ORDINARY NON-LINEAR
DIFFERENTIAL EQUATIONS
IN ENGINEERING
AND PHYSICAL SCIENCES

ORDINARY NON-LINEAR DIFFERENTIAL EQUATIONS IN ENGINEERING AND PHYSICAL SCIENCES

BY

N. W. McLACHLAN

D.SC. (ENGINEERING), LONDON

PROFESSOR OF ELECTRICAL ENGINEERING, EMERITUS,
UNIVERSITY OF ILLINOIS,

WALKER–AMES PROFESSOR OF ELECTRICAL ENGINEERING,
UNIVERSITY OF WASHINGTON (1954)

SECOND EDITION

OXFORD

AT THE CLARENDON PRESS

1956

Oxford University Press, Amen House, London E.C. 4

GLASGOW NEW YORK TORONTO MELBOURNE WELLINGTON
BOMBAY CALCUTTA MADRAS KARACHI CAPE TOWN IBADAN

Geoffrey Cumberlege, Publisher to the University

FIRST EDITION 1950
SECOND EDITION PRINTED LITHOGRAPHICALLY IN GREAT BRITAIN
AT THE UNIVERSITY PRESS, OXFORD
FROM CORRECTED SHEETS OF THE FIRST EDITION
1956

PREFACE TO THE SECOND EDITION

THE first edition was used as a text for some years in a one-semester graduate course for engineers given by the author at the University of Illinois, also in shorter courses at the University of Washington and Michigan State University. The book was supplemented by mimeographed notes on singular points of differential equations, phase trajectories (v–y curves), stability criteria, and fluid flow in two dimensions. These notes constitute Chapters IX and X in the present edition. Wherever possible, references to singular points, etc., have been incorporated into Chapters IV to VIII. The latter should be read in conjunction with Chapter IX. Although partial differential equations are involved in fluid flow, the problems herein reduce ultimately to the solution of ordinary differential equations of the third order.

As well as Chapters IX and X, the following has been incorporated into the text:

(i) Two unpublished theorems on non-driven systems, by the author. Two published theorems on driven systems, by N. Levinson.

(ii) Derivation of the differential equations satisfied by the Jacobian elliptic functions sn, cn, dn, with arguments depending upon the initial conditions, in Chapter III.

(iii) A modified version of the hydro-electric problem in Chapter V, incorporating singular points and v–y curves (phase trajectories).

(iv) New material on the stability of synchronous electrical motors in Chapter VIII.

Fifty-two problems with answers, many of which were given in examination and interim problem papers, have been appended, while there is an additional reference list (C) having sixty-eight entries.

Finally, I am much indebted to Professor T. P. Torda for the comprehensive numerical calculations on which § 10.32 is based.

N. W. M.

June 1955

PREFACE TO THE FIRST EDITION

THE purpose of this book is to provide engineers and physicists with a practical introduction to the important subject of non-linear differential equations, and to give representative applications in engineering and physics. The literature, to date, exceeds 300 memoirs, some rather lengthy, and most of them dealing with applications in various branches of technology. By comparison, the theoretical side of the subject has been neglected. Moreover, owing to the absence of a concise theoretical background, and the need to limit the size of this book for economical reasons, the text is confined chiefly to the presentation of various analytical methods employed in the solution of important technical problems. A wide variety of these is included, and practical details given in the hope that they will interest and help the technical reader. Accordingly, the book is *not* an analytical treatise with technical applications. It aims to show how certain types of non-linear problems may be solved, and how experimental results may be interpreted by aid of non-linear analysis. The reader who desires information on the justification of the methods employed, should consult the references marked with an asterisk in the list at the end of the book.

Much work involving non-linear *partial* differential equations has been done in fluid mechanics, plasticity, and shock waves. The physical and analytical aspects are inseparable, and more than one treatise would be needed to do justice to these subjects. Accordingly, the present text has been confined (apart from Appendix I) to *ordinary* non-linear differential equations. Brief mention of work in plasticity, etc., is made in Chapter I, while the titles of many papers will be found in the reference list, and particularly in [62]. Appendix I has been included on account of the importance of the derived formulae in loudspeaker design.

A method of using Mathieu's equation as a stability criterion of the solutions of non-linear equations is outlined in Appendix II.

I am particularly indebted to Mr. A. L. Meyers for his untiring efforts in checking most of the analytical work in the manuscript, and for his valuable criticisms and suggestions. Professor W. Prager very kindly read the manuscript, and it is to him that I owe the idea of confining the text to *ordinary* non-linear differential equations. I am much indebted to Professor J. Allen for reading and commenting upon §§ 5.170–3; also to Mr. G. E. H. Reuter for doing likewise with §§ 4.196–8, the material in which is the outcome of reading his paper on subharmonics [131*a*].

My best thanks are due to Professor S. Chandrasekhar for permission to use the analysis in §§ 2.30–2 from his book [159]; to Professor R. B. Lindsay for facilities in connexion with § 7.22; and to Sir Richard V. Southwell for permission to use the analysis in §§ 3.180–3 from his book [206].

I am much indebted to the following for either sending or obtaining papers, books, and reports: Sir Edward V. Appleton, Professor W. G. Bickley, Drs. Gertrude Blanch, M. L. Cartwright, and L. J. Comrie, Mr. B. W. Connolly, the Director of Publications Massachusetts Institute of Technology, the Editor of *Engineering*, Professors N. Levinson, C. A. Ludeke, J. Marin, N. Minorsky, and Balth. van der Pol.

Finally I have pleasure in acknowledging permission from the following to reproduce diagrams in the text: American Institute of Physics (*Journal of Applied Physics*), M. Etienne Chiron (*L'Onde Électrique*), the Director of Publications M.I.T., the Editors of the *Philosophical Magazine*, the Institute of Radio Engineers (America), and the U.S.S.R. Embassy (*Technical Physics of the U.S.S.R.*).

N. W. M.

LONDON
May 1950

CONTENTS

ERRATA

p. 18   last para. *read*: In (1) § 2.23 the damping term is larger ...

p. 44   line 1, *for* (14) *read* (12)

p. 123 line 2 above § 7.230 *read*: ... the shape at any instant ...

p. 175 last line but one   *read* $(B/w)^{\frac{1}{2}}$

p. 184 caption for Fig. 89 last line, *for* y *read* $\ddot{y}$

p. 207 line 11 *read*: ... of singularity (except col)

p. 211 Fig. 106 *for* y_2, v_2 *read* y, v

p. 213 line 1 *for* y *read* W

p. 217 first line of (4), *for* $2(A'+B)$ *read* $(2A'+B)$

p. 247 Prob. 13 *for* $C = 3\pi/4KA_0$ *read* $c = 3\pi/4KA_0$

p. 249 Prob. 22 line 1 *for* types and points *read* type, point (singular)

   line 8, *for* $y(0)$ *read* $\dot{y}(0)$

p. 250 Prob. 24, *delete* when $\kappa = 0$

CHAPTER I

GENERAL INTRODUCTION

In the so-called classical theories of different branches of science the differential equations are mainly linear in type. They have been the subject of intense study, and the existence of well-known forms of solutions is now established beyond doubt. If anyone skilled in mathematical analysis encounters a linear differential equation of standard type, the formal solution is usually not difficult to obtain. The comparatively simple nature of such equations is due to the 'characteristic' relationships of the systems, which they describe symbolically, being *assumed* to be linear. For instance the characteristic relationship used in developing the theory of sound propagation in air is the adiabatic law $pv^\gamma = $ a constant. Now the graphical relationship between p and v is a *curve, no finite* portion of which is linear. To overcome this difficulty from a mathematical viewpoint, the theory is based upon infinitesimal pressure variation, so it is assumed that the adiabatic curve may be replaced at the working-point by its tangent. In practice all audible sounds necessitate finite pressure amplitude. Fortunately, however, there is no need to depart from the linear theory based on infinitesimal (and, therefore, inaudible) vibrations, until the sound is fairly intense.

In modern science certain phenomena cannot be explained on the classical linear doctrine, and it is then imperative to resort to non-linear differential equations in order to deduce the desired information. For example, consider an undamped vibrational system whose restoring force is represented by $ay+by^3$ (y the displacement), the system being driven by a force $f\cos \omega t$. When $b = 0$ we have the linear case, and the *single-valued* amplitude is $A = f/(a-\omega^2)$. In the non-linear case, where $b \neq 0$, the second approximation entails a cubic equation for A_1, the amplitude of the fundamental vibration of frequency $\omega/2\pi$. Here

$$\frac{3b}{4} A_1^3 + (a-\omega^2)A_1 - f = 0, \qquad (1)$$

which reduces to the form above when $b = 0$. Thus for given non-zero values of a, b, f, ω, there are *three* possible values of A_1. Over a certain range of ω, all the roots of (1) are real. Outside this range only one root is real. By introducing a viscous damping term into the differential equation, formulae are obtainable from which amplitude–frequency curves may be plotted. Phenomena arising from the multi-valued nature of A_1 may be explained by aid of such curves. One arresting and important feature of the analysis reveals that the *motion is nearly sinusoidal*. Formulae for the *non-linear* case, obtained merely to a second approximation, are adequate to enable a satisfactory explanation of the behaviour of the system to be given, whereas on a linear basis it could not be explained at all!

Some thirty years ago our knowledge of non-linear differential equations might have been compared with that of linear differential equations at the time of Newton, Leibnitz, and the elder Bernoullis (James and John), i.e. about the beginning of the eighteenth century. Until recently the subject of non-linear differential equations has been a happy (!) hunting-ground populated almost exclusively by the technologist. Research into methods of solving these equations has been neglected by the pure mathematician. Like our resources of coal, those of the mathematician in the field of linearity may be exhausted in a finite time!

Interest has been shown in non-linear equations, chiefly in America and in Russia, and research has now started in Britain, with very promising results [26–9, 131 a]. Although the analytical difficulties to be encountered in setting the subject of non-linear differential equations on a firm foundation are formidable, it is here precisely that the pure mathematician can help the technologist. Such assistance will ultimately be 'mirrored in new technical devices destined to benefit the community in general and, therefore, the pure mathematician in particular.

When a problem involving a new kind of non-linear equation arises, or new non-linear boundary conditions are encountered, the technologist may be puzzled as to the proper form of solution to be assumed. Usually these equations cannot be integrated explicitly in terms of known functions. Thus the solution will be an approximate one, but it must be adequate to account for all the salient physical features of the problem. Moreover, theoretical knowledge formulated by the pure mathematician in the guise of suitable forms of solution, existence theorems, and methods of solution would prove invaluable. So far as questions of periodicity, stability, and instability are concerned, we may turn profitably, but not exclusively, to the work of Bendixon [14], Liapounoff [87], and Poincaré [116].

A knowledge of the experimental aspect of a problem may give guidance as regards an appropriate form of solution, e.g. § 7.230. But it will be realized that the accumulation of experimental data may in certain cases be either too costly or impracticable, so that other procedure must then be invoked. Graphical or numerical methods, although tedious, are sometimes useful. Better still is the employment of a differential analyser, or an electronic computing machine. From a purely utilitarian point of view, difficult and troublesome non-linear differential equations involving much numerical work are best solved by a machine. Just as the expert craftsman in various branches of industry has been replaced largely by machines, so in the course of time the technical mathematician may be replaced by differential analysers or other calculating machines. Then the intrinsic interest in mathematical problems will have ceased to exist. At the moment, however, these machines are so rare and the price so high, that they are beyond the reach of the average technologist, and from his standpoint may, therefore, be counted out.

To give a concrete idea of the growing importance of non-linear differential equations, the following typical (but not exhaustive) branches of science where they occur may be cited: acoustics, aerodynamics, astronomy, cable telegraphy, elasticity, electrical power circuits, electrical machinery, electronics, engine governors, fluid jets, hydraulics, hydrodynamics, naval architecture (stabilization of ships), plasticity, wave motion of finite amplitude on fluids and in solids.

One of the earliest non-linear equations of acoustics was given by S. Earnshaw in 1860 [32], and pertained to the propagation of plane sound waves of finite amplitude in air. A general equation for *expanding* sound waves of finite amplitude, of which the above is a particular case, is given by the author in reference [183]. Solutions of this equation for conical and exponential loudspeaker horns have been obtained by S. Goldstein, N. W. McLachlan, and A. L. Meyers [41, 100, 101]. Non-linear equations were encountered by Lord Rayleigh in connexion with an electrically maintained tuning-fork [131], and by C. V. Raman in his experimental work on vibrating strings [127, 128].

An important non-linear equation which occurs in astronomy

concerns the gravitational equilibrium of gaseous configurations (stars). It originated with J. Homer Lane in 1870 [78], and has been discussed at some length by S. Chandrasekhar [159], V. R. Emden [165], R. H. Fowler [36, 37], and Lord Kelvin [68]. Of other non-linear equations in celestial mechanics, those pertaining to the white dwarf stars† [159] and the pulsation of cepheid variables, treated by A. S. Eddington, may be mentioned [164].

About twenty-six years ago the speed of signalling on long submarine telegraph cables was increased some fivefold by 'loading' the inner copper conductor with thin nickel-iron tape or wire. This alloy has an initial permeability (dB/dH as $H \to 0$) of the order 4,000, and with normal sending voltages (40 to 60) it becomes saturated magnetically, thereby introducing non-linearity and consequent distortion of the signals. Using a method of G. Riemann for the propagation of impulses in a gas, H. Salinger showed that a wave front, vertical at the sending end, tilts backwards (on a time basis) with increase in distance along the cable. If the sending voltage exceeds a critical value, the wave front along the cable has both vertical and non-vertical parts [135].

There are a variety of non-linear problems in the theory of elasticity. An early problem is that of the 'elastica' or flexible rod bent in one plane so that the two ends approach each other. It attracted the attention of the Bernoullis, Euler, and Lagrange. R. V. Southwell has given the solution for a uniform bar in terms of elliptic integrals [206], while W. G. Bickley has studied the problem in which fabrics bend under their own weight [16]. In connexion with large deflexions of beams, solutions have been obtained by H. L. Cox, K. O. Friedrichs, Th. von Kármán, J. J. Stoker, J. S. Way [62], and others. Finite deformation of solids has been discussed analytically by M. Biot, J. Boussinesq, G. Kirchhoff, and F. D. Murnaghan [62]. The author has studied the behaviour of steel shells, with non-linear characteristics, due to impulsive forces (§§ 8.20–8.23). In the realm of vibrational mechanical systems having non-linear restoring forces, analytical and experimental work has been done by E. V. Appleton [11], G. Duffing [162], J. P. Den Hartog [47–9], and C. A. Ludeke [91, 92, 92 a]. In certain cases the control stiffness *decreases* with increase in

---

† The radius of such a star is much smaller than that of one of the main stars. Thus for the same luminosity the former will have a much higher effective temperature than the latter. Hence the smaller star will be much 'whiter' than the larger one. This is the origin of the name 'white dwarf'.

amplitude, resulting in instability which is evinced by a 'jump' or discontinuity. Appleton obtained this effect with a 'magnetic' vibration galvanometer [11], and solved the appropriate non-linear equation. The decreasing stiffness characteristic occurs also in connexion with a simple pendulum and a synchronous electrical motor.

Non-linearity arising from iron-cored apparatus in electrical power circuits may introduce oscillations, whose frequency is a sub-multiple of the supply frequency, when the circuit switch is closed. These sub-frequencies must not be confused with sub-harmonics in electrical circuits under different conditions or excited parametrically as in § 7.12. The former have been discussed by J. D. McCrumm and are initiated by 'shock' [99].

An experimental investigation into resonance effects in LCR circuits having iron-cored inductances has been made by C. G. Suits [140]. A variable potential difference (50 c.p.s.) was applied in series with the LCR combination. Provided $R <$ some value R_0, when the potential difference reaches a certain magnitude, the reactance vanishes and the current jumps suddenly to many times its former value. The matter has been investigated analytically by E. G. Keller [64, 65]. R. J. Duffin has discussed the behaviour of electrical networks having positive non-linear resistors [31].

In connexion with transient effects in suddenly loaded synchronous electrical motors, solutions of the non-linear equations have been given by H. E. Edgerton, P. Fourmarier, W. V. Lyon, and F. J. Zak [33, 34, 93]. The solutions were obtained in graphical form by means of a differential analyser.

In the field of electronics the triode oscillator is the outstanding example of a non-linear device. The characteristic is curved, the curvature changing from positive to negative, there being a point of inflexion. During a period of the oscillation the damping of the associated electrical circuit is sometimes negative (maintenance or growth) and at others positive (limitation and loss). The non-linear differential equation of the circuit, namely,

$$\frac{d^2y}{dt^2} + f(y)\frac{dy}{dt} + ay = 0, \tag{2}$$

was first studied by E. V. Appleton and B. van der Pol [8]. Later van der Pol obtained solutions by the isocline method (see § 8.12) with $f(y) = -\epsilon(1-y^2)$, for $\epsilon = 0\cdot1, 1\cdot0, 10$. In the latter case he found that under certain conditions a triode oscillator executed relaxation oscillations, this being a limiting case when the parameter ϵ is large [119]. He also showed that relaxation phenomena occur in a number of branches of science, e.g. physiology, the heart-beat being a relaxation oscillation. B. van der Pol and S. van der Mark constructed an electrical model working on the same principle as the heart and exhibiting similar characteristics [121]. V. Volterra has investigated the variation in the numbers of individuals in animal species which

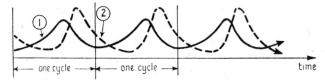

FIG. 1. The ordinates in ① represent the number of soles, and in ② the number of sharks (different vertical scales).

live together, one feeding on the other [147, 209]. The curve of variation is a relaxation type. The problem may be illustrated by the simple case of two species of fish in the sea, e.g. sharks and soles. The sharks eat soles, and the latter live on food in the sea, of which an ever present supply is assumed. If the soles existed alone, they would multiply in number at an ever increasing rate. The sharks, however, take care that this does not happen, by devouring large quantities of soles, so the latter diminish rapidly in number. Ultimately there is an inadequate supply of soles to sustain the sharks which commence to die off at a high rate. Thereafter the soles again begin to increase in number, so the sharks now have more food, thus entailing a growth in the shark population, which reaches a maximum. Then the cycle is repeated indefinitely. The relationship between the two populations and time is depicted in Fig. 1, being in the nature of a relaxation oscillation, although the changes from maxima to minima and vice versa are less precipitous than those in an electronic relaxation oscillation (Fig. 63). The recurrence of epidemics and the problem of parasites show similar characteristics when a time base is used [182]. Other aspects of non-linearity in valve circuits have been treated by E. V. Appleton, W. M. Greaves, and B. van der Pol [7–10], e.g. the 'silent interval' when a valve oscillator is driven by an external source.

The problem of parametric excitation and of oscillations in electrical and other systems having non-linear elements has been studied by A. Andronow, S. Chaikin, N. Kaidanowsky, L. Mandelstam,

A. Mélikian, N. Papalexi, H. Sékerska, S. Strelkow, K. Theodortschik, and A. Witt [94, 95, 139, 142]. Methods of solving the types of non-linear equations occurring in researches of the above kind have been developed by N. Kryloff and N. Bogoliuboff. The procedure is one of successive approximation, being based on rational assumptions relating to such applications. The method may be classified with Lagrange's variation of parameters. It is described in [175] by S. Lefschetz, and in [187] by N. Minorsky. The Poincaré perturbation method, developed primarily for astronomical problems, may be applied (with limitations) to non-linear equations for various types of oscillatory system. Mandelstam and Papalexi have extended the procedure to cover the equations for a self-oscillatory system when acted upon by an external source. The extended analysis enables certain resonance phenomena peculiar to non-linear circuits to be explained, e.g. sub-harmonics in a thermionic valve circuit into which an e.m.f. is injected from an external source [94].

Problems in hydrodynamics involving non-linear equations occur in connexion with rivers, artificial channels, and hydro-electric systems. They have been studied by A. M. Binnie, J. Boussinesq, R. S. Cole, P. Forchheimer, the author, and others [30, 62, 166, 212, 243].

Non-linear problems in the science of plasticity have received attention by various authors, of whom we cite J. Boussinesq, Th. von Kármán, A. Nadai, W. Prager, and G. I. Taylor [62, 125, 126, 189]. Extensive researches in connexion with viscous and with compressible fluids have been conducted by many authors during the past century. Of these W. G. Bickley, A. Busemann, S. Goldstein, D. R. Hartree, Th. von Kármán, C. W. Oseen, L. Prandtl, O. Reynolds, and G. I. Taylor may be mentioned [62].

The theory of ship stabilization by means of anti-rolling tanks and auxiliary mechanism involves non-linear differential equations. This subject has been studied by N. Minorsky [108–11].

Wave motion of finite amplitude on fluid surfaces has been treated analytically by T. H. Havelock, T. Levi-Civita, Lord Rayleigh, G. G. Stokes, D. J. Struik, and others [62].

For additional information on the subject of non-linear equations in general, the reader may consult the references at the end of the book, and also those in [62], which contains a bibliography of 178 items classified under nine heads. The importance of the purely theoretical aspect has been mentioned already. During the past few years the theory of non-linear equations for (*a*) mechanical vibrators, (*b*) triode oscillators (including relaxation oscillations), has been studied by M. L. Cartwright and J. E. Littlewood [26–9], G. E. H. Reuter [131 *a*], H. J. Eckweiler, D. A. Flanders, K. O. Friedrichs, J. J. Stoker, F. John [163], N. Levinson and O. K: Smith [82–6].

Although solutions of a number of the problems mentioned above were obtained either by graphical means or by a differential analyser, the majority of cases to date have been solved approximately by analytical or numerical processes. In some problems the amount of computation is considerable, calculating machines being needed.

The methods of solution used in this book are summarized below:

Chap. II. Integrable exactly, using suitable transformations.

   III. Integrable exactly (with some exceptions) in terms of Jacobian elliptic functions.

   IV. Approximate periodic solutions by (*a*) successive approximation (iteration), (*b*) perturbation method, (*c*) assuming a Fourier series, and determining early coefficients therein.

   V. Approximate periodic and non-periodic solutions by method of slowly varying amplitude and phase.

   VI. Method in V applied to derive equivalent linear equations.

   VII. Approximate periodic solutions, assuming Fourier series, as based upon theory of Mathieu functions.

   VIII. (*a*) Isocline graphical construction, (*b*) Liénard graphical construction, (*c*) Maclaurin series, (*d*) numerical methods.

   X. Maclaurin series.

Appendix I. As at IV (*a*).

CHAPTER II

EQUATIONS READILY INTEGRABLE

2.10. Definition. If in an ordinary differential equation the dependent variable y and its derivatives are of the *first degree* only, there being no products like yy', $y'y''$, y^2, y^3, the equation is said to be linear in y. But when the degree of y and/or its derivatives differs from unity, or if they occur as products, the equation is said to be *non-linear in y*. For example

$$\frac{d^2y}{dx^2} + x^3\frac{dy}{dx} + y = x^5 \tag{1}$$

is a linear equation of the second order. The presence of x^3, x^5 does not constitute non-linearity in y. But

$$\frac{d^2y}{dx^2} + y\frac{dy}{dx} + y^2 = 0, \quad \text{and} \quad \frac{d^2y}{dx^2} + \left(\frac{dy}{dx}\right)^{\frac{1}{2}} + y = 0, \tag{2}$$

are non-linear equations of the second order, $y\,dy/dx$, y^2, $(dy/dx)^{\frac{1}{2}}$ being non-linear terms.

2.11. Examples. In this chapter we shall deal with a brief selection of equations which are integrable exactly without recourse to elliptic integrals. We commence with those of the first order.

1°. Solve

$$\frac{dy}{dx} + \frac{x}{y} = 0, \tag{1}$$

the initial condition being $y = y_0$ when $x = x_0$.

The equation may be written

$$x\,dx + y\,dy = 0, \tag{2}$$

so the second term is non-linear in y. Integrating, we have

$$x^2 + y^2 = A, \text{ a constant.} \tag{3}$$

The initial condition gives $A = x_0^2 + y_0^2 = a^2$, say. Hence the solution is

$$x^2 + y^2 = a^2, \tag{4}$$

the equation of a family of concentric circles radius a (variable). The solution may be written in the form

$$y = \pm(a^2 - x^2)^{\frac{1}{2}}, \tag{5}$$

so y is double-valued, and is also a function of a^2, the constant of integration.

Comparison may be made with the linear equation

$$\frac{dy}{dx}+\frac{y}{x}=0, \tag{6}$$

whose solution is $\qquad y=A_1/x, \tag{7}$

where $A_1 \neq 0$ is an *arbitrary* constant *multiplier* dependent on the initial condition.

2°. Solve $\qquad \dfrac{dy}{dx}=\dfrac{x+y}{x-y}, \tag{1}$

the initial condition being $x=1, y=1$. If the equation is written in the form

$$(x+y)\,dx=(x-y)\,dy, \tag{2}$$

the term $-y\,dy$ is non-linear in y. Let

$$x=r\cos\theta,\qquad y=r\sin\theta, \tag{3}$$

r, θ being variable. Then

$$dx=\cos\theta\,dr-r\sin\theta\,d\theta, \tag{4}$$

and $\qquad dy=\sin\theta\,dr+r\cos\theta\,d\theta. \tag{5}$

Substituting from (4), (5) into (2), we get

$$(\cos\theta+\sin\theta)(\cos\theta\,dr-r\sin\theta\,d\theta)$$
$$=(\cos\theta-\sin\theta)(\sin\theta\,dr+r\cos\theta\,d\theta), \tag{6}$$

so $\qquad \cos^2\theta\,dr-r\sin^2\theta\,d\theta=-\sin^2\theta\,dr+r\cos^2\theta\,d\theta, \tag{7}$

giving $\qquad dr/d\theta=r. \tag{8}$

Thus $\qquad \log r=\theta+A, \tag{9}$

A being the constant of integration, so in terms of x, y we have

$$\tfrac{1}{2}\log(x^2+y^2)-\tan^{-1}y/x=A. \tag{10}$$

Since $y=1$ when $x=1, A=\tfrac{1}{2}(\log_e 2-\tfrac{1}{4}\pi)$, and the solution takes the implicit form $\qquad \log\tfrac{1}{2}(x^2+y^2)-2[\tan^{-1}(y/x)-\tfrac{1}{4}\pi]=0. \tag{11}$

For initial condition $x=x_0, y=y_0$, the solution is

$$\log[(x^2+y^2)/(x_0^2+y_0^2)]-2[\tan^{-1}(y/x)-\tan^{-1}(y_0/x_0)]=0. \tag{12}$$

Here again we see that the solution of a non-linear equation is a function of the initial condition.

3°. Solve $\qquad \dfrac{dy}{dx}+\dfrac{x}{y}=2, \tag{1}$

which is non-linear in y. Write $y=vx$, then $dy/dx=x(dv/dx)+v$ and (1) becomes

$$x\frac{dv}{dx}+v+\frac{1}{v}-2=0, \tag{2}$$

or
$$xv\frac{dv}{dx}+(v-1)^2 = 0. \tag{3}$$

Thus
$$\int\frac{v\,dv}{(v-1)^2}+\int\frac{dx}{x} = \log A, \text{ a constant,} \tag{4}$$

so
$$\frac{1}{2}\int\frac{d(v-1)^2}{(v-1)^2}+\int\frac{dv}{(v-1)^2}+\int\frac{dx}{x} = \log A, \tag{5}$$

and, therefore,
$$\log(v-1)+\log x-\log A = 1/(v-1). \tag{6}$$

Hence
$$\log[x(v-1)/A] = 1/(v-1), \tag{7}$$
which yields the implicit form
$$(y-x) = Ae^{x/(y-x)}, \tag{8}$$

A being the constant of integration. The equation
$$dy/dx+x/y = 2\kappa \quad (\kappa > 0) \tag{9}$$
should be solved by the reader, using the substitution $y = vx$.

2.12. Bernoulli's equation. This may be written

$$\frac{dy}{dx}+f(x)y = g(x)y^{\mu}, \tag{1}$$

where f, g are continuous functions of x, but not of y, and $\mu \neq 0$ or 1, which entails non-linearity in y. Write $u = y^{1-\mu}$ and we get

$$\frac{du}{dx} = (1-\mu)y^{-\mu}\frac{dy}{dx}. \tag{2}$$

Substituting for dy/dx into (1), and replacing $y^{1-\mu}$ by u leads to a standard form of *linear* equation of the first order, namely,

$$\frac{du}{dx}+(1-\mu)f(x)u = (1-\mu)g(x). \tag{3}$$

Now the general solution of

$$\frac{du}{dx}+\xi(x)u = \chi(x) \tag{4}$$

is
$$u = Ae^{-\int^x \xi(x)\,dx}+e^{-\int^x \xi(x)\,dx}\int^x \chi(x)e^{\int^x \xi(x)\,dx}\,dx, \tag{5}$$

A being an arbitrary constant. Hence the solution of (3) is

$$u = Ae^{(\mu-1)\int^x f(x)\,dx}-(\mu-1)e^{(\mu-1)\int^x f(x)\,dx}\int^x g(x)e^{(1-\mu)\int^x f(x)\,dx}\,dx, \tag{6}$$

and finally
$$y = u^{1/(1-\mu)}. \tag{7}$$

2.130. Riccati's equation. We omit the general form of the equation (see ref. 172) and deal with the integrable one, namely,

$$\frac{dy}{dx}+ay^2+yf(x)+g(x) = 0, \tag{1}$$

where $f(x)$ and $g(x)$ are continuous functions of x, independent of y. Write $u = e^{a\int^x y\,dx}$, then

$$u' = ayu, \qquad u'' = (ay'+a^2y^2)u. \tag{2}$$

Thus from (1), (2) we obtain the *linear* equation of the *second order*

$$\frac{d^2u}{dx^2}+f(x)\frac{du}{dx}+a\,g(x)u = 0, \tag{3}$$

whose solution may be derived by well-known methods.
The form given originally by Riccati in 1724 was

$$\frac{dy}{dx}+ay^2-bx^\mu = 0. \tag{4}$$

The foregoing substitution transforms (4) to the second-order *linear* equation

$$\frac{d^2u}{dx^2}-abx^\mu u = 0. \tag{5}$$

This may be solved in terms of Bessel functions as follows:
The solution of

$$\frac{d^2u}{dx^2}-\frac{\alpha}{x}\frac{dy}{dx}+k_1^2 x^\mu u = 0 \tag{6}$$

is [184, p. 39, ex. 50]

$$u = x^p[AJ_\nu(kx^q)+BJ_{-\nu}(kx^q)], \tag{7}$$

where

$p = \frac{1}{2}(\alpha+1)$, $\nu = (\alpha+1)/(\mu+2)$, $k = 2k_1/(\mu+2)$, $q = p/\nu = (\frac{1}{2}\mu+1)$,

and ν is non-integral. The solution of (5) is derived by putting $\alpha = 0$, $k_1^2 = -ab$, then $p = \frac{1}{2}, \nu = 1/(\mu+2), k = 2i(ab)^{\frac{1}{2}}/(\mu+2), q = (\frac{1}{2}\mu+1)$. Now the modified Bessel function $I_\nu(z) = e^{-\frac{1}{2}\nu\pi i}J_\nu(zi)$, so the solution may be expressed in the form

$$u = x^{\frac{1}{2}}[A_1 I_\nu(lx^q)+B_1 I_{-\nu}(lx^q)] = x^{\frac{1}{2}}\Psi, \tag{8}$$

where $l = 2(ab)^{\frac{1}{2}}/(\mu+2)$, and A_1, B_1 are *arbitrary* constants. But $y = u'/au$, so with $\Psi' = d\Psi/dx$ we obtain from (8)

$$y = \{\tfrac{1}{2}x^{-\frac{1}{2}}\Psi+x^{\frac{1}{2}}\Psi'\}/ax^{\frac{1}{2}}\Psi \tag{9}$$

$$= \frac{1}{a}\left\{\frac{1}{2x}+\frac{\Psi'}{\Psi}\right\} \tag{10}$$

$$= \frac{1}{a}\left\{\frac{1}{2x}+\frac{lqx^{q-1}[A_1\,I'_{\nu}(lx^q)+B_1\,I'_{-\nu}(lx^q)]}{\Psi}\right\} \tag{11}$$

$$= \frac{1}{2ax}\left\{1+\frac{2lqx^q[I'_{\nu}+CI'_{-\nu}]}{[I_{\nu}+CI_{-\nu}]}\right\}, \tag{12}$$

where $C = B_1/A_1$ is *the* constant of integration of which y is a function. Since (4) is an equation of unit order, there is only *one* constant of integration.

2.131. Solve $\qquad \dfrac{dy}{dx}+y^2+yxg(x)-g(x) = 0,$ $\qquad\qquad$ (1)

$g(x)$ being a function of x.

This is a Riccati equation of the type (1), § 2.130, with $a = 1$, $f(x) = -xg(x)$. Instead of the substitution in § 2.130, we use the fact that if a *particular* solution of a Riccati equation is known, the general solution may be obtained by quadratures, as exemplified below. Writing (1) in the form

$$\frac{dy}{dx}+y^2+g(x)[yx-1] = 0, \tag{2}$$

a *particular* solution is obviously $1/x$. Accordingly we now put $y = \dfrac{1}{x}+\dfrac{1}{v}$, where v is a once differentiable function of x, and obtain the equation

$$\frac{dv}{dx}-\left(\frac{2}{x}+xg\right)v = 1. \tag{3}$$

Applying (5), § 2.12, leads to

$$v = A\,e^{\int [(2/x)+xg]\,dx}+e^{\int [(2/x)+xg]\,dx}\int^x e^{-\int [(2/x)+xg]\,dx}\,dx, \tag{4}$$

$$= Ax^2 e^{\int xg\,dx}+x^2 e^{\int xg\,dx}\int^x e^{-\int xg\,dx}\,dx/x^2, \tag{5}$$

A being the constant of integration. Substituting for v in terms of x, y, yields the solution

$$1/x(xy-1) = A\,e^{\int xg\,dx}+e^{\int xg\,dx}\int^x e^{-\int xg\,dx}\,dx/x^2. \tag{6}$$

2.14. Simultaneous equations. Solve

$$dy/dx = z+y[(y^2+z^2)^{\frac{1}{2}}-2a], \tag{1}$$

and $\qquad dz/dx = -y+z[(y^2+z^2)^{\frac{1}{2}}-2a]. \tag{2}$

Multiplying (1) by y, (2) by z, and adding, gives

$$yy'+zz' = (y^2+z^2)[(y^2+z^2)^{\frac{1}{2}}-2a], \tag{3}$$

so
$$\frac{1}{2}\frac{d}{dx}(y^2+z^2) = (y^2+z^2)[(y^2+z^2)^{\frac{1}{2}}-2a]. \tag{4}$$

Writing $(y^2+z^2)^{\frac{1}{2}} = u$ and integrating, (4) becomes

$$\int du/(u^2-2au) = \int dx+A_1, \tag{5}$$

or
$$\int du/[(u-a)^2-a^2] = x+A_1, \tag{6}$$

so
$$\frac{1}{2a}\log[u/(2a-u)] = x+A_1 \quad (2a > u). \tag{7}$$

Hence
$$u/(2a-u) = Ae^{2ax}, \tag{8}$$

and the solution has the implicit form

$$(y^2+z^2)^{\frac{1}{2}}/[2a-(y^2+z^2)^{\frac{1}{2}}] = Ae^{2ax}, \tag{9}$$

A being the constant of integration, and $2a > (y^2+z^2)^{\frac{1}{2}}$.

2.20. Equations of the second order. A *linear* differential equation of the second order has two distinct or linearly independent solutions, i.e. they are not proportional. Suppose that y_1, y_2 are two distinct solutions of
$$\ddot{y}+\omega^2 y = 0, \tag{1}$$

then the complete or general solution is

$$y = A_1 y_1 + B_1 y_2, \tag{2}$$

where A_1, B_1 are *arbitrary* non-zero constant multipliers.

If a term by^3 is added to (1), we obtain the non-linear equation (see (1), § 3.10)
$$\ddot{y}+ay+by^3 = 0 \quad (a = \omega^2). \tag{3}$$

The general solution of (3) does *not* take the form at (2), since there cannot be linearly independent solutions of a non-linear differential equation. (3) may be *considered* to have a complete solution which is obtainable by integrating twice, thereby entailing two constants of integration. The general solution is a *function* of these constants which, in a physical problem, are determinable from the initial or the boundary conditions, as the case may be.

In (2) A_1, B_1 are mere multipliers, also determinable from the initial conditions. Their values do not affect the periodic time $(2\pi/\omega)$ of the oscillation of the mechanical system to which (1) refers. But the period corresponding to (3) is a function of the initial conditions. This will be evident from (1), § 3.111, where τ_0 decreases with increase in the initial amplitude y_0, which is a consequence of (3) being non-linear in y.

2.21. Solve
$$\frac{d^2y}{dx^2} = \left(\frac{2y-1}{y^2+1}\right)\left(\frac{dy}{dx}\right)^2. \tag{1}$$

Write $v = dy/dx$, and we get
$$\frac{d^2y}{dx^2} = \frac{dv}{dx} = \frac{dv}{dy}\cdot\frac{dy}{dx} = v\frac{dv}{dy}. \tag{2}$$

Then the variables are separable, and (1) takes the form
$$\frac{v\,dv}{dy} = v^2\left(\frac{2y-1}{y^2+1}\right), \tag{3}$$

so
$$\int\frac{dv}{v} = \int\frac{(2y-1)}{(y^2+1)}dy + A_1, \tag{4}$$

and, therefore, $\log v = \log(y^2+1) - \tan^{-1}y + A_1$, $\qquad$ (5)

from which it follows that
$$\frac{v\,e^{\tan^{-1}y}}{(1+y^2)} = A. \tag{6}$$

Thus $\qquad \int e^{\tan^{-1}y}\,dy/(1+y^2) = A\int dx + B$, $\qquad$ (7)

so $\qquad\qquad\qquad e^{\tan^{-1}y} = Ax + B$, $\qquad$ (8)

and hence $\qquad\qquad y = \tan[\log(Ax+B)]$. $\qquad$ (9)

From (9) we see that y is a function of A, B, the two constants of integration, which are not mere multipliers as they would be in the case of a linear differential equation of the second order. As an exercise the reader may solve
$$d^2y/dx^2 = a[(dy/dx)^2+1]. \tag{10}$$

2.22. Solve
$$\frac{d^2y}{dx^2} + \left(\frac{1-\mu}{\mu y}\right)\left(\frac{dy}{dx}\right)^2 = 0. \tag{1}$$

Put $v = dy/dx$, and (1) becomes
$$\frac{v\,dv}{dy} = \left(\frac{\mu-1}{\mu}\right)\frac{v^2}{y}, \tag{2}$$

the variables now being separable, so
$$\int\frac{dv}{v} = \left(\frac{\mu-1}{\mu}\right)\int\frac{dy}{y} + A_1. \tag{3}$$

Thus
$$\log v = \left(\frac{\mu-1}{\mu}\right)\log y + A_1, \tag{4}$$

or
$$\frac{dy}{dx} = v = Ay^{(1-1/\mu)}. \tag{5}$$

Integrating again, we have
$$\int y^{(1/\mu)-1}\, dy = A \int dx + B, \tag{6}$$

so
$$y^{1/\mu} = \frac{1}{\mu}(Ax+B), \tag{7}$$

giving finally the solution
$$y = (Cx+D)^\mu, \tag{8}$$

where $C = A\mu^{-1}$, $D = B\mu^{-1}$ are the two constants of integration. As before, y is a function of these constants. There is also a particular solution $y = $ a constant.

Equation (1) occurs in a boundary-layer problem in aeronautics, and it is concerned with separation of the fluid from the surface of an aerofoil. (See § 10.33 for the meaning of boundary layer.) Taking

$$\nu = (1-\mu)/\mu, \qquad \text{i.e. } \mu = 1/(1+\nu),$$

(1) may be written
$$y\frac{d^2y}{dx^2} + \nu\left(\frac{dy}{dx}\right)^2 = 0, \tag{9}$$

and by (8) the solution is
$$y = (Cx+D)^{1/(1+\nu)}. \tag{10}$$

Unless all terms of a non-linear equation are of the same degree in y, the solution cannot be multiplied by an arbitrary non-zero constant $A \neq 1$. For example, if y_1 satisfies (3), § 2.20, Ay_1 does not satisfy it. For, on substituting into the equation, we get $\ddot{y}_1 + ay_1 + bA^2y_1^3$, which vanishes only if $y_1 = 0$ or $A = 1$. In (9), both terms are of degree two in y, so that $A(Cx+D)^{1/(1+\nu)}$ is a solution, as may be checked by substitution.

Singular point of (1). With $v = dy/dx$, (9) may be written
$$\frac{dv}{dy} = -\frac{\nu v}{y}. \tag{11}$$

If $\nu > 0$, by 4°, § 9.11, the origin $y = v = 0$ is a col, whereas if $\nu < 0$, by 1°, § 9.11, it is a node.

2.23. Solve
$$y'' + 3yy' + y^3 = f(x). \tag{1}$$

Write $u = e^{\int^x y\, dx}$, then

$$\frac{du}{dx} = uy, \qquad \frac{d^2u}{dx^2} = uy^2 + uy' = u(y' + y^2), \qquad (2)$$

and
$$\frac{d^3u}{dx^3} = u(y'' + 3yy' + y^3). \qquad (3)$$

Thus by (1), (3) we obtain a standard form of *linear* equation of the third order, namely,

$$\frac{d^3u}{dx^3} - uf(x) = 0. \qquad (4)$$

If u_1, u_2, u_3 are linearly independent solutions of (4), and A_1, A_2, A_3 arbitrary constants, the complete solution is

$$u = A_1 u_1 + A_2 u_2 + A_3 u_3. \qquad (5)$$

Since $u = e^{\int^x y\, dx}$, we get $y = u'/u$, and the solution may be expressed in the form
$$y = \frac{A_1 u_1' + A_2 u_2' + A_3 u_3'}{A_1 u_1 + A_2 u_2 + A_3 u_3} \qquad (6)$$

$$= (u_1' + Au_2' + Bu_3')/(u_1 + Au_2 + Bu_3), \qquad (7)$$

where $A = A_2/A_1$, $B = A_3/A_1$. Thus solution (7) is a rational function of the two constants of integration A, B.

Particular case of (1). Let $f(x) = 0$, and we get

$$y'' + 3yy' + y^3 = 0. \qquad (8)$$

Also (4) becomes
$$d^3u/dx^3 = 0, \qquad (9)$$

so
$$d^2u/dx^2 = A_0, \qquad du/dx = A_0 x + B_0, \qquad (10)$$

and
$$u = \tfrac{1}{2}A_0 x^2 + B_0 x + C_0. \qquad (11)$$

Hence
$$y = u'/u = 2(A_0 x + B_0)/(A_0 x^2 + 2B_0 x + 2C_0),$$
$$= 2(x + A)/(x^2 + 2Ax + B), \qquad (12)$$

with $A = B_0/A_0$, $B = 2C_0/A_0$, these being the two constants of integration, of which y is a rational function.

2.24. Dynamical illustration of (8), § 2.23.

Imagine a body of unit mass constrained by frictionless guides to move in a straight line on a frictionless horizontal plane as in Fig. 2, without the damping device. A displacement y from an equilibrium or zero position is opposed by a massless spring whose 'characteristic' is defined by restoring force $= y^3$. To the body is attached a device which introduces a damping force $3y\dot{y}$, where $\dot{y} = dy/dt$, this being three times the product of displacement and velocity. If the body is moved a distance y_0 from its equilibrium position and released at time $t = 0$, what is its subsequent motion?

The first step is to determine A, B in (12), § 2.23, using t instead of x. Substituting $y = y_0$, $t = 0$, gives

$$A = \tfrac{1}{2}By_0. \tag{1}$$

Differentiating (12), § 2.23, we obtain

$$\dot{y} = \frac{2}{(t^2+2At+B)}\left[1 - \frac{2(t+A)^2}{(t^2+2At+B)}\right]. \tag{2}$$

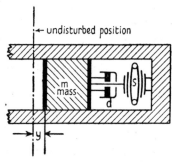

←undisturbed position

FIG. 2. Schematic diagram of mass-spring system with viscous damping proportional to the velocity. m = mass, s = spring, d = damping device.

Since the body starts from rest, $\dot{y} = 0$ at $t = 0$, so (2) yields

$$B = 2A^2. \tag{3}$$

Hence from (1), (3)

$$A = 1/y_0, \quad \text{and} \quad B = 2/y_0^2. \tag{4}$$

Inserting these into (12), § 2.23, with t for x, leads to

$$y = 2(t+1/y_0)/[(t+1/y_0)^2+1/y_0^2]. \tag{5}$$

There are two cases to be considered, namely, (i) when $y_0 > 0$, (ii) when $y_0 < 0$.

(i) It is evident from (5) that $y \to +0$ monotonically as $t \to +\infty$, and since $\dot{y} = 0$ when $t = 0$, the relationship between y and t has the form illustrated in Fig. 3 A. The inflexional point, where $\ddot{y} = 0$, occurs at $t_1 = (3^{\frac{1}{2}}-1)/y_0$. Thus the larger y_0, the smaller t_1, because the damping increases with increase in y.

(ii) Here we write $-y_0$ for y_0 (> 0) in (5), thereby obtaining

$$y = 2(t-1/y_0)/[(t-1/y_0)^2+1/y_0^2]. \tag{6}$$

When $t = 0$, $\dot{y} = 0$, $y = -y_0$, and when $t = 1/y_0$, $y = 0$, after which y is positive. Moreover, the y–t relationship now takes the form depicted in Fig. 3 B, where y becomes positive and attains a maximum value y_0 at $t = 2/y_0$, before tending monotonically to zero as $t \to +\infty$. The curve $P_3 P_4$ in Fig. 3 B is identical with that in Fig. 3 A, since (5) is obtained by writing $(t+2/y_0)$ for t in (6).

In (1) the damping term is much larger than would be expected in a practical application, where the motion would be more likely to have the form of a weakly damped oscillation.

2.25. Derivation of non-linear equation. Consider the linear third-order equation

$$\frac{d^3u}{dx^3}+f(x)\frac{d^2u}{dx^2}+g(x)\frac{du}{dx}=0,\tag{1}$$

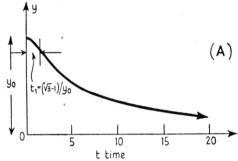

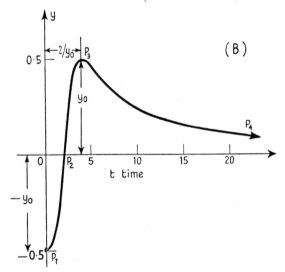

Fig. 3 A. Illustrating solution curve for (5), § 2.24.
B. Illustrating solution curve for (6), § 2.24. When $t \geqslant 4$, curve (B) is identical with (A) for $t \geqslant 0$.

where $f(x)$, $g(x)$ are functions of x independent of y. Then by aid of (2), (3), § 2.23, we have

$$u(y''+3yy'+y^3)+uf(x)(y'+y^2)+u\,g(x)y=0,\tag{2}$$

and since $u \neq 0$, (2) yields the non-linear differential equation of the second order

$$y''+[3y+f(x)]y'+g(x)y+f(x)y^2+y^3=0.\tag{3}$$

Then if u_1, u_2, u_3 are linearly independent solutions of (1), the general solution of (3) takes the form at (7), § 2.23.

2.26. Solve
$$3\epsilon\frac{d^3y}{dx^3}+y\frac{d^2y}{dx^2}+\left(\frac{dy}{dx}\right)^2 = 0, \tag{1}$$

subject to the conditions $y = y'' = 0$ when $x = 0$, $y' = 0$ when $x \to +\infty$. This equation occurs in the theory of the plane jet in hydrodynamics [17].

The first step is to remove the constant ϵ, so we write $x = 3u$, $y(x) = 2\epsilon w(u)$, where w is a thrice differentiable function of u. Then (1) becomes
$$\frac{2}{9}\epsilon^2\frac{d^3w}{du^3}+\frac{4}{9}\epsilon^2 w\frac{d^2w}{du^2}+\frac{4}{9}\epsilon^2\left(\frac{dw}{du}\right)^2 = 0, \tag{2}$$

or
$$w'''+2(ww''+w'^2) = 0, \tag{3}$$

the accents denoting differentiation with respect to u. (3) may be written
$$\frac{d}{du}(w''+2ww') = 0, \tag{4}$$

so
$$w'' = -2ww'+A, \quad \text{a constant.} \tag{5}$$

By virtue of the above conditions, with $\epsilon > 0$, $w = w'' = 0$ when $u = 0$, and $w' = 0$ when $u \to +\infty$, so $A = 0$. Thus, from (5),
$$w''+2ww' = 0, \tag{6}$$

or
$$\frac{d}{du}(w'+w^2) = 0, \tag{7}$$

so
$$w' = a^2-w^2, \tag{8}$$

$B = a^2$ being a non-zero constant of integration. Hence
$$\int dw/(a^2-w^2) = u+C, \quad \text{a constant,} \tag{9}$$

giving
$$\frac{1}{a}\tanh^{-1}(w/a) = u+C. \tag{10}$$

Since $w = 0$ when $u = 0$, it follows that $C = 0$, so
$$w = a\tanh au, \tag{11}$$

which satisfies the three conditions above. Restoring the original variables leads to the solution
$$y = 2\epsilon a\tanh(ax/3), \tag{12}$$

which is a function of the constant $B = a^2$. Since the differential equation is of the third order, there are three constants of integration, namely, $A = C = 0$, and B.

2.27. Solution of (1), § 2.26 when A, B, $C \neq 0$. We commence with (5), § 2.26, then

$$\frac{d}{du}(w' + w^2) = A, \tag{1}$$

so

$$w' + w^2 = Au + B. \tag{2}$$

Writing $z = Au + B$, we get

$$\frac{dw}{du} = \frac{dw}{dz}\frac{dz}{du} = A\frac{dw}{dz}, \tag{3}$$

so (2) becomes

$$\frac{dw}{dz} + \frac{w^2}{A} - \frac{z}{A} = 0. \tag{4}$$

This is the Riccati type of equation at (4), § 2.130, with $a = b = 1/A$, $\mu = 1$, so *mutatis mutandis* the solution is (12), § 2.130. In the present case $\alpha = 0$, $p = 1/2$, $v = 1/3$, $q = 3/2$, $l = 2/3A$, which gives

$$w(z) = (A/2z)\left\{1 + (2z^{\frac{3}{2}}/A)\left[\frac{I'_{\frac{1}{3}}(2z^{\frac{3}{2}}/3A) + CI'_{-\frac{1}{3}}(2z^{\frac{3}{2}}/3A)}{I_{\frac{1}{3}}(2z^{\frac{3}{2}}/3A) + CI_{-\frac{1}{3}}(2z^{\frac{3}{2}}/3A)}\right]\right\}, \tag{5}$$

C being a constant of integration. Finally by § 2.26 with

$$z = [A(x/3) + B]$$

in (5) above, we obtain

$$y = 2\epsilon w[A(x/3) + B], \tag{6}$$

which is a function of the three constants of integration A, B, and C.

2.30. The Lane–Emden equation [159] This occurs in connexion with the gravitational equilibrium of a gaseous configuration in stellar structure. Here the total pressure is due to the usual gas pressure plus that in virtue of radiation. It is given by the formula

$$p = \tfrac{1}{3}aT^4 + RT/v, \tag{1}$$

where p = pressure, T = absolute temperature, a = radiation constant, v = volume of unit mass, R = gas constant. The pressure p and density $\rho = 1/v$ both vary with the radius r, the relationship between the two former is

$$p = K\rho^{1+1/\mu}, \tag{2}$$

K, μ being constants. If m is the mass of matter within a sphere of radius r, and G the gravitational constant, namely, $6{\cdot}67 \times 10^{-8}$ dynes cm.^{2} gm.$^{-2}$, the equations of equilibrium for the configuration are

$$\frac{dp}{dr} + \frac{Gm\rho}{r^2} = 0, \tag{3}$$

and
$$\frac{dm}{dr} - 4\pi r^2 \rho = 0. \tag{4}$$

From (3)
$$\frac{r^2}{\rho}\frac{dp}{dr} + Gm = 0, \tag{5}$$

and by aid of (4), this becomes

$$\frac{1}{r^2}\frac{d}{dr}\left(\frac{r^2}{\rho}\frac{dp}{dr}\right) + 4\pi G\rho = 0. \tag{6}$$

Write $\rho = \lambda\theta^\mu$, where λ is, for the time being, an arbitrary constant. Then from this and (2) we get

$$p = K\lambda^{(1+1/\mu)}\theta^{\mu+1}. \tag{7}$$

Substituting from (7) into (6) yields

$$\frac{1}{r^2}\frac{d}{dr}\left(\frac{r^2}{\theta^\mu}\frac{d}{dr}\theta^{\mu+1}\right) + \frac{4\pi G}{K}\lambda^{(1-1/\mu)}\theta^\mu = 0, \tag{8}$$

or
$$\frac{1}{r^2}\frac{d}{dr}\left(r^2\frac{d\theta}{dr}\right) + k^2\theta^\mu = 0, \tag{9}$$

with $k^2 = 4\pi G\lambda^{(1-1/\mu)}/(\mu+1)K$. Putting $\xi = kr$ in (9) leads to

$$\frac{1}{\xi^2}\frac{d}{d\xi}\left(\xi^2\frac{d\theta}{d\xi}\right) + \theta^\mu = 0, \tag{10}$$

or
$$\frac{d^2\theta}{d\xi^2} + \frac{2}{\xi}\frac{d\theta}{d\xi} + \theta^\mu = 0. \tag{11}$$

This is known as the Lane–Emden equation. Unless $\mu = 0$ or 1, it is non-linear. So far λ is arbitrary, but we now fix it by making $\theta = 1$ at $r = 0$, the centre of the sphere, which gives $\lambda = \rho_c$, the central density, and we have $\theta = 1$, and $d\theta/d\xi = 0$ when $\xi = 0$. A solution which satisfies these boundary conditions is termed a Lane–Emden function of index μ. Tabular values of some of the functions are given in reference [105].

2.31. Transformation of (10), § 2.30 [159]. The substitution $\xi = 1/x$, $d/d\xi = -x^2 d/dx$ transforms the equation to

$$x^4\frac{d^2\theta}{dx^2} + \theta^\mu = 0. \tag{1}$$

We shall consider the integrable case where $\mu = 5$. Substituting $\theta = (\tfrac{1}{4})^{\tfrac{1}{4}}x^{\tfrac{1}{2}}y$ into (1) gives

$$x^2 y'' + xy' - \tfrac{1}{4}y(1-y^4) = 0, \tag{2}$$

while with $x = e^u$, (2) becomes

$$\frac{d^2y}{du^2} - \tfrac{1}{4}y(1-y^4) = 0, \tag{3}$$

which is non-linear by virtue of the term $\tfrac{1}{4}y^5$.

2.32. Solution of (3), § 2.31 [159]. Write $v = dy/du$, $du = dy/v$, and we get

$$v\frac{dv}{dy} = \tfrac{1}{4}y(1-y^4), \tag{1}$$

so

$$\int v\,dv = \tfrac{1}{4}\int (y-y^5)\,dy + A, \tag{2}$$

or

$$v^2 = \tfrac{1}{4}y^2(1-\tfrac{1}{3}y^4) + 2A. \tag{3}$$

When $r = 0$, $\xi = d\theta/d\xi = 0$, and it may be shown that $y = v = 0$, so $A = 0$. Thus (3) gives

$$v = \frac{dy}{du} = \pm\tfrac{1}{2}y(1-\tfrac{1}{3}y^4)^{\frac{1}{2}}. \tag{4}$$

Either sign in (4) will yield the result at (11). We choose the lower sign, so that when $u \to +\infty$, $r \to 0$. From (4) we have

$$u = -2\int (dy/y)/(1-\tfrac{1}{3}y^4)^{\frac{1}{2}} + B_1. \tag{5}$$

Let $\sin^2 w = \tfrac{1}{3}y^4$, and (5) becomes

$$u = -\int dw/\sin w + B_1 \tag{6}$$

$$= -\log(\tan\tfrac{1}{2}w) + B_1, \tag{7}$$

so

$$\tan\tfrac{1}{2}w = Be^{-u} = B\xi. \tag{8}$$

Now $\sin^2 w = 4\tan^2\tfrac{1}{2}w/(1+\tan^2\tfrac{1}{2}w)^2 = \tfrac{1}{3}y^4$,

so

$$y = [12B^2\xi^2/(1+B^2\xi^2)^2]^{\frac{1}{4}}. \tag{9}$$

But $\theta = (\tfrac{1}{4})^{\frac{1}{4}}x^{\frac{1}{2}}y$, and $x = \xi^{-1}$, so $\theta = (\tfrac{1}{4})^{\frac{1}{4}}y\xi^{-\frac{1}{2}}$, and on substituting for y from (9), we get

$$\theta = [3B^2/(1+B^2\xi^2)^2]^{\frac{1}{4}}. \tag{10}$$

For the Lane–Emden function of index $\mu = 5$, we take $\theta = 1$, $d\theta/d\xi = 0$ at $\xi = 0$, which gives $B^2 = 1/3$. Hence the function of index 5 is

$$\theta_5 = (1+\tfrac{1}{3}\xi^2)^{-\frac{1}{2}}. \tag{11}$$

CHAPTER III

EQUATIONS INTEGRABLE BY ELLIPTIC INTEGRALS AND FUNCTIONS

3.10. Solve $$\ddot{y}+ay+by^3 = 0, \tag{1}$$

where $a > 0$, $b \gtrless 0$, and the initial conditions are $y = y_0$, $\dot{y} = 0$, when $t = 0$. This equation refers to a mass-spring system of the type illustrated in Fig. 2, but the 'characteristic' of the spring is $s_1 y + s_3 y^3$, and there is no damping. The differential equation of the system is

$$m\ddot{y}+s_1 y+s_3 y^3 = 0, \tag{2}$$

so $a = s_1/m$, and $b = s_3/m$, m being the mass. A spring control of the form $s_1 y + s_3 y^3$ may be obtained by using a flat bar and suitably shaped blocks, as shown in Fig. 4 A, provided $s_3 > 0$. The effective length of the spring decreases with increase in the amplitude of vibration. The stiffness is defined to be the derivative of the restoring force, so

$$s = s_1+3s_3 y^2. \tag{3}$$

Thus the stiffness increases or decreases with increase in the displacement, according as $s_3 >$ or < 0. A case where $s_3 > 0$ is illustrated in Fig. 12 B, C. We shall see later that in the case of a simple pendulum $s_3 < 0$. Herein we take $s_3 > 0$, so in (1) $b > 0$.

Another example of a non-linear restoring force is that of a mass m at the centre of a taut uniform vertical wire, as illustrated in Fig. 4 B. It is left to the reader to show that if $y/l \ll 1$, and m moves in a horizontal straight line, the approximate differential equation of motion takes the form at (1), with $a = 2T/ml$, $b = EA/ml^3$, T being the tension when $y = 0$, A the cross-sectional area, and E the modulus of elasticity.

Solution of (1). Write $v = dy/dt$ and (1) becomes

$$v\frac{dv}{dy} = -(ay+by^3), \tag{4}$$

so $$\int_0^v v\,dv = -\int_{y_0}^y (ay+by^3)\,dy \tag{5}$$

and $$v^2 = a(y_0^2-y^2)+\tfrac{1}{2}b(y_0^4-y^4). \tag{6}$$

Choosing the negative root, we have

$$v = dy/dt = -a^{\frac{1}{2}}(y_0^2-y^2)^{\frac{1}{2}}[1+(b/2a)(y_0^2+y^2)]^{\frac{1}{2}}, \tag{7}$$

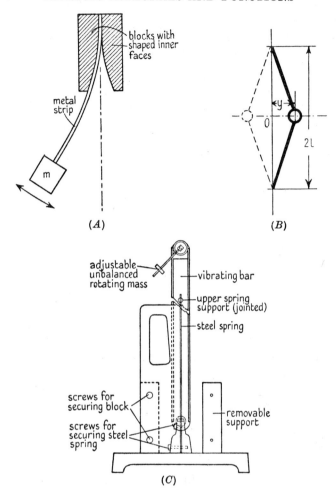

FIG. 4 A, B, C. Illustrating how a non-linear spring control may be obtained. C is described in § 4.193.

and, therefore,

$$t = -a^{-\frac{1}{2}} \int_{y_0}^{y} dw/(y_0^2 - w^2)^{\frac{1}{2}}[1 + (b/2a)(y_0^2 + w^2)]^{\frac{1}{2}}. \qquad (8)$$

Let $w = y_0 \cos\psi$, and we get

$$t = a^{-\frac{1}{2}} \int_{0}^{\varphi} d\psi/[1 + (b/2a)y_0^2(1 + \cos^2\psi)]^{\frac{1}{2}}, \qquad (9)$$

with $\cos\varphi = y/y_0$, or $\varphi = \cos^{-1}(y/y_0)$. Thus if $\lambda^2 = by_0^2/2(a + by_0^2)$,

(9) may be written

$$t = \frac{1}{(a+by_0^2)^{\frac{1}{2}}} \int_0^{\varphi} d\psi/(1-\lambda^2\sin^2\psi)^{\frac{1}{2}}. \tag{10}$$

Apart from the external multiplier, the right-hand side of (10) is an incomplete elliptic integral of the first kind with modulus λ. Thus in standard notation [173] we have

$$t = \frac{1}{(a+by_0^2)^{\frac{1}{2}}} F(\lambda, \varphi), \tag{11}$$

where

$$u = F(\lambda, \varphi) = \int_0^{\varphi} d\psi/(1-\lambda^2\sin^2\psi)^{\frac{1}{2}}. \tag{12}$$

If we put $x = \sin\psi$, (12) becomes

$$u = \int_0^{\sin\varphi} dx/[(1-x^2)^{\frac{1}{2}}(1-\lambda^2x^2)^{\frac{1}{2}}]. \tag{13}$$

By definition $u = \text{sn}^{-1}\sin\varphi =$ the right-hand side of (13),   (14)

so

$$\text{sn}\,u = \sin\varphi, \tag{15}$$

where sn u is the sine type of Jacobian elliptic function. This definition will be understood more readily if we make comparison with the inverse function defined by

$$u = \sin^{-1}y = \int_0^y dx/(1-x^2)^{\frac{1}{2}}, \qquad |y| \leqslant 1, \tag{16}$$

from which we obtain the well-known result

$$du/dy = 1/(1-y^2)^{\frac{1}{2}}, \tag{17}$$

or

$$\sin u = y. \tag{18}$$

The Jacobian elliptic function corresponding to $\cos u$, which applies to our solution, is

$$\text{cn}\,u = \cos\varphi, \tag{19}$$

so by (15), (19) $\text{sn}^2u+\text{cn}^2u = 1,$ (20)

which compares with $\sin^2u+\cos^2u = 1$.

The solution (10), (11) is expressed in the form of an 'inverse' function, and the values of F corresponding to given values of $\varphi°$ may be extracted from tables of elliptic integrals [173]. Then, as shown in § 3.13, t may be computed from (11). The other coordinate is $y = y_0\cos\varphi = y_0\,\text{cn}\,u$, so the y–t relationship may be plotted, the 'elliptic' cosine being obtained.

3.110. The energy equation. Multiplying (6), § 3.10, throughout by $\frac{1}{2}m$ and rearranging, we obtain

$$\tfrac{1}{2}mv^2 + \tfrac{1}{2}may^2 + \tfrac{1}{4}mby^4 = \tfrac{1}{2}may_0^2 + \tfrac{1}{4}mby_0^4, \tag{1}$$

or $\qquad \tfrac{1}{2}mv^2 + (\tfrac{1}{2}s_1 y^2 + \tfrac{1}{4}s_3 y^4) = \tfrac{1}{2}s_1 y_0^2 + \tfrac{1}{4}s_3 y_0^4, \tag{2}$

so Kinetic energy + Potential energy = Total energy (p.e. at $t = 0$). (3)

Equations of the type (6), § 3.10, may be regarded as energy equations. (1) is used in 1°, § 9.23, to show that the motion is periodic.

3.111. Periodic time of oscillation. The dynamical system to which (1), § 3.10 refers, is devoid of damping, and the spring control is an anti-symmetrical or odd function of y (see Figs. 12 A, B). It follows that if the mass were displaced initially by an amount $\pm y_0$, after release it would execute a periodic oscillation about the central position $y = 0$. The periodic nature of the motion follows from the relationship $y = y_0 \cos\varphi$ obtained in § 3.10, since $\cos\varphi$ is periodic in φ, with period 2π. The quarter period is the time taken for the mass to move from the initial position $y = y_0$ to the central or equilibrium position $y = 0$, and corresponds to the interval $\varphi = (0, \frac{1}{2}\pi)$. Thus by (10), (11), § 3.10, the complete period of the motion is given by

$$\tau_0 = [4/(a+by_0^2)^{\frac{1}{2}}] \int_0^{\frac{1}{2}\pi} d\psi/(1-\lambda^2 \sin^2\psi)^{\frac{1}{2}} = [\ \ ]F(\lambda, \tfrac{1}{2}\pi), \tag{1}$$

where $F(\lambda, \frac{1}{2}\pi)$ is a complete elliptic integral of the first kind with modulus λ. In virtue of the multiplier $(a+by_0^2)^{-\frac{1}{2}}$, the periodic time decreases with increase in a, b, y_0 either individually or collectively. If y_0 is fixed, an increase in a, b, or both of them, entails a stiffer spring, and therefore a smaller period τ_0, and higher fundamental frequency $\omega/2\pi = \tau_0^{-1}$. On the other hand, if a, b are fixed, an increase in y_0 means greater initial acceleration in virtue of the enhanced *average* stiffness† $(s_1 + s_3 y_0^2)$, which corresponds to $(a+by_0^2)$. In this respect it is of interest to remark that, approximately,

$$\tau_0 \propto (a+by_0^2)^{-\frac{1}{2}} = [m/(s_1+s_3 y_0^2)]^{\frac{1}{2}} = (\text{mass/average stiffness})^{\frac{1}{2}}, \tag{2}$$

or $\qquad \tau_0 = (\text{mass/average stiffness})^{\frac{1}{2}} \times \text{a factor}. \tag{3}$

The factor is $4F(\lambda, \frac{1}{2}\pi)$ which we shall now determine for certain values of a, b, and y_0.

---

† Stiffness $= s_1 + 3s_3 y^2$. Average stiffness $= \dfrac{1}{y_0} \displaystyle\int_0^{y_0} (s_1 + 3s_3 y^2)\, dy = s_1 + s_3 y_0^2$.

3.12. Numerical illustration of (1), § 3.111. Take $y_0 = 1, a = 10,$ $b = 100$, then the modulus

$$\lambda = [by_0^2/2(a+by_0^2)]^{\frac{1}{2}} = (100/2\times110)^{\frac{1}{2}} \tag{1}$$

$$= 0\cdot674. \tag{2}$$

By (1), § 3.111,
$$\tau_0 = (4/110^{\frac{1}{2}})F(0\cdot674, \tfrac{1}{2}\pi) \tag{3}$$

$$= 4\times1\cdot82/10\cdot48 = 0\cdot695, \tag{4}$$

by aid of elliptic integral tables [173]. It follows that the constant in § 3.111 is $4\times1\cdot82 \simeq 7\cdot28$. In a system with *linear* spring control it would be $2\pi \simeq 6\cdot28$. The frequency of occurrence of the oscillation is, therefore,

$$\omega/2\pi = \tau_0^{-1} \simeq 1\cdot44. \tag{5}$$

If $b = 0$, $y = y_0 \cos a^{\frac{1}{2}}t,$ (6)
so the frequency is

$$\omega/2\pi = a^{\frac{1}{2}}/2\pi = 10^{\frac{1}{2}}/2\pi \simeq 0\cdot5. \tag{7}$$

Thus the influence of adding the term by^3 to the stiffness control is almost to treble the frequency of the oscillation when $y_0 = 1$. The frequency ratio either increases or decreases, according as $y_0 >$ or < 1.

3.13. Graphical representation. To exhibit the relationship between y and t we use the formula

$$t = F(0\cdot674, \varphi)/110^{\frac{1}{2}}, \tag{1}$$

i.e. (11), § 3.10, with the numerical values inserted, and a table of elliptic integrals of the first kind [173]. Then $\lambda = 0\cdot674 = \sin\alpha$, so $\alpha \simeq 42\cdot5°$. Also $y = y_0\cos\varphi = \cos\varphi$. The data in Table 1 were obtained.

TABLE 1

$\varphi°$	$F(42\cdot5°, \varphi°)$	$t = F/10\cdot48$	$t\ (radians)$	$y = \cos\varphi$
0	0·000	0·0000	0·000	1·000
10	0·175	0·0167	0·151	0·985
20	0·352	0·0336	0·304	0·940
30	0·535	0·0510	0·461	0·866
40	0·724	0·0691	0·625	0·766
50	0·923	0·0881	0·797	0·643
60	1·132	0·1080	0·976	0·500
70	1·353	0·1292	1·168	0·342
80	1·58:	0·1510	1·365	0·174
90	1·82:	0·1738	1·571	0·000

By plotting the points corresponding to the last two columns in Table 1 we obtain the first quarter period of the Jacobian elliptic function $\operatorname{cn} t = \cos\varphi$, i.e. the elliptic cosine. A quarter period of the curve is depicted in Fig. 5, and the ordinary or circular cosine of equal period and amplitude is shown by the broken curve for comparison. There is no marked difference between the ordinates of the two curves. Thus although the addition of by^3 to the spring control ay causes the rate of oscillation to increase nearly threefold when $y_0 = 1$, *the motion is almost simple harmonic notwithstanding.*

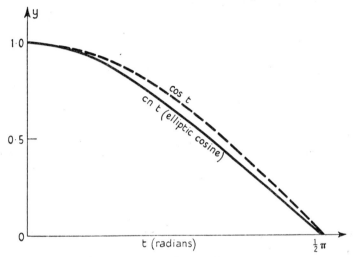

FIG. 5. Graphs of $\operatorname{cn} t$ and $\cos t$.

3.14. Approximate solution of (1), § 3.10.

It is evident from Fig. 5 that the solution curve $y = \cos\varphi = \operatorname{cn} t$ may be analysed into a Fourier series. Its shape is such that in a first approximation we may write

$$y = A_1 \cos \omega t + A_3 \cos 3\omega t, \tag{1}$$

where $|A_1| \gg |A_3|$. Substituting (1) into (1), § 3.10, with $\psi = \omega t$ we get

$$\left.\begin{aligned}
\ddot{y} &= -\omega^2(A_1 \cos\psi + 9A_3 \cos 3\psi) \\
ay &= a(A_1 \cos\psi + A_3 \cos 3\psi) \\
by^3 &= \tfrac{1}{4}bA_1^3(3\cos\psi + \cos 3\psi) + \tfrac{3}{4}bA_1^2 A_3 \cos\psi + \tfrac{3}{2}bA_1^2 A_3 \cos 3\psi
\end{aligned}\right\}. \tag{2}$$

In the last line, terms involving A_3 (except two) have been omitted as negligible.

Equating the coefficient of $\cos\psi$ to zero, gives

$$\omega^2 = a + \tfrac{3}{4}bA_1^2 + \tfrac{3}{4}bA_1 A_3, \tag{3}$$

since $A_1 \neq 0$. It follows from (3) that the frequency is dependent upon the amplitude of the motion, which is a characteristic of non-linear dynamical or other physical systems. When $b = 0$, $A_3 = 0$, the system is linear, and ω is independent of A_1, this being a feature of such a system.

Equating the coefficient of $\cos 3\psi$ to zero, we have

$$-9\omega^2 A_3 + aA_3 + \tfrac{1}{4}bA_1^3 + \tfrac{3}{2}bA_1^2 A_3 = 0. \tag{4}$$

Substituting for a from (3), and omitting the term in $A_1 A_3^2$, yields

$$A_3 \simeq bA_1^3 \Big/ 32\left(\omega^2 - \frac{3}{32} bA_1^2\right). \tag{5}$$

Using (3), without the term in A_3, in (5) we get

$$A_3/A_1 \simeq bA_1^2/(32a + 21bA_1^2) \tag{6}$$
$$= 1/[21 + (32a/bA_1^2)], \tag{7}$$

which is always $\ll 1$, provided $b > 0$.

Since $y = y_0$ when $t = 0$, it follows that

$$y_0 = A_1 + A_3, \tag{8}$$

with $|A_1| \gg |A_3|$. Substituting from (8) into (3) we obtain

$$\omega^2 \simeq a + \tfrac{3}{4}by_0^2 - \tfrac{3}{4}by_0 A_3. \tag{9}$$

Take $a = 10$, $b = 100$, $y_0 = 1$, and neglect the term in A_3. Then to a first approximation

$$\omega^2 \simeq 10 + 75 = 85. \tag{10}$$

Using this in (5) with $A_1 \simeq 1$ we get

$$A_3 \simeq 0 \cdot 04, \tag{11}$$

so $A_1 \simeq 25A_3$. Substituting into (9) for the various quantities yields

$$\omega^2 \simeq 85 - 75 \times 0 \cdot 04 = 82, \tag{12}$$

so the periodic time is

$$\tau_0 = 2\pi/\omega = 0 \cdot 69_8, \tag{13}$$

which compares favourably with the more accurate value at (4), § 3.12.

By (8), (11), $A_1 = (y_0 - A_3) = 1 - 0 \cdot 04 = 0 \cdot 96$. Substituting into (1) we obtain the approximate solution

$$y = 0 \cdot 96 \cos \omega t + 0 \cdot 04 \cos 3\omega t, \tag{14}$$

so the amplitude of the third harmonic is only about $\tfrac{1}{24}$th that of the fundamental, i.e. the motion is essentially simple harmonic. Using the formula given at (12), § 3.19, the reader should compute the coefficients in the Fourier series for $\operatorname{cn} t$, and compare them with those in (14).

3.15. Application of §§ 3.13, 3.14. The results therein may be used for the following problem: A large mass m is dropped from a height h on a steel shell whose vertical force-displacement relationship is $f = s_1 y + s_3 y^3$, the two bodies interlocking at the instant of impact. Neglecting (a) the mass of the shell, (b) the displacement due to mg after impact, (c) damping, determine the subsequent motion of the system if the base of the shell is clamped to a rigid foundation.

The differential equation is

$$m\frac{d^2y}{dt^2} + s_1 y + s_3 y^3 = 0, \tag{1}$$

or
$$\ddot{y} + ay + by^3 = 0, \tag{2}$$

where $a = s_1/m$, $b = s_3/m$. The maximum displacement y_0 may be calculated from the energy relation. Thus equating the strain energy to the loss in potential energy of m, we have

$$s_1 \int_0^{y_0} y\, dy + s_3 \int_0^{y_0} y^3\, dy = \tfrac{1}{2}s_1 y_0^2 + \tfrac{1}{4}s_3 y_0^4 = mg(h+y_0). \tag{3}$$

If $h \gg y_0$, (3) yields

$$y_0 = \left(\frac{s_1}{s_3}\right)^{\frac{1}{2}}\left[\left(1 + 4mgh\frac{s_3}{s_1^2}\right)^{\frac{1}{2}} - 1\right]^{\frac{1}{2}}. \tag{4}$$

After reaching $y = y_0$, the motion is identical with that discussed in §§ 3.13, 3.14, so the y–t curve is the elliptic cosine $cn\,t$. Since damping is absent, the initial part of the curve from $y = 0$ to y_0 is obtained by reflecting the first quadrant of $cn\,t$ in the y-axis, so that it comes behind the origin. In § 3.14 we assumed

$$y = A_1 \cos \omega t + A_3 \cos 3\omega t. \tag{5}$$

Thus if we commence at $t = 0$ when the impact occurs, we must write $(\omega t - \tfrac{1}{2}\pi)$ for ωt, which gives the approximate solution

$$y = A_1 \sin \omega t - A_3 \sin 3\omega t. \tag{6}$$

A_1 and A_3 are calculated as in § 3.14, the value of y_0 being that in (4) above.

3.160. The simple pendulum. Referring to Fig. 6 A the equation of motion is

$$\text{mass} \times \text{acceleration} + \text{restoring force} = 0, \tag{1}$$

or
$$m(ld^2\theta/dt^2) + mg\sin\theta = 0, \tag{2}$$

so
$$d^2\theta/dt^2 + \frac{g}{l}\sin\theta = 0. \tag{3}$$

Since $\sin\theta = \theta - \dfrac{\theta^3}{3!} + \dfrac{\theta^5}{5!} - \ldots$, the degree of the equation differs from unity, so it is non-linear. Owing to the shape of a sine curve, the control 'stiffness' decreases with increase in θ (Fig. 6 B).

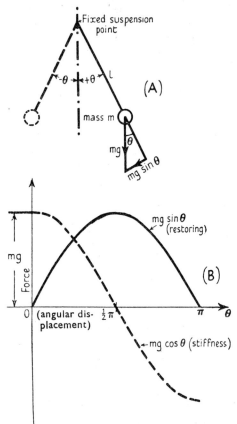

FIG. 6 A. Schematic diagram for simple pendulum. B. Restoring force and 'stiffness' curves for simple pendulum, showing non-linearity.

Write $v = d\theta/dt$, $g/l = a$, and (3) becomes

$$\frac{v\,dv}{d\theta} + a\sin\theta = 0, \tag{4}$$

so

$$\int v\,dv = -a \int \sin\theta\,d\theta + \tfrac{1}{2}A, \tag{5}$$

giving

$$v^2 = 2a\cos\theta + A. \tag{6}$$

If the maximum swing (amplitude) is $\theta = \psi$,

$$v = 0, \quad \text{and} \quad A = -2a\cos\psi.$$

Thus $\quad v = \pm(2a)^{\frac{1}{2}}(\cos\theta - \cos\psi)^{\frac{1}{2}} = \pm 2a^{\frac{1}{2}}(\sin^2\frac{1}{2}\psi - \sin^2\frac{1}{2}\theta)^{\frac{1}{2}}.$ (7)

Put $\sin\frac{1}{2}\psi = k$, $\sin\frac{1}{2}\theta = k\sin\varphi$, and (7) becomes

$$d\theta/dt = v = -2a^{\frac{1}{2}}k\cos\varphi,$$ (8)

the negative sign being chosen, since θ decreases with increase in t, as reckoned from the instant of maximum deflexion. Also

$$\tfrac{1}{2}\cos\tfrac{1}{2}\theta\,d\theta = k\cos\varphi\,d\varphi,$$

or $\qquad\qquad d\theta = 2k\cos\varphi\,d\varphi/(1 - k^2\sin^2\varphi)^{\frac{1}{2}}.$ (9)

Equating the expressions for $d\theta$ from (8), (9) gives

$$dt = -d\varphi/a^{\frac{1}{2}}(1 - k^2\sin^2\varphi)^{\frac{1}{2}}.$$ (10)

When $t = 0$, $v = 0$ and $\varphi = \tfrac{1}{2}\pi$, and when $t = \tfrac{1}{4}\tau_0$, $\theta = 0$, $\varphi = 0$. Accordingly on integrating (10) between the limits $\varphi = (\tfrac{1}{2}\pi, 0)$, we obtain the quarter period, so

$$\tfrac{1}{4}\tau_0 = a^{-\frac{1}{2}}\int_0^{\frac{1}{2}\pi} d\varphi/(1 - k^2\sin^2\varphi)^{\frac{1}{2}} = (l/g)^{\frac{1}{2}}F(k, \tfrac{1}{2}\pi),$$ (11)

where $F(k, \tfrac{1}{2}\pi)$ is a complete elliptic integral of the first kind, modulus $k = \sin\frac{1}{2}\psi$. Hence the time for a complete period is given by

$$\tau_0 = 4(l/g)^{\frac{1}{2}}F(k, \tfrac{1}{2}\pi).$$ (12)

From a table of elliptic integrals we find that F increases with increase in k, and, therefore, the greater the amplitude the longer the periodic time. Consequently the motion is not isochronous, i.e. the time of swing is a function of the amplitude, which is to be expected, since (3) is non-linear in θ. See problem 47, p. 255 for singular points of (3).

3.161. Approximate solution of (3), § 3.160. If $|\theta| < \tfrac{1}{6}\pi$, we may write $\sin\theta \simeq \theta - \tfrac{1}{6}\theta^3$. Then the non-linear equation to be solved is

$$\ddot{\theta} + a\theta + b\theta^3 = 0,$$ (1)

with $a = g/l$ and $b = -g/6l$. In this case, as before, the 'stiffness' decreases with increase in θ. Then to a first approximation we have by (3), § 3.14, for an amplitude ψ,

$$\omega^2 \simeq a + \tfrac{3}{4}b\psi^2 = (g/l)[1 - \tfrac{1}{8}\psi^2].$$ (2)

Thus the periodic time is approximately

$$\tau_0 = 2\pi/\omega \simeq 2\pi(l/g)^{\frac{1}{2}}(1 + \tfrac{1}{16}\psi^2),$$ (3)

being a function of the amplitude ψ.

3.17. Motion with viscous damping. If a term representing this is introduced into (1), § 3.10, it becomes

$$\ddot{y} + 2\kappa\dot{y} + (ay + by^3) = 0.$$ (1)

D

When $\kappa = 0$, by (7), § 3.14,

$$A_3/A_1 \ll 1, \tag{2}$$

and the motion is nearly cosinusoidal with angular frequency

$$\omega \simeq (a+3bA_1^2/4)^{\frac{1}{2}}. \tag{3}$$

Hence we may write

$$y = y_0 \cos \omega t, \text{ approximately.} \tag{4}$$

Thus when $\kappa > 0$, but small enough, and (2) is satisfied, the equation to be solved takes the approximate equivalent linear form

$$\ddot{y}+2\kappa\dot{y}+\omega^2 y = 0. \tag{5}$$

For the initial conditions $y = y_0$, $\dot{y} = 0$ at $t = 0$, it follows that

$$y = y_0 e^{-\kappa t} \cos \omega t, \tag{6}$$

is an approximate solution of (1). Since $A_1 \simeq y_0 e^{-\kappa t}$, from (3) we obtain

$$\omega \simeq (a+3by_0^2 e^{-2\kappa t}/4)^{\frac{1}{2}}, \tag{7}$$

so $\omega \to a^{\frac{1}{2}}$ as $t \to +\infty$.

Singular points of (1). As shown in 2°, § 9.23, for $a, b > 0$, and $\kappa > $ or < 0, $y = v = 0$ is the only singular point. If $\kappa^2 < a$, $\kappa > 0$, the motion is oscillatory for any y_0, and y, $\dot{y} \to 0$ as $t \to +\infty$. For $\kappa^2 > a$, $\kappa > 0$, and y_0 large enough, the motion is a damped oscillation at the start. Ultimately, the control stiffness $s = a+3by^2$ is too small for oscillation to continue, and then $y \to 0$ monotonically as $t \to +\infty$. Progressive decrease in s is accompanied by increase in the time interval between successive zeros of y.

When $b < 0$, the singularities are investigated in 2°, § 9.30. With $\kappa > 0$, the origin is either a stable node or a stable spiral point, according as $\kappa \geqslant a^{\frac{1}{2}} > 0$, or $0 < \kappa < a^{\frac{1}{2}}$. There is, however, a restriction to be imposed on the amplitude of motion to avoid instability. The v–y curves have a form akin to those in Fig. 101, where the cols occur at $y = \pm(a/b)^{\frac{1}{2}} = \pm 2^{\frac{1}{2}}$, $v = 0$. If $|y| > (a/b)^{\frac{1}{2}}$, the v–y curve lies in an unstable region of the v–y plane. Also $f'(y)$ is negative, which indicates instability. Moreover, for stable motion about the origin, the initial conditions point (y_0, v_0) must lie in a stable region of the v–y plane.

3.180. The elastica. In the linear theory of elasticity it is assumed that (1) stress is proportional to strain, i.e. Hooke's law is obeyed; (2) the deflexions are small so that in the formulae for the strain, squares and products of the deflexions and their derivatives may be neglected. The elastica is a thin strut deflected beyond the Euler critical or buckling load. Here assumption (1) is maintained, but (2) is not. Consequently the differential equation for the strut is a non-linear type.

In Fig. 7 A the axis of the strut $CDEF$ is bent in the plane of the

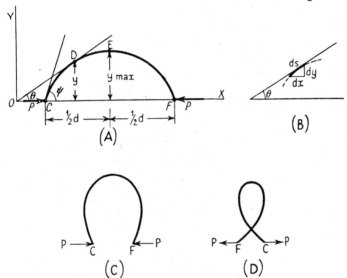

FIG. 7. A. Schematic diagram for the elastica CEF. C, D. Bent form of elastica.

paper as shown, by two equal but opposite forces P acting along the line OX. Let

l = axial length of strut assumed constant,
P = forces applied along the line OX as in Fig. 7 A,
s = arc length measured from C,
ψ, θ = angles of tangent to strut at C, and D, respectively,
y = ordinate at D,
$B = EI$ = flexural rigidity,
I = moment of inertia of cross-section,
E = modulus of elasticity.

The differential equation is [206]

$$\frac{B \, d\theta}{ds} + Py = 0, \tag{1}$$

or

$$\frac{d^2\theta}{ds^2} + a\frac{dy}{ds} = 0, \tag{2}$$

with $a = P/B$. From Fig. 7 B, $dy/ds = \sin\theta$, so (2) becomes

$$\frac{d^2\theta}{ds^2} + a\sin\theta = 0, \qquad (3)$$

which is identical with (3), § 3.160 if we write s for t. Consequently we take (10), § 3.160, and make this change, so

$$ds = -d\varphi/a^{\frac{1}{2}}(1-k^2\sin^2\varphi)^{\frac{1}{2}}. \qquad (4)$$

At C in Fig. 7 A, $y = 0$, $\psi = 0$, so $\varphi_0 = \frac{1}{2}\pi$, while at any point on the strut between C and E, $\varphi_1 = \sin^{-1}(\sin\frac{1}{2}\theta/\sin\frac{1}{2}\psi)$ by virtue of the substitutions in § 3.160. Also

$$d\varphi/ds = \frac{\cos\frac{1}{2}\theta}{2k\cos\varphi}\frac{d\theta}{ds},$$

which is negative since θ decreases with increase in s. Hence the negative sign in (4) is correct. Then

$$s = -a^{-\frac{1}{2}}\int_{\frac{1}{2}\pi}^{\varphi_1} d\varphi/(1-k^2\sin^2\varphi)^{\frac{1}{2}} \qquad (5)$$

$$= a^{-\frac{1}{2}}\left[\int_0^{\frac{1}{2}\pi} - \int_0^{\varphi_1}\right] \qquad (6)$$

$$= a^{-\frac{1}{2}}[F(k,\tfrac{1}{2}\pi) - F(k,\varphi_1)], \qquad (7)$$

where, as usual, F represents an elliptic integral of the first kind. When $\varphi_1 = 0$ at E, (7) gives

$$l = 2a^{-\frac{1}{2}}F(k,\tfrac{1}{2}\pi). \qquad (8)$$

3.181. Maximum deflexion y_{max}. From (1), § 3.180, and (8), § 3.160,

$$y = -\frac{1}{a}\frac{d\theta}{ds} = \frac{1}{a}2a^{\frac{1}{2}}k\cos\varphi, \qquad (1)$$

$$= 2ka^{-\frac{1}{2}}\cos\varphi. \qquad (2)$$

When $\varphi = 0$, $\qquad y_{max} = 2ka^{-\frac{1}{2}} = kl/F(k,\tfrac{1}{2}\pi). \qquad (3)$

3.182. Relationship between load and maximum deflexion. When the strut is about to buckle, $\psi = 0$, $k = 0$, $y_{max} = 0$. Then in (8), § 3.180, $F = \frac{1}{2}\pi$, so taking $a = P_c/B$, the Euler critical load is given by the well-known formula

$$P_c = \pi^2 B/l^2 \simeq 10B/l^2. \qquad (1)$$

Writing (8), § 3.180, in the form

$$P = 4BF^2/l^2, \qquad (2)$$

we get $$P/P_c = 4F^2/\pi^2. \tag{3}$$

Also, by (3), § 3.181, $$y_{max}/l = k/F. \tag{4}$$

Using tables of F, we plot P/P_c against y_{max}/l for various values of $k = \sin \frac{1}{2}\psi$. The graph is shown in Fig. 8 A [206]. The maximum value of y_{max}/l corresponds to the configuration of the strut (see Figs. 7 c, d) when the ends C and F meet. For greater values of ψ and, therefore, of $k = \sin \frac{1}{2}\psi$, the ends are thrust apart as in Fig. 7 d, so y_{max}/l decreases with increase in P/P_c. The reader should plot the

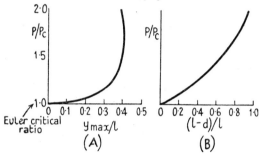

Fig. 8. A. Relation between (load/critical load) and (y_{max}/l) for elastica. B. Relation between (load/critical load) and ($l-d)/l$ for elastica, from critical load where strut buckles, to that where the two ends meet.

curve of Fig. 8 A and also bend a thin strip of metal to the shapes shown in Fig. 7 c, d.

3.183. The distance d in Fig. 7 A. This is given by

$$d = \int dx = 2 \int_0^{\frac{1}{2}l} \cos\theta \, ds. \tag{1}$$

Since $\cos\theta = 1 - 2\sin^2\frac{1}{2}\theta = 1 - 2k^2\sin^2\varphi$, from (1) and (4), § 3.180, we obtain

$$d = 2a^{-\frac{1}{2}} \int_0^{\frac{1}{2}\pi} \frac{(1-2k^2\sin^2\varphi)}{(1-k^2\sin^2\varphi)^{\frac{1}{2}}} \, d\varphi \tag{2}$$

$$= 2a^{-\frac{1}{2}} \int_0^{\frac{1}{2}\pi} [2(1-k^2\sin^2\varphi)^{\frac{1}{2}} - 1/(1-k^2\sin^2\varphi)^{\frac{1}{2}}] \, d\varphi \tag{3}$$

$$= 2a^{-\frac{1}{2}}[2E(k,\tfrac{1}{2}\pi) - F(k,\tfrac{1}{2}\pi)], \tag{4}$$

where F, E are complete elliptic integrals of the first and second kinds, respectively. We can now compute the ratio $(l-d)/l = $ [contraction/original length] for various values of k. Then the graph of Fig. 8 B may be obtained showing the relationship between P/P_c and $(l-d)/l$, i.e. in effect between load and contraction [206]. The curved nature of the graph is accounted for by (3), § 3.180, being a non-linear equation.

3.19. Jacobian elliptic functions continued. From § 3.10,

$$\operatorname{sn} u = \sin\varphi, \tag{1}$$

and
$$\operatorname{cn} u = \cos\varphi. \tag{2}$$

A third function is defined by

$$\operatorname{dn} u = (1-k^2\sin^2\varphi)^{\frac{1}{2}} = \{(1-k^2)+k^2\cos^2\varphi\}^{\frac{1}{2}} \tag{3}$$

$$= (1-k^2\operatorname{sn}^2u)^{\frac{1}{2}} = \{(1-k^2)+k^2\operatorname{cn}^2u\}^{\frac{1}{2}}. \tag{4}$$

Then from (1), (2), and (4)

$$\operatorname{sn}^2u+\operatorname{cn}^2u = k^2\operatorname{sn}^2u+\operatorname{dn}^2u = 1. \tag{5}$$

Graphs of these *periodic* functions are given in Figs. 8 C, D, E.

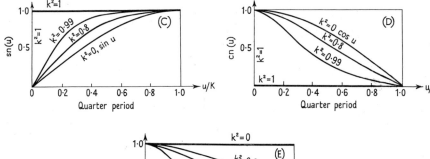

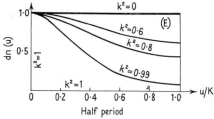

FIG. 8 C, D, E. Graphs of the Jacobian elliptic functions. C. sn u. D. cn u.

E. dn u. $K = F(k, \tfrac{1}{2}\pi) = \int_{0}^{\frac{1}{2}\pi} d\psi/(1-k^2\sin^2\psi)^{\frac{1}{2}}$. As $k \to 1$, dn $u \to$ cn u.

Derivatives.
$$\frac{d}{du}\operatorname{sn} u = \operatorname{sn}' u = \frac{d}{d\varphi}\sin\varphi\frac{d\varphi}{du} \tag{6}$$

$$= (1-k^2\sin^2\varphi)^{\frac{1}{2}}\cos\varphi, \tag{7}$$

by (12), § 3.10, with k for λ, so

$$\text{sn}'u = \text{cn}\,u\,\text{dn}\,u. \tag{8}$$

Similarly $$\text{cn}'u = -\text{sn}\,u\,\text{dn}\,u, \tag{9}$$

and $$\text{dn}'u = -k^2\text{sn}\,u\,\text{cn}\,u. \tag{10}$$

Fourier series. With $K = F(k, \tfrac{1}{2}\pi)$,

$$q^{\frac{1}{4}} = p(1+2p^4+15p^8+150p^{12}+1707p^{16}+...), \quad p = k^{\frac{1}{2}}/2, \ |k| < 1,$$

$$\text{sn}\,u = \frac{2\pi}{Kk}\sum_{r=0}^{\infty}\left(\frac{q^{r+\frac{1}{2}}}{1-q^{2r+1}}\right)\sin(2r+1)\frac{\pi u}{2K}, \tag{11}$$

$$\text{cn}\,u = \frac{2\pi}{Kk}\sum_{r=0}^{\infty}\left(\frac{q^{r+\frac{1}{2}}}{1+q^{2r+1}}\right)\cos(2r+1)\frac{\pi u}{2K}, \tag{12}$$

and $$\text{dn}\,u = \frac{\pi}{2K}+\frac{2\pi}{K}\sum_{r=1}^{\infty}\left(\frac{q^r}{1+q^{2r}}\right)\cos\frac{r\pi u}{K}. \tag{13}$$

Application of (12). At (14), § 3.14, in the second approximation solution of $\ddot{y}+10y+100y^3 = 0$, the amplitude ratio of the third harmonic to the fundamental is $0\cdot042$, while by the method of iteration (exemplified in § 4.130) it is $0\cdot038$. We shall compare these with the 'exact' result calculated from (12). By § 3.12, $k = \lambda = 0\cdot674$, so $p = 0\cdot411$, and this gives $q = 0\cdot038$. Then by (12)

$$A_3/A_1 = q/(1-q+q^2) = 0\cdot0395. \tag{14}$$

Thus we have the three values for comparison, (i) Fourier series $0\cdot042$, (ii) iteration $0\cdot038$, (iii) elliptic function $0\cdot0395$, each of which is less than 5 per cent.

3.20. Differential equations satisfied by $\text{sn}\,u$, $\text{cn}\,u$, $\text{dn}\,u$

$1°$. *Equation for* $\text{sn}\,u$. Differentiating (8), § 3.19, with respect to u, we obtain

$$\text{sn}'' = \text{dn}\,\text{cn}'+\text{cn}\,\text{dn}'$$
$$= -\text{sn}(\text{dn}^2+k^2\,\text{cn}^2). \tag{1}$$

But $\text{dn}^2+k^2\text{sn}^2 = 1$, $\text{sn}^2+\text{cn}^2 = 1$, so

$$\text{dn}^2+k^2\,\text{cn}^2 = 1-k^2\text{sn}^2+k^2(1-\text{sn}^2)$$
$$= (1+k^2)-2k^2\,\text{sn}^2. \tag{2}$$

Hence from (1), (2),

$$\text{sn}'' = -\text{sn}\{(1+k^2)-2k^2\,\text{sn}^2\}, \tag{3}$$

and if $y = \text{sn}\,u$, the required equation is

$$y''+(1+k^2)y-2k^2y^3 = 0. \tag{4}$$

Let $y = A\,\text{sn}\,u$, where A is a non-zero real constant. Substituting into (4) and dividing through by A, the last term on the left-hand side is $-2k^2A^2\mathrm{sn}^3$. Then it follows that $y = A\,\mathrm{sn}\,u$ satisfies

$$y'' + (1+k^2)y - 2k^2A^{-2}y^3 = 0. \tag{5}$$

Now put $u = \alpha t$ in (5), and we obtain

$$\ddot{y} + (1+k^2)\alpha^2 y - 2k^2\alpha^2 A^{-2}y^3 = 0, \tag{6}$$

whose solution is $y = A\,\mathrm{sn}\,\alpha t$. Let $(1+k^2)\alpha^2 = a$, $2k^2\alpha^2 A^{-2} = b$, $a,\ b > 0$, and we get $\alpha^2 = (a - \tfrac{1}{2}bA^2)$, $k^2 = bA^2/(2a - bA^2)$. Since $|k| < 1$, we must have $|A| < (a/b)^{\frac{1}{2}}$ or $a > bA^2$, which is the condition for a periodic stable solution (see §§ 9.20, 9.22 and Fig. 94). Thus

$$y = A\,\mathrm{sn}\,u = A\,\mathrm{sn}\{t(a - \tfrac{1}{2}bA^2)^{\frac{1}{2}}\}$$

is the solution of $\ddot{y} + ay - by^3 = 0.$ (7)

Comparing the argument here with that in the first term on the right-hand side of (11), § 3.19, we have

$$\frac{\pi u}{2K} = \frac{\pi t(a - \tfrac{1}{2}bA^2)^{\frac{1}{2}}}{2K} = \omega t, \tag{8}$$

so the periodic time $2\pi/\omega$ is given by

$$\tau = 4F(k, \tfrac{1}{2}\pi)/(a - \tfrac{1}{2}bA^2)^{\frac{1}{2}}. \tag{9}$$

2°. *Equation for $A\,\mathrm{cn}\,u$.* Proceeding as in 1°, we find that the solution of $\ddot{y} + ay + by^3 = 0$ $(a,\ b > 0)$ (1)

is $y = A\,\mathrm{cn}\{t(a + bA^2)^{\frac{1}{2}}\},$ (2)

where $k^2 = bA^2/2(a + bA^2)$, and

$$\tau = 4F(k, \tfrac{1}{2}\pi)/(a + bA^2)^{\frac{1}{2}}. \tag{3}$$

Since $a, b > 0$, $|k| < 1$ for A real, and therefore, the solution is always periodic and stable (see § 9.23 and Fig. 96).

3°. *Equation for $A\,\mathrm{dn}\,u$.* The solution of

$$\ddot{y} - ay + by^3 = 0 \qquad (a,\ b > 0) \tag{1}$$

is $y = A\,\mathrm{dn}\{At(b/2)^{\frac{1}{2}}\},$ (2)

with $k^2 = 2(1 - a/bA^2)$, and

$$4F(k, \tfrac{1}{2}\pi)/A(b/2)^{\frac{1}{2}}. \tag{3}$$

For a periodic solution about $y = 0$, k must be real, so $|A| > (a/b)^{\frac{1}{2}}$ (see above (8), 4°, § 9.11, also §§ 9.20, 9.22).

In 1°–3° the respective initial conditions $y(0) = 0$, $\dot{y}(0) = 0$, and $\dot{y}(0) = 0$, are satisfied automatically by the solutions given. The values of A may be found by assigning either $\dot{y}(0)$ or $y(0)$, as the case may be.

CHAPTER IV

EQUATIONS HAVING PERIODIC SOLUTIONS

4.10. Self-oscillatory thermionic valve circuit. This is shown schematically in Fig. 9 A, but the applied potential difference

$$E_0 \cos(\omega t + \varphi)$$

is replaced by a short circuit. The sum of the potential differences

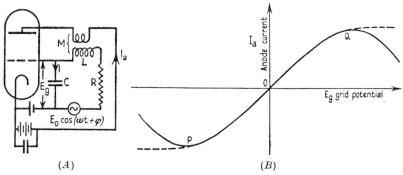

(A) (B)

Fɪɢ. 9. A. Circuit diagram for thermionic valve oscillator, with oscillatory circuit between grid and cathode, together with 'driving' potential difference $E_0 \cos(\omega t + \varphi)$ applied in series therewith. B. Assumed cubical-parabolic relation between anode current and grid potential. The working part of the curve lies between P and Q; O is the centre of oscillation. The 'actual' curve beyond P, Q takes the form indicated by the broken lines, i.e. the current tends to zero at P, and to a saturation value at Q.

round the grid circuit must vanish, so in the absence of grid current the differential equation is

$$L\frac{dI}{dt} + RI + \frac{1}{C}\int I\,dt - M\frac{dI_a}{dt} = 0. \qquad (1)$$

The sign of M is minus, this being a known condition for self-oscillation. Assume that the anode current is given by

$$I_a = \sigma[E_g - E_g^3/3E_s^2], \qquad (2)\dagger$$

where σ is the transconductance of the valve, and E_s is the grid potential corresponding to the anode saturation current. The

   † This relationship applies when the grid potential is adjusted so that the valve operates about the point of inflexion of the curve (see Fig. 9 B). Otherwise a term in E_g^2 must be included. (5) then takes the form $\ddot{y} - b(1 - y^2 - b_1 y)\dot{y} + ay = 0$, which introduces unnecessary complication into the analysis.

relationship at (2) is shown graphically in Fig. 9 B. If we write $E_g/E_s = u$, since $E_g = (1/C) \int I\, dt$, (1) becomes

$$LCE_s \ddot{u} + RCE_s \dot{u} + E_s u - \sigma M E_s \left[\dot{u} - \frac{1}{3} \frac{d(u^3)}{dt} \right] = 0, \qquad (3)$$

or
$$\ddot{u} - b\dot{u} + c\frac{d(u^3)}{dt} + au = 0, \qquad (4)$$

with $a = 1/LC$, $b = (\sigma M/LC) - (R/L)$, $c = \sigma M/3LC$. Writing $u = (b/3c)^{\frac{1}{2}}y$, (4) takes the form [122]

$$\ddot{y} - b(1 - y^2)\dot{y} + ay = 0. \qquad (5)$$

Replacing t by $a^{-\frac{1}{2}}t$, and $a^{-\frac{1}{2}}b$ by ϵ, (5) becomes

$$\ddot{y} - \epsilon(1 - y^2)\dot{y} + y = 0. \qquad (6)$$

By §§ 4.311, 8.12, and 3°, § 9.23, equation (5) has a periodic solution if $b > 0$, so

$$\sigma M/LC > R/L, \qquad (7)$$

or
$$M > CR/\sigma. \qquad (8)$$

Thus to obtain a sustained self-oscillation, the mutual inductance between the grid and anode coils must exceed a certain critical value.

The factor $-b(1 - y^2)$ represents the damping coefficient, which alternates in sign during the steady oscillatory state. When positive, energy is dissipated in the circuit, but when negative, energy is supplied from the external source and compensates exactly for the loss, since the motion is periodic. If in (5), $a^{-\frac{1}{2}}b \ll 1$, as shown below $y \simeq 2\sin\omega_0 t$, where $\omega_0 = a^{\frac{1}{2}}$, which gives

$$-b(1 - y^2) \simeq -b(2\cos 2\omega_0 t - 1),$$

so the damping coefficient changes sign at twice the frequency of the steady oscillation, as illustrated in Fig. 9 c. When M is increased sufficiently to make $1 \ll a^{-\frac{1}{2}}b$, relaxation oscillations occur (see Fig. 63). They will be considered later. At the moment we shall take $0 < a^{-\frac{1}{2}}b \ll 1$, and obtain an approximate periodic solution of (5).

Let $y = A\sin\omega_0 t$, then substituting into (5), multiplying by $\cos\omega_0 t$ and integrating from $t = 0$ to $2\pi/\omega_0$, with $\psi = \omega_0 t$, we get

$$-A\omega_0^2 \int_0^{2\pi/\omega_0} \sin\psi\cos\psi\, dt - \omega_0 bA \int_0^{2\pi/\omega_0} (1 - A^2\sin^2\psi)\cos^2\psi\, dt +$$

$$+ aA \int_0^{2\pi/\omega_0} \sin\psi\cos\psi\, dt = 0. \qquad (9)$$

The first and third integrals vanish, and the second may be written

$$-\omega_0 bA \int\limits_{0}^{2\pi/\omega_0} \left(\cos^2\psi - \frac{A^2}{4}\sin^2 2\psi\right) dt = -bA\pi(1-A^2/4). \qquad (10)$$

For this to vanish, we must have $A = 2$.

Repeating the above procedure but multiplying by $\sin\omega_0 t$, we find that
$$\omega_0^2 = a \qquad (11)$$

is a rough approximation. Hence we obtain the approximate periodic solution
$$y = 2\sin a^{\frac{1}{2}}t. \qquad (12)$$

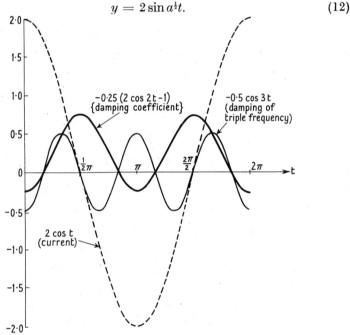

FIG. 9. c. Curves for periodic solution of $\ddot{y}-\epsilon(1-y^2)\dot{y}+y = 0$, $\epsilon = 0.25$. $y = 2\sin t$ is a first approximation, and corresponds to E_g in Fig. 9 A when $E_0 = 0$; $\dot{y} = 2\cos t$ corresponds to I in Fig. 9 A when $E_0 = 0$; $-\epsilon(1-y^2) = -0.25(2\cos 2t-1)$ corresponds to the oscillatory damping *coefficient* of double frequency; $-\epsilon(1-y^2)\dot{y} = -0.5\cos 3t$ corresponds to variable damping of triple frequency. Energy loss per cycle at fundamental frequency $= \epsilon \int\limits_{0}^{2\pi} (1-y^2)\dot{y}\,dy = \int\limits_{0}^{2\pi} (1-4\sin^2 t)\cos^2 t\,dt = 0$, which corresponds to periodic motion, since the *net* energy lost or gained per cycle is zero.

4.110. Perturbation method applied to (5), § 4.10. We employ this method, which was used extensively by Lindstedt and Poincaré for the solution of perturbation problems in celestial mechanics, to obtain a better approximation than (14), § 4.10 [90, 193]. Assume that the *periodic* solution may be expressed in the form

$$y = y_0 + by_1 + b^2 y_2 + \dots \tag{1}$$

where $y_0, y_1, \dots$, are twice-differentiable functions of t to be determined, and $0 < b \ll 1$ is the perturbation parameter. Also let

$$a = \alpha_0 + b\alpha_1 + b^2\alpha_2 + \dots, \tag{2}$$

$\alpha_0, \alpha_1, \dots$, being constants to be determined. We shall take the initial conditions
$$y(0) = 0, \qquad \dot{y}(0) = \omega_0 A.$$
Since these are to hold for $0 < b \leqslant b_0$, it follows that

$$y_0(0) = y_1(0) = \dots = 0, \quad \dot{y}_0(0) = \omega_0 A, \quad \dot{y}_1(0) = \dot{y}_2(0) = \dots = 0.$$

Substituting (1), (2) into (5), § 4.10, leads to

$$(1-y^2) = (1-y_0^2) - 2by_0 y_1 - b^2(y_1^2 + 2y_0 y_2) - \dots,$$
$$\dot{y} = \dot{y}_0 + b\dot{y}_1 + b^2 \dot{y}_2 + \dots;$$
$$-b(1-y^2)\dot{y} = -b\dot{y}_0(1-y_0^2) - b^2[\dot{y}_1(1-y_0^2) - 2y_0 \dot{y}_0 y_1] - \dots,$$
$$\ddot{y} = \ddot{y}_0 + b\ddot{y}_1 + b^2 \ddot{y}_2 + \dots;$$
$$ay = \alpha_0 y_0 + b(\alpha_1 y_0 + \alpha_0 y_1) + b^2(\alpha_0 y_2 + \alpha_2 y_0 + \alpha_1 y_1) + \dots. \tag{3}$$

Equating coefficients of b^r to zero for $r = 0, 1, 2, \dots$, we obtain

b^0:
$$\ddot{y}_0 + \alpha_0 y_0 = 0, \tag{4}$$

so
$$y_0 = A_0 \sin \omega_0 t + B_0 \cos \omega_0 t, \tag{5}$$

with $\alpha_0 = \omega_0^2$. Since $y_0(0) = 0$, $\dot{y}_0 = \omega_0 A$, it follows that $B_0 = 0$, $A_0 = A$, so with $\psi = \omega_0 t$,

$$y_0 = A \sin \psi. \tag{6}$$

b:
$$\ddot{y}_1 + \alpha_0 y_1 = -\alpha_1 y_0 + \dot{y}_0(1-y_0^2) \tag{7}$$
$$= -\alpha_1 A \sin \psi + A\omega_0 \cos \psi (1 - A^2 \sin^2 \psi) \tag{8}$$
$$= -\alpha_1 A \sin \psi + A\omega_0(1 - \tfrac{1}{4}A^2)\cos \psi + \tfrac{1}{4}A^3 \omega_0 \cos 3\psi. \tag{9}$$

The particular integrals of (9) corresponding to the terms in $\sin \psi$, $\cos \psi$ take the non-periodic form $t \cos \psi$, $t \sin \psi$, respectively. Since the solution is to be periodic, it follows that the coefficients of $\sin \psi$, $\cos \psi$ must vanish independently. Hence

$$\alpha_1 = 0, \qquad A = 2, \tag{10}$$

so
$$y_0 = 2 \sin \psi. \tag{11}$$

Thus (9) becomes

$$\ddot{y}_1 + \alpha_0 y_1 = 2\omega_0 \cos 3\psi, \tag{12}$$

of which the complete solution is

$$y_1 = A_1 \sin\psi + B_1 \cos\psi - (1/4\omega_0)\cos 3\psi, \tag{13}$$

and since $y_1(0) = \dot{y}_1(0) = 0$, we find that $A_1 = 0$, $B_1 = 1/4\omega_0$. Thus we have

$$y_1 = (1/4\omega_0)(\cos\psi - \cos 3\psi). \tag{14}$$

b^2:
$$\ddot{y}_2 + \alpha_0 y_2 = -(\alpha_2 y_0 + \alpha_1 y_1) + \dot{y}_1(1 - y_0^2) - 2y_0 \dot{y}_0 y_1. \tag{15}$$

Substituting from (11), (14) into the right-hand side of (15) gives

$$\ddot{y}_2 + \alpha_0 y_2 = -2\alpha_2 \sin\psi + (-\tfrac{1}{4}\sin\psi + \tfrac{3}{4}\sin 3\psi)(1 - 4\sin^2\psi) - $$
$$-\sin 2\psi(\cos\psi - \cos 3\psi), \tag{16}$$
$$= -(2\alpha_2 - \tfrac{1}{4})\sin\psi - \tfrac{3}{2}\sin 3\psi + \tfrac{5}{4}\sin 5\psi. \tag{17}$$

Since the solution is to be periodic, the coefficient of $\sin\psi$ must vanish, so
$$\alpha_2 = 1/8. \tag{18}$$
Then (17) becomes

$$\ddot{y}_2 + \alpha_0 y_2 = -\tfrac{3}{2}\sin 3\psi + \tfrac{5}{4}\sin 5\psi, \tag{19}$$

of which the complete solution is

$$y_2 = A_2 \sin\psi + B_2 \cos\psi + \frac{3}{16\omega_0^2}\sin 3\psi - \frac{5}{96\omega_0^2}\sin 5\psi. \tag{20}$$

Since $y_2(0) = \dot{y}_2(0) = 0$, we find that $A_2 = -29/96\omega_0^2$, $B_2 = 0$, and, therefore,

$$y_2 = -\frac{29}{96\omega_0^2}\sin\psi + \frac{3}{16\omega_0^2}\sin 3\psi - \frac{5}{96\omega_0^2}\sin 5\psi. \tag{21}$$

Whence from (1), (11), (14), (21), to the second order in b, the solution of (5), § 4.10, is
$$y = y_0 + by_1 + b^2 y_2, \tag{22}$$

$$= \left(2 - \frac{29b^2}{96\omega_0^2}\right)\sin\psi + \frac{b}{4\omega_0}(\cos\psi - \cos 3\psi) + \frac{b^2}{16\omega_0^2}(3\sin 3\psi - \tfrac{5}{6}\sin 5\psi). \tag{23}$$

Also by (2), (10), (18), to order two in b,

$$a = \alpha_0 + \tfrac{1}{8}b^2 = \omega_0^2 + \tfrac{1}{8}b^2, \tag{24}$$
so
$$\omega_0 \simeq a^{\frac{1}{2}}(1 - b^2/16a). \tag{25}$$

From (23), (25) it is evident that when b is small enough and a large enough, the approximate solution (14), § 4.10, is satisfactory. (25) shows that the influence of damping is to reduce the angular frequency of the oscillation by a small amount. In this respect it is of interest to compare (25) with the angular frequency obtained from the linear equation

$$\ddot{y} + b\dot{y} + ay = 0. \tag{26}$$

Here
$$\omega_0^2 = (a - \tfrac{1}{4}b^2), \tag{27}$$

so
$$\omega_0 \simeq a^{\frac{1}{2}}(1 - b^2/8a). \tag{28}$$

The reduction in ω_0 due to damping in (28) is twice that in (25).

It should be observed that the method of solution is one where successive approximations are found by solving *linear* differential equations, such that the initial conditions are satisfied.

4.111. Remarks on amplitude limitation.
Writing θy for y in (5), § 4.10, θ being a real constant, we obtain

$$\ddot{y} - b(1 - \theta^2 y^2)\dot{y} + ay = 0. \tag{1}$$

Thus (5), § 4.10, is reproduced only if $|\theta| = 1$. It follows, therefore, that the solution of *this* non-linear differential equation *cannot be multiplied by an arbitrary constant*. For given a, b, the coefficients of the various terms in the solution are unique. When the differential equation has the form (5), § 4.10, the amplitude of the fundamental oscillation is nearly 2, $0 < a^{-\frac{1}{2}}b \leqslant 0 \cdot 1$. If the equation were (1) above, the solution would be (23), § 4.110, multiplied by θ^{-1}. (1) may be derived from (4), § 4.10, by writing $\theta^2 = 3c/b$.

Amplitude limitation may also be considered in the following way. During growth, when the amplitude is small, the c term in (4), § 4.10, is negligible, so the equation becomes

$$\ddot{u} - b\dot{u} + au = 0. \tag{2}$$

The solution of (2) takes the form $e^{\frac{1}{2}bt}\sin(\omega t + \theta)$, with $\omega = (a - \tfrac{1}{4}b^2)^{\frac{1}{2}}$. Under this condition the anode current–grid potential relationship $(I_a–E_g)$ is linear. Moreover, a linear characteristic of unlimited extent would entail an amplitude which $\to \infty$ as $t \to +\infty$, by virtue of the negative resistance property of the valve. Owing to curvature of the characteristic (Fig. 9 B), amplitude limitation occurs. By aid of the differential equations (4), (5), § 4.10, we see that non-linear damping represented by the term $by^2\dot{y}$ is introduced as a consequence of the curved characteristic. Thus stabilization is effected by the inherent non-linear property of the valve.

Frequently if a system, electrical, mechanical, etc., is unstable, it may be stabilized by introducing some form of non-linear element, e.g. the systems described in §§ 7.13, 7.14, 7.420, 7.422 where the damping is non-linear. The action of a non-linear spring-control element in a mechanical system may be compared with the detuning of a resonant mass-spring arrangement, when either the mass or the spring stiffness varies with amplitude, e.g. §§ 7.20–7.22, 7.410.

4.12. Self-oscillations with electric motor-generator combination.

The schematic diagram of Fig. 10 A shows an electric motor with separately excited field, coupled mechanically and electrically to a dynamo having a series field. If I is the circuital

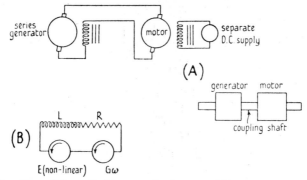

FIG. 10. A. Schematic diagram of series-wound D.C. generator and separately excited D.C. motor. B. Circuit diagram for A.

current, the potential difference at the generator terminals is approximately

$$E = \alpha_1 I - \alpha_3 I^3, \tag{1}$$

α_1, α_3 being positive constants. Since the sum of the potential differences round a closed circuit is zero, we must have

$$L \, dI/dt + RI + G\omega - E = 0, \tag{2}$$

where L, R are the total circuit inductance and resistance, respectively, and G is the back e.m.f. at the motor terminals per unit angular velocity ω. Inserting (1) in (2) and differentiating with respect to t gives

$$L \, d^2I/dt^2 - (\alpha_1 - R) \, dI/dt + \alpha_3 \, d(I^3)/dt + G \, d\omega/dt = 0. \tag{3}$$

Apart from ohmic loss, the power to the motor is the product of back e.m.f. and current, i.e. $G\omega I$. In absence of mechanical loss, this is equal to the rate of change of the kinetic energy of the rotating system. Thus if $\mathbf{I}$ is the moment of inertia,

$$G\omega I = \frac{d}{dt}(\tfrac{1}{2}\mathbf{I}\omega^2), \tag{4}$$

so

$$d\omega/dt = GI/\mathbf{I}. \tag{5}$$

Substituting from (5) into the last term of (3), and dividing throughout by L, yields the equation

$$\ddot{I}-b\dot{I}+cd(I^3)/dt+aI = 0, \qquad (6)$$

with $a = G^2/\mathbf{I}L, b = (\alpha_1-R)/L, c = \alpha_3/L$. (6) is identical in form with (4), § 4.10, for a thermionic valve circuit. Hence if $b > 0$, i.e. $\alpha_1 > R$, the system will be self-oscillatory, but non-oscillatory if $\alpha_1 < R$. When the former condition is satisfied, the motor-generator combination rotates periodically in each direction. For a relaxation type oscillation (sudden reversal),† b must be large enough and a small enough.

4.130. Solve $\ddot{y}+ay+by^2 = 0$ $(a > 0, \quad b > 0)$.   (1)

This equation pertains to an *undamped* mass-spring system (see Fig. 2) in which the spring control‡ takes the asymmetrical form $ay+by^2$, illustrated in Fig. 11 A. If the spring is extended and the mass released, the ensuing motion is periodic.§ We write (1) in the form

$$\ddot{y}+\omega^2 y = (\omega^2-\omega_0^2)y-by^2 \quad (\omega_0^2 = a) \qquad (2)$$

and use the method of successive approximation (iteration). First we assume the right-hand side to be negligible, so with $\psi = \omega t$, the complete solution is

$$y = A_1\cos\psi+B_1\sin\psi. \qquad (3)$$

Taking the initial conditions $y = y_0$, $\dot{y} = 0$, we obtain the first approximation

$$y = y_0\cos\psi. \qquad (4)$$

Substituting this in the right-hand side of (2) yields

$$\ddot{y}+\omega^2 y = (\omega^2-\omega_0^2)y_0\cos\psi-\tfrac{1}{2}by_0^2(1+\cos 2\psi). \qquad (5)$$

Since the solution is to be periodic, the coefficient of $\cos\psi$ must vanish, so

$$\omega^2 = \omega_0^2 = a. \qquad (6)$$

The complete solution of (5) is, therefore,

$$y = A\cos\psi+B\sin\psi+\frac{by_0^2}{6\omega^2}\cos 2\psi-\frac{by_0^2}{2\omega^2}. \qquad (7)$$

---

† A relaxation oscillation is a self-excited type in which a physical quantity, e.g. current, velocity, alternates abruptly between two levels, where it remains approximately constant for a relatively long time. This is illustrated by the curve in Fig. 63.

‡ As in § 3.10, (1) is a suitable form for the equation $m\,d^2y/dt^2+s_1 y+s_2 y^2 = 0$, with $a = s_1/m$, $b = s_2/m$. Although the spring control is $s_1 y+s_2 y^2$, it is convenient to refer to $ay+by^2$ as the control. It is the control corresponding to unit mass.

§ Provided $0 < y_0 < a/2b$. Periodicity is demonstrable by aid of §§ 9.22, 9.23. See Fig. 103 and problem 18, p. 248.

Now $y = y_0$, $\dot{y} = 0$, at $t = 0$, so it follows that

$$A = (y_0 + by_0^2/3\omega^2), \quad \text{and} \quad B = 0. \tag{8}$$

Hence, in the second approximation,

$$y = -\frac{by_0^2}{2\omega^2} + (y_0 + by_0^2/3\omega^2)\cos \omega t + \frac{by_0^2}{6\omega^2}\cos 2\omega t \tag{9}$$

with $\omega^2 = \omega_0^2 = a$. If $by_0/6a \ll 1$, the coefficient of $\cos 2\omega t$ will be

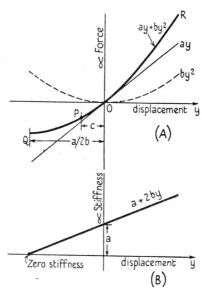

FIG. 11. A. Asymmetrical curve showing combination of linear and parabolic spring controls ay, by^2, respectively: $ay + by^2$ is neither an odd nor an even function of y. B. Stiffness-displacement curve for case (A).

small in comparison with that of $\cos \omega t$. The values of y and ω, in the third approximation, are given in problem 11, p. 246.

The constant term $(-by_0^2/2a)$ implies that the central point about which the oscillation occurs is displaced by this amount. In the language of the radio engineer, there is a rectification effect, since in an electrical circuit $(-by_0^2/2a)$ would correspond to a unidirectional current. In §§ 3.111, 3.14 we found that, in the non-linear system considered, the frequency of the oscillation was dependent upon the amplitude, whereas in (6) this is not so, since in our first approximation we neglected the term in b. We shall, therefore, obtain a better approximate value of $\omega/2\pi$ using the method of perturbation.

4.131. More accurate solution of (1), § 4.130. Let

$$y = y_0 + by_1 + b^2 y_2 + \ldots \tag{1}$$

and

$$a = \omega_0^2 + b\omega_1^2 + b^2\omega_2^2 + \ldots \tag{2}$$

with initial conditions $y = A$, $\dot{y} = 0$. From these it follows as in § 4.110 that

$$y_0(0) = A, \quad y_1(0) = y_2(0) = y_3(0) = \ldots = 0, \quad \dot{y}_0(0) = \dot{y}_1(0) = \ldots = 0.$$

Substituting for y and a from (1), (2) into the differential equation, we get

$$(\ddot{y}_0 + b\ddot{y}_1 + b^2\ddot{y}_2 + \ldots) + (\omega_0^2 + b\omega_1^2 + b^2\omega_2^2 + \ldots)(y_0 + by_1 + b^2 y_2 + \ldots) +$$
$$+ by_0^2 + 2b^2 y_0 y_1 + b^3(y_1^2 + 2y_0 y_2)\ldots = 0. \tag{3}$$

Equating the coefficients of $b^0, b, b^2, \ldots$ to zero, we have

b^0:
$$\ddot{y}_0 + \omega_0^2 y_0 = 0, \tag{4}$$

so
$$y_0 = A \cos \omega_0 t; \tag{5}$$

b:
$$\ddot{y}_1 + \omega_0^2 y_1 = -(\omega_1^2 y_0 + y_0^2) \tag{6}$$
$$= -[\tfrac{1}{2}A^2 + \omega_1^2 A \cos \omega_0 t + \tfrac{1}{2}A^2 \cos 2\omega_0 t], \tag{7}$$

by (5). To avoid a non-periodic term in the particular integral, we must have $\omega_1^2 = 0$, so the complete solution of (7) is

$$y_1 = -\frac{A^2}{2\omega_0^2} + A_1 \cos \omega_0 t + B_1 \sin \omega_0 t + \frac{A^2}{6\omega_0^2} \cos 2\omega_0 t. \tag{8}$$

With the above initial conditions, we find that

$$A_1 = A^2/3\omega_0^2, \qquad B_1 = 0, \tag{9}$$

so
$$y_1 = (A^2/\omega_0^2)[-\tfrac{1}{2} + \tfrac{1}{3} \cos \omega_0 t + \tfrac{1}{6} \cos 2\omega_0 t]. \tag{10}$$

b^2:
$$\ddot{y}_2 + \omega_0^2 y_2 = -(\omega_1^2 y_1 + \omega_2^2 y_0 + 2y_0 y_1) \tag{11}$$
$$= -\left[\frac{A^3}{3\omega_0^2} + A(\omega_2^2 - 5A^2/6\omega_0^2)\cos \omega_0 t + \frac{A^3}{3\omega_0^2} \cos 2\omega_0 t + \right.$$
$$\left. + \frac{A^3}{6\omega_0^2} \cos 3\omega_0 t \right]. \tag{12}$$

To avoid a non-periodic term in the particular integral of (12), the coefficient of $\cos \omega_0 t$ must vanish, so

$$\omega_2^2 = 5A^2/6\omega_0^2. \tag{13}$$

Then the complete solution of (12) is

$$y_2 = -\frac{A^3}{3\omega_0^4} + A_2 \cos \omega_0 t + B_2 \sin \omega_0 t + \frac{1}{9}\frac{A^3}{\omega_0^4} \cos 2\omega_0 t + \frac{1}{48}\frac{A^3}{\omega_0^4} \cos 3\omega_0 t. \tag{14}$$

Using the initial conditions above, we obtain

$$A_2 = 29A^3/144\omega_0^4, \quad \text{and} \quad B_2 = 0. \tag{15}$$

Hence by (1), (5), (10), (14), (15) to the second order in b, the solution of (1), § 4.130, is

$$y = -[(bA^2/2\omega_0^2)+(b^2A^3/3\omega_0^4)]+$$
$$+[A+(bA^2/3\omega_0^2)+(29b^2A^3/144\omega_0^4)]\cos\omega_0 t+$$
$$+[(bA^2/6\omega_0^2)+(b^2A^3/9\omega_0^4)]\cos 2\omega_0 t+(b^2A^3/48\omega_0^4)\cos 3\omega_0 t. \tag{16}$$

So long as $A \gg bA^2/6\omega_0^2$, i.e. $bA/6a \ll 1$, the second and third harmonics will be small in comparison with the fundamental. Also by (2), (13), since $\omega_1^2 = 0$, to the second order in b

$$\omega_0^2 = (a-5b^2A^2/6\omega_0^2). \tag{17}$$

If $a \gg 5b^2A^2/6\omega_0^2$, we obtain

$$\omega_0 \simeq a^{\frac{1}{2}}(1-5b^2A^2/12a^2). \tag{18}$$

It follows from (18) that the frequency *decreases* with increase in amplitude, which is just the opposite to the result in § 3.14. At first sight the term by^2 in the equation might be expected to ensure an increase in the spring control with increase in amplitude. The stiffness, however, is $(d/dy)(ay+by^2) = a+2by$ (see § 3.111 and Fig. 11 B), so it increases and decreases by equal amounts for $\pm y$. But the oscillation centre is now at the point defined by the constant term in (16), so the effective decrease in control exceeds numerically the increase, as the amplitude increases (see Fig. 11 A). Thus the frequency reduction is explained by the 'rectification' effect. Referring to Fig. 11 A, the two spring control terms ay, by^2 are plotted separately and collectively (QPR). For the latter curve, we see that the oscillation centre moves to the negative side of O, where the slope is less than that at O. Also $|c|$ increases with increase in A owing to the curve QPR being asymmetrical. Thus ω_0 decreases with increase in A. For a spring control $ay+by^3$, the stiffness is $(a+3by^2)$ and increases with increase in y, whether $\pm$, i.e. it is an even function of y (see Fig. 12 c). The graph of $ay+by^3$ is anti-symmetrical, so ω_0 increases with increase in amplitude. In Fig. 11 A, curve RQ if continued would intersect the y-axis at $-a/b$, which by § 9.30 corresponds to a col. Thus for stability $y_{\min} > -a/b$.

It is apposite to remark in connexion with the foregoing analysis that a tone of double frequency (the octave) is audible when a tuning-fork vibrates with a large amplitude. As the latter decreases, the pitch of the fundamental tone rises. This is in accord with the analysis.

EXAMPLE. The reader should solve (1), § 3.10, by the perturbation method using the initial conditions $y = A, \dot{y} = 0$. The result to order three in b is:

$$y = \left(A - \frac{bA^3}{32\omega_0^2} - \frac{b^2A^5}{256\omega_0^4} - \frac{b^3A^7}{32768\omega_0^2}\right)\cos \omega_0 t +$$
$$+ \left(\frac{bA^3}{32\omega_0^2} + \frac{3b^2A^5}{1024\omega_0^4} - \frac{3b^3A^7}{32768\omega_0^6}\right)\cos 3\omega_0 t +$$
$$+ \left(\frac{b^2A^5}{1024\omega_0^4} + \frac{3b^3A^7}{32768\omega_0^6}\right)\cos 5\omega_0 t + \frac{b^3A^7}{32768\omega_0^6}\cos 7\omega_0 t, \quad (19)$$

with
$$\omega_0^2 = a + \tfrac{3}{4}bA^2 + \frac{3b^2A^4}{128a} - \frac{21b^3A^6}{1024a^2}. \quad (20)$$

4.132. Effect of viscous damping. The equation to be solved is

$$\ddot{y} + 2\kappa\dot{y} + ay + by^2 = 0 \qquad (\kappa > 0). \quad (1)$$

Write $y = e^{-\kappa t}u(t)$, and we get

$$\ddot{u} + (a - \kappa^2)u + be^{-\kappa t}u^2 = 0. \quad (2)$$

If κ is small enough, by § 4.131, writing $be^{-\kappa t}$ for b, and ω_0^2 for $(a - \kappa^2) > 0$, an approximate solution of (1) is

$$y = e^{-\kappa t}\left[-\frac{bA^2e^{-\kappa t}}{2\omega_0^2} + \left(A + \frac{1}{3}\frac{bA^2e^{-\kappa t}}{\omega_0^2}\right)\cos \omega_0 t + \frac{1}{6}\frac{bA^2e^{-\kappa t}}{\omega_0^2}\cos 2\omega_0 t\right]. \quad (3)$$

When $t = 0, y = A, \dot{y} = -\kappa A$ which is small enough to be neglected. By §§ 9.20, 9.22, (1) has a col at $y = -a/b, v = 0$, and a stable spiral point or a stable node at $y = v = 0$, according as $\kappa^2 <$ or $> a$.

4.140. Solve

$$\ddot{y} + ay + by^3 = f\cos \omega t \quad (a > 0, b \gtrless 0). \quad (1)$$

This is the equation for a loss-free mass-spring system, with control proportional to $ay + by^3$, driven by a force $f\cos \omega t$ as shown schematically in Fig. 12 A. The inevitable transient follows the application of the driving force at $t = 0$, but we may assume that there is sufficient damping to extinguish this and enable the periodic state to be attained after a short time interval. The damping is supposed to be small enough to have negligible influence on the amplitude of the motion.

When a, b, ω, f have appropriate values, a subharmonic of

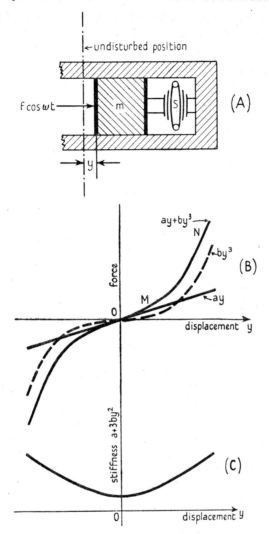

FIG. 12. A. Schematic diagram of mass m and non-linear spring s, driven by an alternating force $f\cos\omega t$. B. Anti-symmetrical curve showing combination of linear and cubical springs ay, by^3, respectively. The restoring force is an odd function of y. C. Stiffness-displacement curve for case B: $a + 3by^2$ is an even function of y.

frequency $\omega/6\pi$ occurs. This aspect is considered in § 4.190 et seq. For the time being we shall assume that the conditions for the existence of a subharmonic are not satisfied. In analytical work herein, it is tacitly presumed that the reaction of the system on the driving agent may be neglected. Thus the amplitude and functional form of the applied force is invariable.

By theorem (3), § 9.50, (1) has a solution of period $2\pi/\omega$. Since $ay+by^3$ is an odd function of y, the corresponding force-displacement graph in Fig. 12 B is anti-symmetrical about the force axis. It follows that the solution may take the form

$$y = A_1 \cos\psi + A_3 \cos 3\psi + A_5 \cos 5\psi + ..., \tag{2}$$

where $\psi = \omega t$. We shall restrict ourselves to two terms in (2). Substituting into (1), we get

$$\left.\begin{aligned}
\ddot{y} &= -\omega^2(A_1 \cos\psi + 9A_3 \cos 3\psi) \\
ay &= a(A_1 \cos\psi + A_3 \cos 3\psi) \\
by^3 &= b[\tfrac{1}{4}A_1^3(3\cos\psi + \cos 3\psi) + \\
&\quad + \tfrac{3}{4}A_1^2 A_3(\cos\psi + 2\cos 3\psi + \cos 5\psi) + \\
&\quad + \tfrac{3}{4}A_1 A_3^2(2\cos\psi + \cos 5\psi + \cos 7\psi) + \\
&\qquad\qquad\qquad + \tfrac{1}{4}A_3^3(3\cos 3\psi + \cos 9\psi)].
\end{aligned}\right\} \tag{3}$$

Equating the coefficients of $\cos\psi$ on each side of (1), by aid of (3), we have

$$(a - \omega^2 + \tfrac{3}{4}bA_1^2)A_1 + \tfrac{3}{4}bA_1^2 A_3 + \tfrac{3}{2}bA_1 A_3^2 = f, \tag{4}$$

or

$$\omega^2 = (a + \tfrac{3}{4}bA_1^2 - f/A_1) + \tfrac{3}{4}bA_1^2\left[\frac{A_3}{A_1} + 2\left(\frac{A_3}{A_1}\right)^2\right]. \tag{5}$$

This may be regarded as an approximation to the amplitude-frequency relation.

For the coefficient of $\cos 3\psi$, we obtain

$$(a - 9\omega^2)A_3 + \tfrac{1}{4}bA_1^3 + \tfrac{3}{2}bA_1^2 A_3 + \tfrac{3}{4}bA_3^3 = 0, \tag{6}$$

so

$$A_3 = \tfrac{1}{4}bA_1^3/(9\omega^2 - a - \tfrac{3}{2}bA_1^2 - \tfrac{3}{4}bA_3^2). \tag{7}$$

In (5) assume $|A_3/A_1| \ll 1$, so that we may neglect the third member.

Then

$$\omega^2 = (a + \tfrac{3}{4}bA_1^2 - f/A_1), \tag{8}$$

a condition which must be satisfied (approximately) for the solution of (1) to be periodic. If f and A_1 are fixed, ω is given by (8). For fixed ω and f, the amplitude of the fundamental vibration may be ascertained if (8) is written in the form

$$\tfrac{3}{4}bA_1^3 + (a - \omega^2)A_1 - f = 0. \tag{9}$$

If $b = 0$, we obtain the well-known formula for a linear system, namely,

$$A_1 = f/(a - \omega^2). \tag{10}$$

(9) is a cubic equation for A_1 which will, therefore, for fixed a, b, ω, f, have three values: (i) all real, (ii) one real, two complex conjugate. The consequences of A_1 being multivalued will be discussed later.

Next we consider (7). Substituting therein for ω^2 from (8), and neglecting $\frac{3}{4}bA_3^2$, leads to

$$A_3 = bA_1^3\bigg/\bigg(32a+21bA_1^2-\frac{36f}{A_1}\bigg). \tag{11}$$

Thus $A_3/A_1 \simeq 1/[21+\{32a-36f/A_1\}/bA_1^2], \tag{12}$

so $|A_3/A_1| \ll 1, \quad \text{if} \quad |21+(32a-36f/A_1)/bA_1^2| \gg 1, \tag{13}$

which includes the two cases $b > 0, b < 0$. Hence if (13) is satisfied, the forced motion of the system is *nearly cosinusoidal*. In the foregoing procedure, the non-linear equation is solved directly, whereas the methods of iteration, e.g. in § 4.130, and perturbation, e.g. in §§ 4.110, 4.131, entail the solution of linear differential equations, in the various stages of approximation.

4.141. Energy considerations.   Writing $v = dy/dt$, (1), § 4.140, takes the form $v\,dv/dy+ay+by^3 = f\cos\omega t, \tag{1}$

so $\int v\,dv+a\int y\,dy+b\int y^3\,dy = f\int\cos\omega t\,dy. \tag{2}$

By (2), § 4.140,

$$dy = -\omega(A_1\sin\psi+3A_3\sin 3\psi+...)\,dt. \tag{3}$$

Substituting (3) into the right-hand side of (2), and integrating over a period $t = (0, 2\pi/\omega)$, the left-hand side vanishes by virtue of periodicity, and the right-hand side by virtue of orthogonality of the circular functions. Hence during steady motion, no energy is supplied to the system from the driving mechanism, as we should expect, since there is no dissipation.

4.142. Effect of large f and small ω.   Experiments using an analog computer are described in [270]. The differential equation was that in § 4.16, taking $\varphi = -\frac{1}{2}\pi$. With $\kappa = 0\cdot 1, a = b = 1$, and $f \simeq 0\cdot 32$, the $|A_1|-\omega$ curve was similar to that in Fig. 17 A, but more peaked at Q. With $f \simeq 3\cdot 2$, pronounced irregularities occurred in $0 < \omega < 1$, in virtue of instability. Higher harmonics of relatively large amplitude were present (see [270] for details).

4.15. Experimental illustration of analysis in § 4.140 [92].   The apparatus shown schematically in Fig. 13 A, B has been used to obtain wave forms for a system akin to one represented symbolically by (1), § 4.140. A beam is mounted on a fulcrum so that oscillation occurs about the latter in a vertical plane. The mechanical construction is such as to reduce friction to a small amount. One end of the beam is constrained by a non-linear type of spring while a mass m rotates at

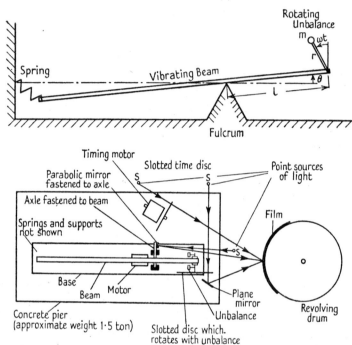

FIG. 13. A. Schematic diagram of apparatus for investigating system with non-linear restoring force. B. Plan view of apparatus.

radius r with angular velocity ω about the other end of the beam, thereby causing unbalance. If $\mathbf{I}$ is the moment of inertia of the oscillating parts about the fulcrum, $f(\theta)$ the spring-control torque, l the distance of the centre of rotation of m from the fulcrum, neglecting loss, we have

$$\mathbf{I}\, d^2\theta/dt^2 + f(\theta) = l(m\omega^2 r \cos \omega t), \tag{1}$$

where $-m(\omega^2 r \cos \omega t)$ is the accelerational force due to the rotation of m, and the right-hand side of (1) the corresponding driving torque. The motion of the lever was recorded photographically, and a record is reproduced in Fig. 14. The torque-deflexion curve $f(\theta)$ for the spring is depicted in Fig. 15, being such that $f(\theta) = -f(-\theta)$, i.e. it is an odd

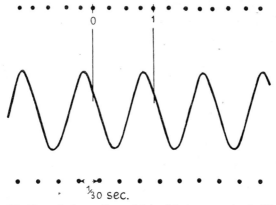

FIG. 14. Record of wave form obtained from apparatus in Fig. 13
using load-deflexion curve of Fig. 15.

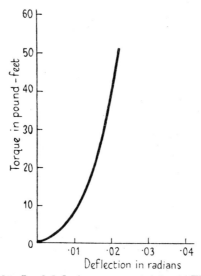

FIG. 15. Load-deflexion curve pertaining to Fig. 14.

function of θ, and the curve is anti-symmetrical about the torque
axis. Despite appreciable departure from linearity in Fig. 15, the
wave form in Fig. 14 is almost a simple harmonic type.

4.16. Amplitude-frequency relation for

$$\ddot{y}+2\kappa\dot{y}+ay+by^3 = f\cos(\omega t+\varphi).$$

This equation is for a dynamical system of the type considered in
§ 4.140, but with a term $2\kappa\dot{y}$ representing viscous damping. The

driving force will now be out of phase with the displacement corresponding to the fundamental vibration, so to simplify the analysis we have introduced the phase angle φ. By 3°, § 9.50, a periodic solution exists, so we assume as an approximation that with $\psi = \omega t$

$$y = A_1 \cos\psi + A_3 \cos 3\psi. \tag{1}$$

Then

$$2\kappa\dot{y} = -2\omega\kappa(A_1 \sin\psi + 3A_3 \sin 3\psi), \tag{2}$$

while

$$f\cos(\omega t + \varphi) = f(\cos\varphi \cos\psi - \sin\varphi \sin\psi). \tag{3}$$

Using (2), (3), (3), § 4.140, and equating the coefficients of $\cos\psi$, $\sin\psi$ on each side of the above differential equation, we obtain

$$\left.\begin{array}{r}(a - \omega^2 + \tfrac{3}{4}bA_1^2)A_1 = f\cos\varphi \\ \text{and} \qquad\qquad 2\omega\kappa A_1 = f\sin\varphi \end{array}\right\}, \tag{4}$$

terms involving A_3, A_3^2, A_3^3 being neglected by virtue of their relative smallness (see § 4.140).

Squaring and adding, (4) yields

$$[(a - \omega^2 + \tfrac{3}{4}bA_1^2)^2 + 4\omega^2\kappa^2]A_1^2 = f^2, \tag{5}$$

which is the amplitude-frequency relation for the non-linear system with viscous damping. When $\kappa = 0$, (5) degenerates to (8), § 4.140.

4.170. Amplitude-frequency curves.

These are obtained by plotting the relationship between ω and $|A_1|$ in (5), § 4.16, for given values of a, b, κ, and different values of f. The general trend of the curves will be gleaned from Figs. 16 A, B, C, which correspond to $b > 0$, $b < 0$, and $b = 0$. The curve through $\omega = a^{\frac{1}{2}}$, $|A_1| = 0$, is given by (5), § 4.16, when $f = \kappa = 0$, i.e.

$$|A_1| = \left[\frac{4}{3b}(\omega^2 - a)\right]^{\frac{1}{2}} \text{ for } b > 0, \tag{1}$$

and

$$|A_1| = \left[\frac{4}{3|b|}(a - \omega^2)\right]^{\frac{1}{2}} \text{ for } b < 0. \tag{2}$$

It is evident from Figs. 16 A, B, C that the curves for $b >$ or < 0 correspond to those for $b = 0$ sheared over to the right or left, respectively. In Fig. 16 A with $f = f_3$, if $\omega < \omega_1$, $|A_1|$ is single-valued so two roots of (5), § 4.16, are complex conjugate. If $\omega_1 \leqslant \omega \leqslant \omega_2$, all the roots are real, and $|A_1|$ is triple-valued, there being coincident pairs at ω_1, ω_2. If $\omega_2 < \omega$, $|A_1|$ is again single-valued, and two roots are complex conjugate. The curves of Fig. 16 B may be considered similarly, but of course with the proviso that $\omega > 0$. When $\kappa = 0$, the amplitude-frequency relation is that at (8) or (9), § 4.140. The curves resemble those in Figs. 16 A, B except that they are not closed at their upper ends. They approach the curves (1), (2) for $b > 0$, < 0. When $\omega^2 \gg a$, the amplitude-frequency curves for $b > 0$ are asymptotic to the straight line $|A_1| = 2\omega/(3b)^{\frac{1}{2}}$.

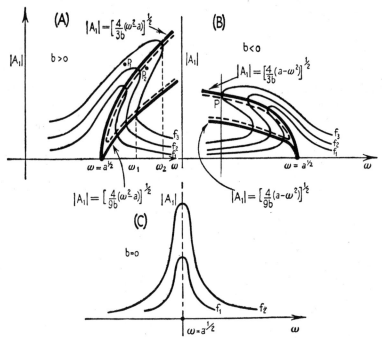

FIG. 16. Amplitude-frequency curves for driven mass-spring system, with spring characteristic of the form $ay + by^3$. For $b < 0$ use $|b|$ in formulae.

Jump phenomenon. Consider the mechanism of Fig. 13 whose motion is represented (*mutatis mutandis*) by the differential equation in § 4.16. Starting at P in Fig. 17 A with $b > 0$, let the frequency be increased gradually. The operating point will travel to Q, where $|A_1|$ drops suddenly to R and continues to move along to S with increase in ω. From S suppose the frequency is decreased gradually. On reaching T, $|A_1|$ jumps suddenly to U and then follows the curve down to P. Thus a form of hysteresis is exhibited. A similar behaviour is evinced when $b < 0$, as indicated in Fig. 17 B. Operation along TQ cannot be realized in practice, and the explanation is as follows: In Fig. 16 A there are three amplitude curves for forces $f_3 > f_2 > f_1$. The point P_1 lies on a curve f_2' such that $f_3 > f_2' > f_2$. If ω is constant, an increase

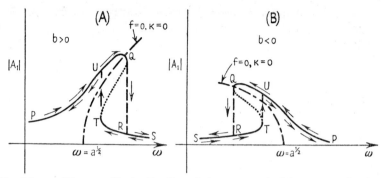

FIG. 17 A, B. Diagrams illustrating 'jump' phenomenon in driven system having spring characteristic of the form $ay+by^3$. See [11] respecting B.

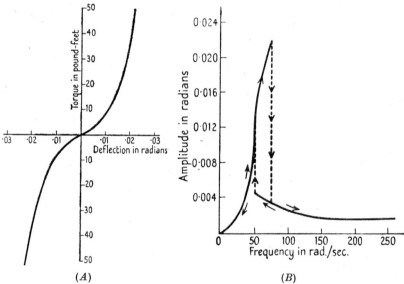

FIG. 18. A. Load-deflexion curve pertaining to amplitude-frequency curve in FIG. 18 B. B. Amplitude-frequency curve obtained from apparatus of Fig. 13 using load-deflexion curve of Fig. 18 A.

in f_2' entails an increase in A_1, so $d|A_1|/df > 0$, and the system is stable. But at P_2, constancy of ω entails a decrease in $|A_1|$ when f increases, so $d|A_1|/df < 0$ and the system is unstable.

Experimental illustration. Using the apparatus of Fig. 13, and a spring whose control-torque graph is shown in Fig. 18 A, the curve depicted in Fig. 18 B was obtained. The jump phenomenon is exhibited distinctly [92].

4.171. Loci of vertical tangents in Figs. 16 A, B. The values of ω, $|A_1|$ for which the tangents of (5), § 4.16, are parallel to the $|A_1|$ axis, satisfy $d\omega/dA_1 = 0$. Differentiating (5), § 4.16, with respect to A_1, we get

$$2A_1[(a-\omega^2+\tfrac{3}{4}bA_1^2)^2+4\kappa^2\omega^2]+$$

$$+A_1^2\{2(a-\omega^2+\tfrac{3}{4}bA_1^2)(\tfrac{3}{2}bA_1-2\omega\omega')+8\kappa^2\omega\omega'\}= 0, \quad (1)$$

or

$$2\omega\omega'A_1^2\{4\kappa^2-2(a-\omega^2+\tfrac{3}{4}bA_1^2)\}+3bA_1^3(a-\omega^2+\tfrac{3}{4}bA_1^2)+2A_1[\ ] = 0.$$

$$(2)$$

If $\omega' = d\omega/dA_1 = 0$, then

$$3bA_1^2(a-\omega^2+\tfrac{3}{4}bA_1^2)+2[(a-\omega^2+\tfrac{3}{4}bA_1^2)^2+4\kappa^2\omega^2] = 0, \quad (3)$$

so

$$(a-\omega^2+\tfrac{3}{4}bA_1^2)[\tfrac{3}{2}bA_1^2+(a-\omega^2+\tfrac{3}{4}bA_1^2)]+4\kappa^2\omega^2 = 0, \quad (4)$$

i.e.

$$(a-\omega^2+\tfrac{3}{4}bA_1^2)(a-\omega^2+\tfrac{9}{4}bA_1^2)+4\kappa^2\omega^2 = 0. \quad (5)$$

When $\kappa = 0$, (5) gives

$$a-\omega^2+\tfrac{3}{4}bA_1^2 = 0, \quad \text{or} \quad |A_1| = [(4/3b)(\omega^2-a)]^{\frac{1}{2}}, \quad (6)$$

and

$$a-\omega^2+\tfrac{9}{4}bA_1^2 = 0, \quad \text{or} \quad |A_1| = [(4/9b)(\omega^2-a)]^{\frac{1}{2}}, \quad (7)$$

with $b > 0$. When $b < 0$, write $(a-\omega^2)$ for (ω^2-a). The graphs corresponding to (6), (7) are marked accordingly in Figs. 16 A, B. There are no vertical tangents corresponding to the curve represented by (6), since the amplitude-frequency curves never cross it. However, we may consider the case to be that for $\kappa \to 0$ when the tangents exist. For $\kappa > 0$, the graphs of (5) take the form of the broken line curves in Figs. 16 A, B. Referring back to § 4.170, we may infer that the region within the broken curve in Fig. 16 A (also 16 B) is one where the motion of the system is unstable. This may be compared with the unstable region in Fig. 38 between b_1 and a_1 which corresponds to equation (1), § 7.10.

4.18. Energy considerations. Proceeding as in § 4.141, we obtain

$$\int v\,dv+a\int y\,dy+b\int y^3\,dy+2\kappa\omega^2\int(A_1\sin\psi+3A_3\sin3\psi+...)^2\,dt$$

$$= -\omega f\int\cos(\psi+\varphi)(A_1\sin\psi+3A_3\sin3\psi+...)\,dt. \quad (1)$$

Integrating over a period $t = (0, 2\pi/\omega)$, the first three integrals on the left-hand side of (1) vanish by virtue of periodicity. Thus

$$2\kappa\omega^2\int_0^{2\pi/\omega}(A_1\sin\psi+3A_3\sin3\psi+...)^2\,dt$$

$$= -\omega f\int_0^{2\pi/\omega}\cos(\psi+\varphi)(A_1\sin\psi+3A_3\sin3\psi+...)\,dt, \quad (2)$$

so we obtain the relationship

$$\pi\left(\frac{2\kappa}{\omega}\right)[\omega^2 A_1^2 + (3\omega)^2 A_3^2 + (5\omega)^2 A_5^2 + ...] = \pi f A_1 \sin\varphi. \tag{3}$$

The expression on the left-hand side of (3) represents the work done in overcoming viscous loss per period. The right-hand side represents the energy supplied by the driving mechanism. Each term on the left-hand side represents the loss for the corresponding harmonic. The energy is supplied by the driving mechanism at the fundamental frequency $\omega/2\pi$, since the only contribution from the right-hand side of (2) comes from the term involving $(\sin\psi)^2$. This must be so from a physical viewpoint, since the driving force has no higher harmonic components.

Owing to the approximate nature of the analysis, the two sides of (3) are not equal. To demonstrate this, substitute $\sin\varphi = 2\omega\kappa A_1/f$ from (4), § 4.16, and we get

$$2\pi\omega\kappa A_1^2[1 + (3A_3/A_1)^2 + (5A_5/A_1)^2 + ...] \tag{4}$$

for the left-hand side, and

$$2\pi\omega\kappa A_1^2 \tag{5}$$

for the right-hand side. Since $[(2r+1)A_{2r+1}/A_1]^2 \ll 1$, the approximation at (3) is in keeping with that in the rest of the analysis.

4.190. Harmonic of order $\frac{1}{3}$. Under certain conditions a periodic solution of the differential equation

$$\ddot{y} + ay + by^3 = f\cos\omega t \quad (a, b, f > 0) \tag{1}$$

has a term involving $\cos\frac{1}{3}\omega t$. Since (1) is unaltered if $(t + 2n\pi/\omega)$ replaces t, it follows that if $\cos\frac{1}{3}\omega t$ is a solution, so also is $\cos\frac{1}{3}(\omega t + 2\pi)$ and $\cos\frac{1}{3}(\omega t + 4\pi)$. Thus from a mathematical viewpoint, there are three subharmonics of order 3 having the same amplitude, but differing in phase by $2\pi/3$ radians.

The analysis given below *does not prove the existence* of a subharmonic. It is based on the hypothesis that (1) has a subharmonic solution if $b/a \ll 1$. An experimental demonstration for (1) with a small damping term $2\kappa\dot{y}$, and $b/a \gg 1$, is reported in [92 b]. Moreover, it *may* happen that (2)–(6), (8), (9) are usable when b/a is much larger than we have contemplated.

As a first approximation we assume that

$$y = A_{\frac{1}{3}}\cos\frac{1}{3}\omega t + A_1\cos\omega t. \tag{2}$$

Substituting (2) into (1) and equating the coefficients of $\cos \frac{1}{3}\omega t$, $\cos \omega t$ on each side, leads to

$$[(a-\tfrac{1}{9}\omega^2)+\tfrac{3}{4}b(A_{\frac{1}{3}}^2+A_{\frac{1}{3}}A_1+2A_1^2)]A_{\frac{1}{3}} = 0, \tag{3}$$

and
$$(a-\omega^2)A_1+\tfrac{1}{4}b(A_{\frac{1}{3}}^3+6A_{\frac{1}{3}}^2A_1+3A_1^3) = f. \tag{4}$$

Eliminating ω^2 between (3), (4) gives

$$A_{\frac{1}{3}}^3-A_1(21A_{\frac{1}{3}}^2+27A_{\frac{1}{3}}A_1+51A_1^2+32a/b) = 4f/b, \tag{5}$$

provided $A_{\frac{1}{3}} \neq 0$, for only then does the equation

$$(a-\tfrac{1}{9}\omega^2)+\tfrac{3}{4}b(A_{\frac{1}{3}}^2+A_{\frac{1}{3}}A_1+2A_1^2) = 0 \tag{6}$$

hold. When $A_{\frac{1}{3}} = 0$, by (4) there is the single relationship (writing $\bar{A}_1$ for A_1)
$$\tfrac{3}{4}b\bar{A}_1^3-(\omega^2-a)\bar{A}_1-f = 0. \tag{7}$$

(4), (6) must be compatible for the subharmonic to exist.

Solving (6) for $A_{\frac{1}{3}}$ gives the two values

$$A_{\frac{1}{3}} = -\frac{1}{2}\Big[A_1\pm\Big\{\frac{16}{27b}(\omega^2-9a)-7A_1^2\Big\}^{\frac{1}{2}}\Big]. \tag{8}$$

Since $A_{\frac{1}{3}}$ must be real, it follows from (8) that

$$\omega^2 \geqslant 9(a+21A_1^2b/16), \tag{9}$$

the equality sign corresponding to $A_{\frac{1}{3}} = -\tfrac{1}{2}A_1$, when the subharmonic starts. Substituting into (5), after reduction we obtain

$$\tfrac{343}{32}bA_1^3+8aA_1+f = 0, \tag{10}$$

which has only one real root, since a, b, f are positive. Neglecting the first term gives
$$A_1 \simeq -f/8a, \tag{11}$$

which is an adequate approximation if

$$A_1^2 \ll 256a/343b, \quad \text{or} \quad 0 \cdot 02bf^2/a^3 \ll 1. \tag{12}$$

Inserting $A_1^3 = -(f/8a)^3$ into (10) and solving, yields the second approximation

$$A_1 \simeq -\frac{f}{8a}\Big(1-\frac{343bf^2}{16384a^3}\Big) \simeq -\frac{f}{8a}(1-0\cdot02bf^2/a^3), \tag{13}$$

which is the value when the subharmonic starts. Also

$$\omega^2 \simeq 9(a+21bf^2/1024a^2), \tag{14}$$

so $\omega \simeq 3a^{\frac{1}{2}}$, provided $21bf^2/1024a^3 \ll 1$.

Using the equality sign in (9) and substituting into (7), we obtain the equation
$$\tfrac{354}{32}b\bar{A}_1^3+8a\bar{A}_1+f = 0. \tag{15}$$

From (10), (15) it follows that to the degree of approximation envisaged, there is little alteration in A_1 when the subharmonic starts. The value of A_1 at (11) indicates that it is almost on curve ① in Fig. 19.

Solving (6) gives

$$A_1 = -\frac{1}{4}\left[A_{\frac{1}{3}} \pm \left\{\frac{32}{27b}(\omega^2 - 9a) - 7A_{\frac{1}{3}}^2\right\}^{\frac{1}{2}}\right], \tag{16}$$

provided $A_{\frac{1}{3}} \neq 0$. If in (5), (6) we put $A_1 = 0$,

$$A_{\frac{1}{3}} = (4f/b)^{\frac{1}{3}} = \left[\frac{4}{27b}(\omega^2 - 9a)\right]^{\frac{1}{2}}, \tag{17}$$

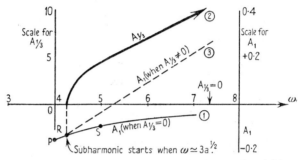

Fig. 19. Curves showing amplitude of fundamental and $\frac{1}{3}$ harmonic in the periodic solution of $\ddot{y} + 2y + 0 \cdot 05y^3 = 2\cos\omega t$. ① A_1 when $A_{\frac{1}{3}} = 0$; ② $A_{\frac{1}{3}}$, ③ A_1 when $A_{\frac{1}{3}} \neq 0$. When $\omega = 4$, $A_1 = OP$, and if ω increases, $|A_1|$ decreases until at R the subharmonic starts with $\omega \simeq 3a^{\frac{1}{2}} = 3\sqrt{2}$. Thereafter A_1 follows curve ③. ① corresponds to the curve in Fig. 17 A to the right of S, where A_1 (not $|A_1|$) is negative.

the negative sign being inadmissible, since (4) is not satisfied. When $A_1 = 0$, and $A_{\frac{1}{3}} = (4f/b)^{\frac{1}{3}}$, (6) gives

$$\omega^2 = 9a + 27(bf^2/4)^{\frac{1}{3}}, \tag{18}$$

and the solution of (1) is then

$$y = (4f/b)^{\frac{1}{3}} \cos\tfrac{1}{3}\omega t. \tag{19}$$

These results enable us to obtain an equation which has a subharmonic solution $A\cos\omega t$. Writing 3ω for ω, $4f/b = A^3$ in (18), gives $a = (\omega^2 - 3f/A)$, so (1) becomes

$$\ddot{y} + (\omega^2 - 3f/A)y + 4fy^3/A^3 = f\cos 3\omega t. \tag{20}$$

The other subharmonic solutions are $A\cos(\omega t + 2\pi/3)$, $A\cos(\omega t + 4\pi/3)$.

A similar equation is given in [27]. If $3f = A\omega^2$, then $A\cos\omega t$ is a subharmonic solution of

$$\ddot{y} + (4\omega^2/3A^2)y^3 = (A\omega^2/3)\cos 3\omega t. \tag{21}$$

4.191. Example. To illustrate the analysis in § 4.190, we take $a = 2$, $b = 0.05$, $f = 2$. When the subharmonic starts

$$A_1 \simeq -f/8a = -0.125, \quad \text{and} \quad A_{\frac{1}{3}} = -\tfrac{1}{2}A_1 = 0.0625. \tag{1}$$

Using (9), § 4.190, we find that

$$\omega^2 = 18.004, \quad \text{and} \quad \omega = 4.243 \simeq 3a^{\frac{1}{2}}. \tag{2}$$

Assigning values to $A_{\frac{1}{3}}$, and using (5), (6), § 4.190, we obtain the data given in Table 2. These are exhibited graphically in Fig. 19. The graph of A_1 corresponding to $A_{\frac{1}{3}} = 0$ is inserted also.

TABLE 2

Data relating to $\frac{1}{3}$ harmonic

$A_{\frac{1}{3}}$	A_1	$|A_{\frac{1}{3}}/A_1|$	ω
0.0625	−0.125	0.5	4.24
1.0000	−0.122	8.2	4.28
4.0000	−0.0594	67.3	4.83
5.43	0.0000	∞	5.29
10.0000	0.24	41.6	7.25

The relationship between A_1 and ω is sensibly linear. An examination of the case when $b < 0$ is left as an exercise for the reader.

4.192. Effect of viscous damping. The differential equation is now

$$\ddot{y} + 2\kappa\dot{y} + ay + by^3 = f\cos\omega t. \tag{1}$$

For a first approximation we assume that

$$y = A_{\frac{1}{3}}\cos\tfrac{1}{3}\omega t + B_{\frac{1}{3}}\sin\tfrac{1}{3}\omega t + A_1\cos\omega t + B_1\sin\omega t \tag{2}$$

$$= C_{\frac{1}{3}}\cos(\tfrac{1}{3}\omega t - \theta_{\frac{1}{3}}) + C_1\cos(\omega t - \theta_1). \tag{3}$$

In (3)

$C_{\frac{1}{3}} = (A_{\frac{1}{3}}^2 + B_{\frac{1}{3}}^2)^{\frac{1}{2}}$, the amplitude of the subharmonic

$C_1 = (A_1^2 + B_1^2)^{\frac{1}{2}}$, the amplitude of the fundamental

$\theta_{\frac{1}{3}} = \tan^{-1}(B_{\frac{1}{3}}/A_{\frac{1}{3}})$, the phase angle of the subharmonic ⎫
$\quad$ due to viscous damping; compare (2), § 4.190.
$\theta_1 = \tan^{-1}(B_1/A_1)$, the phase angle of the fundamental ⎭

Substituting either (2) or (3) into (1) and proceeding as in previous sections, we find ultimately that if $b > 0$, $\kappa \geqslant 0$ are not too large, the $\frac{1}{3}$ harmonic is present provided that

$$\omega^2 \geqslant 9\{a + (21bf^2/1024a^2)\}/\{1 - \kappa^2 a^2[(2048/9bf^2) - (1/2a^3)]\}. \tag{4}$$

(1) has no exact subharmonic solution $A_{\frac{1}{3}}\cos\tfrac{1}{3}\omega t + B_{\frac{1}{3}}\sin\tfrac{1}{3}\omega t$, unless $\kappa = 0$, and then $B_{\frac{1}{3}} = 0$ as in (19), § 4.190. To confirm, sub-

stitute into (1) and equate the coefficients of $\cos\frac{1}{3}\omega t$, $\sin\frac{1}{3}\omega t$ to zero. For $A_{\frac{1}{3}}$, $B_{\frac{1}{3}} \neq 0$, $(9a-\omega^2+27bA_{\frac{1}{3}}^2/4)^2+36\kappa^2\omega^2 = 0$, which is impossible since each term > 0.

Since an alteration in the motion is associated with a change of energy, the 'jumps' must be interpreted accordingly. As ω approaches a critical value, there will be a transition stage during which the amplitude of vibration either increases or decreases at a *finite* rate. In other words the diagrams showing 'vertical jumps' refer to the *steady* state. Diagrams having time bases are needed to show the nature of the vibration at either a 'jump', or at the initiation or the cessation of a subharmonic. Oscillograms are given in references [92b, 234, 235].

4.193. Experimental illustration of subharmonics of higher order.

It seems likely that when the 'spring control' is representable by a polynomial of the form $ay+by^3+cy^5+...$, odd in y, there will be harmonics of order $\frac{1}{3}$, $\frac{1}{5}$,... (see [38, p. 113]). This is illustrated by the oscillograms reproduced in Figs. 20 A, B. They show $\frac{1}{3}$ and $\frac{1}{5}$ harmonics which were obtained with the apparatus of Fig. 13 and a control characteristic of the form depicted in Fig. 20 C. In these experiments there was a small amount of damping, so $\kappa \neq 0$. The fundamental vibration is present in both cases, being of smaller amplitude than the subharmonic, and this agrees qualitatively with the data in Table 2. Subharmonics of this type may occur in aeroplane structures, the rate of vibration being a sub-multiple of the engine speed.

Subharmonics down to $\frac{1}{10}$th the fundamental frequency have been demonstrated with the apparatus described in reference [92a]. The oscillating member is a bar of I-section pivoted at its lower end (see Fig. 4 A, C). A metal strip, anchored as shown, passes between two shaped blocks which cause a variation in its effective length when the bar oscillates. In this way a non-linear spring control may be obtained, whose characteristic is determined by the shape of the inner faces of the blocks. The oscillation is maintained by a harmonic force due to the rotation of an unbalanced mass near the upper end of the bar.

4.194. Solution of $\ddot{y}+ay+by^2 = f\cos\omega t$.

We make the same basic assumptions relating to damping, subharmonics, etc., as in § 4.140, while the amplitude must be limited in accordance with the last paragraph of § 4.198. Writing $\omega t = \psi$, the equation becomes

$$\omega^2 y''+ay+by^2 = f\cos\psi \quad (a,b > 0), \tag{1}$$

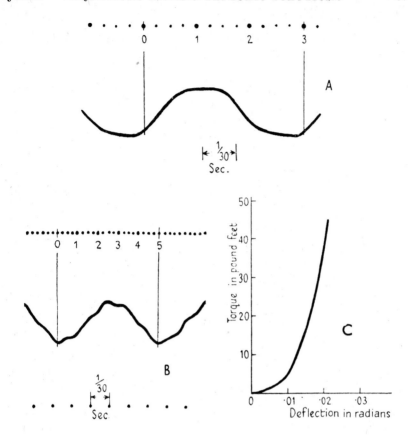

FIG. 20. A. Record illustrating ⅓ harmonic. B. Record illustrating ¼ harmonic. C. Load-deflexion curve used in apparatus of Fig. 13 to obtain records Fig. 20 A, B.

differentiation being with regard to ψ. We choose b (small) as the perturbation parameter, put $bF = f$, and seek a solution having period 2π in ψ, which satisfies the initial conditions $y(0) = A$, $y'(0) = 0$. We now assume that

$$(a) \qquad y = y_0 + by_1 + b^2y_2 + \dots$$

where the y_r are twice differentiable functions of ψ to be determined;

$$(b) \qquad \omega^2 = \omega_0^2 + b\omega_1^2 + b^2\omega_2^2 + \dots$$

the ω_r^2 being determinable constants. Here we expand ω^2 (not a) in ascending powers of b (see §§ 4.110, 4.131).

$$(2)$$

Substituting from (2) into (1) gives

$$(\omega_0^2+b\omega_1^2+b^2\omega_2^2+...)(y_0''+by_1''+b^2y_2''+...)+a(y_0+by_1+b^2y_2+...)+$$
$$+b(y_0^2+2by_0y_1+...) = bF\cos\psi. \quad (3)$$

Equating the coefficients of b^r, $r = 0, 1, 2,...$ on each side of (3) yields:

b^0: $\qquad\qquad \omega_0^2 y_0''+ay_0 = 0,$ or $y_0''+(a/\omega_0^2)y_0 = 0.$ $\qquad$ (4)

For period 2π in ψ, we must have

$$\omega_0^2 = a, \quad (5)$$

so the complete solution of (4) is

$$y_0 = A_0\sin\psi+B_0\cos\psi. \quad (6)$$

As in § 4.110, the initial conditions entail

$$y_0(0) = A,\ y_1(0) = y_2(0) = ... = 0 = y_0'(0) = y_1'(0) = ... = 0,$$

so the appropriate solution is

$$y_0 = A\cos\psi. \quad (7)$$

b: $\qquad\qquad \omega_0^2 y_1''+ay_1 = F\cos\psi-(\omega_1^2 y_0''+y_0^2),$ $\qquad$ (8)

and by (5), (7)

$$y_1''+y_1 = [(F+\omega_1^2 A)\cos\psi-\tfrac{1}{2}A^2(1+\cos 2\psi)]/a. \quad (9)$$

To avoid a non-periodic term in the particular integral of (9), the coefficient of $\cos\psi$ must vanish, so

$$F+\omega_1^2 A = 0, \quad \text{giving} \quad \omega_1^2 = -F/A. \quad (10)$$

Thus the complete solution of (9) is

$$y_1 = A_1\sin\psi+B_1\cos\psi+\frac{A^2}{6a}\cos 2\psi-\frac{A^2}{2a}. \quad (11)$$

The initial conditions $y_1(0) = y_1'(0) = 0$, necessitate $A_1 = 0$, $B_1 = A^2/3a$, and, therefore,

$$y_1 = -\frac{A^2}{2a}+\frac{A^2}{3a}(\cos\psi+\tfrac{1}{2}\cos 2\psi). \quad (12)$$

b^2: $\qquad\qquad \omega_0^2 y_2''+ay_2 = -(\omega_2^2 y_0''+\omega_1^2 y_1''+2y_0 y_1),$ $\qquad$ (13)

and by (5), (7), (12)

$$y_2''+y_2 = \frac{A}{a}\left(\omega_2^2+\frac{\omega_1^2 A}{3a}+\frac{5A^2}{6a}\right)\cos\psi-\frac{A}{3a^2}(A^2-2\omega_1^2 A)\cos 2\psi-$$
$$-\frac{A^3}{6a^2}\cos 3\psi-\frac{A^3}{3a^2}. \quad (14)$$

To avoid a non-periodic term in the particular integral, we must have

$$\omega_2^2 = -\frac{1}{3a}(\omega_1^2 A + \tfrac{5}{2}A^2) = \frac{F}{3a} - \frac{5A^2}{6a}, \tag{15}$$

by (10). Then the complete solution of (14) is

$$y_2 = A_2\sin\psi + B_2\cos\psi + \frac{A}{9a^2}(A^2+2F)\cos 2\psi + \frac{A^3}{48a^2}\cos 3\psi - \frac{A^3}{3a^2}. \tag{16}$$

The initial conditions $y_2(0) = y_2'(0) = 0$, necessitate

$$A_2 = 0, \qquad B_2 = \frac{A}{3a^2}(\tfrac{29}{48}A^2 - \tfrac{2}{3}F),$$

so the appropriate complete solution of (14) is

$$y_2 = -\frac{A^3}{3a^2} + \frac{A}{3a^2}(\tfrac{29}{48}A^2 - \tfrac{2}{3}F)\cos\psi + \frac{A}{9a^2}(A^2+2F)\cos 2\psi + \frac{A^3}{48a^2}\cos 3\psi. \tag{17}$$

Hence to the second order in b

$$y = y_0 + by_1 + b^2 y_2$$

$$= -\frac{bA^2}{a}\left(\frac{1}{2}+\frac{bA}{3a}\right) + A\left(1+\frac{bA}{3a}+\frac{29b^2A^2}{144a^2}-\frac{2bf}{9a^2}\right)\cos\omega t +$$

$$+\frac{bA^2}{3a}\left(\frac{1}{2}+\frac{bA}{3a}+\frac{2f}{3aA}\right)\cos 2\omega t + \frac{b^2A^3}{48a^2}\cos 3\omega t. \tag{18}$$

Also to order two in b

$$\omega^2 = \omega_0^2 + b\omega_1^2 + b^2\omega_2^2 = a - \frac{5b^2A^2}{6a} - f\left(\frac{1}{A} - \frac{b}{3a}\right). \tag{19}$$

In virtue of the constant term in (18), what may be regarded as the 'centre of oscillation' is on the negative side of the origin of the force-displacement curve $ay + by^2$ (Fig. 11 A).

We showed in Chapter II that the solution of a non-linear differential equation depends upon the initial conditions. If (1) is solved such that the coefficient of $\cos\psi$ is A for all t, the coefficients of the various terms will differ from those in (18), and the initial condition will not be $y(0) = A$. Also the last term in (19) will not appear. The reader should verify these remarks as an exercise.

4.195. Amplitude-frequency relation. (18), § 4.194, was derived subject to the conditions $y = A$, $y' = 0$ at $t = 0$. But (19), § 4.194, must be satisfied also, which means that for fixed values of a, b, and f,

ω^2 complies with this equation. Written in the form

$$\frac{5b^2}{6a}A^3 - \left(a - \omega^2 + \frac{fb}{3a}\right)A + f = 0, \tag{1}$$

it is a cubic equation for A, which may be compared with (9), § 4.140. The consequences of such a relation are examined in § 4.16 et seq. From the analysis therein it appears that a physical system operating in accordance with the equation

$$\ddot{y} + 2\kappa\dot{y} + ay + by^2 = f\cos\omega t \tag{2}$$

should exhibit the jump phenomenon described in § 4.170. Consideration of the signs of the terms in (1), where $b > 0$, shows that it is of the same type as (9), § 4.140, with $b < 0$, so the $(|A|, \omega)$ relationship for $\kappa > 0$, should be akin to that in Figs. 16 B, 17 B.

4.196. Harmonics of order $\frac{1}{2}$.

In this case we shall solve the equation

$$\ddot{y} + 2\kappa\dot{y} + ay + by^2 = f\cos 2\omega t \tag{1}$$

for subharmonics of order 2 (period $2\pi/\omega$), using the method of perturbation. Let $\omega t = z$, $2\kappa = \epsilon b^2$, $f = bF$, with $a > 0$, b, $\kappa > 0$ small, and (1) becomes

$$\omega^2 y'' + \omega\epsilon b^2 y' + ay + by^2 = bF\cos 2z. \tag{2}$$

Assume that

$$y = y_0 + by_1 + b^2 y_2 + ..., \tag{3}$$

the y_r being periodic twice differentiable functions of z, and that

$$\omega = \omega_0 + b\omega_1 + b^2\omega_2 + ..., \tag{4}$$

where the ω_r are to be determined. Substituting from (3), (4) into (2) gives

$$\{\omega_0^2 + 2b\omega_0\omega_1 + b^2(\omega_1^2 + 2\omega_0\omega_2) + ...\}(y_0'' + by_1'' + b^2 y_2'' + ...) +$$
$$+ \epsilon(b^2\omega_0 + ...)(y_0' + by_1' + ...) + a(y_0 + by_1 + b^2 y_2 + ...) +$$
$$+ (by_0^2 + 2b^2 y_0 y_1 + ...) = bF\cos 2z. \tag{5}$$

Equating coefficients of b^r, $r = 0, 1, 2,...$, on each side of (5), yields

b^0:
$$\omega_0^2 y'' + ay = 0, \tag{6}$$

so for a solution with period 2π, we must have $\omega_0^2 = a$, and, therefore,

$$y_0 = A\sin z + B\cos z. \tag{7}$$

A, B, are functions of a, b, f, κ, ω; to effect simplification of the algebra we shall keep them the same throughout. Since the equation is non-linear, the ultimate initial conditions (unknown at the present stage) differ from $y(0) = B$, $y'(0) = A$.

b:
$$\omega_0^2 y_1'' + ay_1 = -2\omega_0\omega_1 y_0'' - y_0^2 + F\cos 2z, \tag{8}$$

so

$$y_1'' + y_1 = 2(\omega_1/\omega_0)(A \sin z + B \cos z) -$$
$$- (1/a)\{(A^2 + B^2)/2 + AB \sin 2z - [(A^2 - B^2)/2 + F]\cos 2z\}. \quad (9)$$

To avoid non-periodic terms in y_1, we must have $\omega_1 = 0$. Thus with $g = (A^2 + B^2)/2$, $h = F + (A^2 - B^2)/2$, we get

$$y_1 = -(g/a) + (AB/3a)\sin 2z - (h/3a)\cos 2z. \quad (10)$$

$$b^2: \quad \omega_0^2 y_2'' + a y_2 = -\epsilon\omega_0 y_0' - 2\omega_0 \omega_2 y_0'' - 2y_0 y_1 \quad (11)$$

$$= -\epsilon\omega_0(A \cos z - B \sin z) + 2\omega_0 \omega_2(A \sin z + B \cos z) -$$
$$- 2(A \sin z + B \cos z)\{-(g/a) + (AB/3a)\sin 2z - (h/3a)\cos 2z\}$$

so

$$\qquad (12)$$

$$y_2'' + y_2 = P \sin z + Q \cos z + (A/3a^2)(h - B^2)\sin 3z + (B/3a^2)(h + A^2)\cos 3z \quad (13)$$

where P, Q are given below. To avoid non-periodic terms in y_2, P and Q must vanish, and with A, B, non-zero we have

$$P/A = 2(\omega_2/\omega_0) + 2(g/a^2) - (h/3a^2) - (B^2/3a^2) + (\epsilon B/\omega_0 A) = 0, \quad (14)$$

$$Q/B = 2(\omega_2/\omega_0) + 2(g/a^2) + (h/3a^2) - (A^2/3a^2) - (\epsilon A/\omega_0 B) = 0. \quad (15)$$

Adding (14), (15) and multiplying throughout by $a/2 = \omega_0^2/2$, gives

$$2\omega_0 \omega_2 = -5(A^2 + B^2)/6a + (\kappa\omega_0/b^2)(A/B - B/A). \quad (16)$$

Subtracting (14), (15), and multiplying throughout by

$$\omega_0/\epsilon = b^2\omega_0/2\kappa,$$

we obtain $\qquad (A/B + B/A) = bf/3\kappa\omega_0^3 = \beta. \quad (17)$

Solving (17) yields

$$A/B = \{\beta \pm (\beta^2 - 4)^{\frac{1}{2}}\}/2, \quad (18)$$

so $\qquad \kappa\omega_0(A/B - B/A) = \pm\{(bf/3a)^2 - 4\kappa^2 a\}^{\frac{1}{2}}. \quad (19)$

By (4) $\qquad \omega^2 = \omega_0^2 + 2b\omega_0 \omega_1 + b^2(\omega_1^2 + 2\omega_0 \omega_2) + ..., \quad (20)$

and since $\omega_0^2 = a$, $\omega_1 = 0$, by aid of (16), (19), we get

$$\omega^2 = a - 5b^2(A^2 + B^2)/6a \pm \{(bf/3a)^2 - 4\kappa^2 a\}^{\frac{1}{2}}. \quad (21)$$

Thus

$$Y = (A^2 + B^2)^{\frac{1}{2}} = \pm\{(6a/5b^2)[(a - \omega^2) \pm \{(bf/3a)^2 - 4\kappa^2 a\}^{\frac{1}{2}}]\}^{\frac{1}{2}} \quad (22)$$

which gives the amplitudes of the subharmonics.

To order one in b (small) the solution is $y = y_0 + by_1$, so

$$y = A \sin z + B \cos z + (bAB/3a)\sin 2z - (bh/3a)\cos 2z - (bg/a) \quad (23)$$

$$= -(b/2a)Y^2 + Y \cos(z - \theta_1) - (b/6a)Y^2 \cos(2z + \theta_2) - (f/3a)\cos 2z, \quad (24)$$

where $\tan\theta_1 = A/B$, $\tan\theta_2 = AB/\{(A^2-B^2)/2\}$, $\theta_2 = -2\theta_1$. This solution is valid only for Y real > 0, i.e. when there are subharmonics. The first term represents a unidirectional displacement, and as in § 4.195 the 'centre of oscillation' is on the left of the origin. The second and third terms represent, respectively, the subharmonic and its first overtone, while the last term gives the forced oscillation which has the same period as the driving force.

4.197. Subharmonics and stability.

The motion is defined to be stable (unstable), if after being subjected to a small disturbance it returns to (moves away from) its former state. In [131 a], by aid of stability criteria given in [85], it is shown that the upper (lower) internal and the two external signs in (22), § 4.196 correspond to a pair of stable (unstable) subharmonics. Thus there are four subharmonics, two stable and two unstable. By virtue of the two external signs in (22), § 4.196, the components of each pair differ in phase by π radians or π/ω sec. Under certain conditions specified in [131 a], the forced oscillation of driving frequency becomes unstable (see remarks in § 4.198). Nevertheless, there is still the oscillation due to the overtone of the subharmonic. The analysis pertaining to stability is beyond our present purview, so we shall merely state what results may be expected on the basis of reference [131 a].

4.198. Forms of oscillation.

For Y to be real, whatever the values of a and ω, we must have

$$f > 6\kappa a^{\frac{3}{2}}/b. \tag{1}$$

This gives the threshold of f, below which subharmonics cannot occur. Also for the existence of the stable pair of subharmonics, we must have

$$\{(bf/3a)^2-4\kappa^2 a\}^{\frac{1}{2}} > (\omega^2-a), \tag{2}$$

and for the unstable pair,

$$(a-\omega^2) > \{(bf/3a)^2-4\kappa^2 a\}^{\frac{1}{2}}. \tag{3}$$

Variation in f.

(i) For $\omega^2 <$ or $> a$, as f is increased from zero, there is a stable forced oscillation of amplitude $X \simeq f/(4\omega^2-a)$, but no subharmonics.

(ii) For $a > \omega^2$, when $f = 6\kappa a^{\frac{3}{2}}/b$ the threshold is reached, and for $f > 6\kappa a^{\frac{3}{2}}/b$ there is a pair of stable (unstable) subharmonics having amplitude given by (22), § 4.196 with the upper (lower) internal sign. When

$$[a-\omega^2-\{(bf/3a)^2-4\kappa^2 a\}^{\frac{1}{2}}] = 0, \tag{4}$$

the unstable subharmonics vanish while the stable ones remain. At this point, however, the forced oscillation becomes unstable and the amplitude jumps† to that for *one* of the stable subharmonics, as given by (22), § 4.196 with the upper internal sign. Increase in f is accompanied by that of Y and also in the amplitude of the subharmonic overtone. If f is now decreased, the stable subharmonic persists but with decreasing Y, until the threshold $f = 6\kappa a^{\frac{3}{2}}/b$ is reached. It then

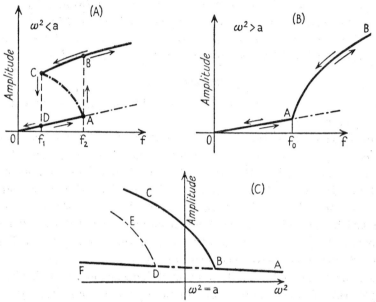

Fig. 21. A. OA = forced oscillation; CA = unstable subharmonics; CB = stable subharmonics. At A, B, $f_2 = (3a/b)\{(a-\omega^2)^2+4\kappa^2a\}^{\frac{1}{2}}$; at C, D, $f_1 = 6\kappa a^{\frac{3}{2}}/b$. For f increasing from O, the forced oscillation becomes unstable at A, and there is a jump to *one* of the stable subharmonics at B. B. OA = forced oscillation; AB = stable subharmonics. c. $ABDF$ = forced oscillation which is unstable between B and D; BC = stable subharmonics; DE = unstable subharmonics.

vanishes and the amplitude of the motion jumps† down to that for the forced oscillation (now stable), namely, $X \simeq f/(4\omega^2-a)$. The cycle of changes is portrayed in Fig. 21 A, and there is a type of 'hysteresis' as in Fig. 16 A. In the first case two frequencies are involved, but only one in the second.

If the system were started suddenly by applying a force f ($f_1 < f < f_2$ in Fig. 21 A), the subsequent motion would entail either the forced oscillation or the subharmonic, depending upon the values of the initial displacement and velocity. Fig. 21 A indicates that

† See remarks on 'jumps' in § 4.192.

conditions yielding a relatively small (large) displacement would be needed to initiate the forced oscillation (subharmonic).

(iii) For $\omega^2 > a$, Y in (22), § 4.196 cannot be real with the lower internal sign, so there are no unstable subharmonics. The stable pair cannot occur unless (1), (2) are satisfied. As f in (2) increases from zero, there is the forced oscillation with $X \simeq f/(4\omega^2 - a)$, and when $f = f_0$ the stable subharmonics commence with amplitude X_0. The forced oscillation is now unstable, but there is the subharmonic overtone. Increase in f is accompanied by that in Y. These remarks are illustrated in Fig. 21 B. There is no hysteresis effect [131 a].

Variation in ω.

(i) If (1) is not satisfied, there are no subharmonics, but there is a stable forced oscillation.

(ii) If (1) is satisfied and $\omega^2 > a + \{(bf/3a)^2 - 4\kappa^2 a\}^{\frac{1}{2}}$, there is a stable forced oscillation but no subharmonics, since Y is imaginary. But when $|a - \omega^2| < \{(bf/3a)^2 - 4\kappa^2 a\}^{\frac{1}{2}}$, the forced oscillation is unstable and there is *one* pair of stable subharmonics, provided a is not too near† to $\omega^2 - \{ \ \}^{\frac{1}{2}}$. If $a - \{(bf/3a)^2 - 4\kappa^2 a\}^{\frac{1}{2}} > \omega^2$ there is a stable forced oscillation, also the *two* pairs of subharmonics, provided a is not too near† to $\omega^2 + \{ \ \}^{\frac{1}{2}}$. The trend of these remarks is illustrated in Fig. 21 C. Subharmonic resonance does not occur.

In general the forced oscillation is unstable when accompanied by a single pair of subharmonics, but remains stable if another pair of subharmonics is present to 'counteract' the instability. This remark is exemplified in Figs. 21 A, B, C [131 a].

Amplitude limitation. In Fig. 11 A the slope of the force-displacement curve changes sign to the left of the minimum, and if

$$y_{\min} < -a/b,$$

the displacement increases continually with increase in time. Usually the characteristic for a physical system has no minimum, but it may have a point of inflexion. In the case considered in § 4.199, where the restoring force is pneumatic, neither a minimum nor an inflexion occurs.

4.199. Example. Imagine a hollow circular cylinder, of working length l, closed by a rigid disk of mass‡ m which is driven axially by a

---

† The approximate analysis does not hold if a is too near to these values.

‡ This includes 'accession to inertia' due to the external air [183].

force $F \cos 2\omega t$, such that the displacement ξ is 'finite'. If p_0 is the atmospheric pressure, and v_0 the corresponding undisturbed volume, for adiabatic operation we have

$$pv^\gamma = p_0 v_0^\gamma = \text{a constant.} \tag{1}$$

If the displacement during *expansion* is $+\xi$, then

$$p(l+\xi)^\gamma = p_0 l^\gamma, \tag{2}$$

so $\qquad p = p_0(1+\xi/l)^{-\gamma} = p_0[1-\gamma\xi/l+\gamma(\gamma+1)\xi^2/2l^2-...]. \tag{3}$

Thus the 'spring control' per unit cross-sectional area, due to the air within the cylinder, is given by

$$p_0-p_0[1-\gamma\xi/l+\gamma(\gamma+1)\xi^2/2l^2-...] = \gamma p_0\xi/l-\gamma(\gamma+1)p_0\xi^2/2l^2+.... \tag{4}$$

Accordingly if $\xi/l \ll 1$, the approximate equation of motion of the disk is

$$m\ddot{\xi}+r\dot{\xi}+s_1\xi+s_2\xi^2 = F \cos 2\omega t, \tag{5}$$

with $s_1 = \gamma p_0 A/l$, $s_2 = -\gamma(\gamma+1)p_0 A/2l^2$, A being the cross-sectional area of the cylinder. Here the slope of the p–v curve is negative, and what may be regarded as the 'centre of oscillation' moves *down* this curve (see (18), § 4.194 with $b < 0$). The adiabatic curve has no minimum value, so ξ need not be limited as in § 4.198. A relatively large ξ would entail additional terms involving $\xi^3, \xi^4,...$ in (5). The solution of this equation on the lines of previous sections is left as an exercise for the reader.

4.20. Intermodulation frequencies.

Consider a loudspeaker diaphragm of the type illustrated in Fig. 22 and suppose the relationship between force and axial displacement takes the form $F = ay+by^3$ as shown graphically in Fig. 12 B. This relationship has been chosen in the interest of analytical simplification. In practice, especially when y is large, the relationship is likely to be complicated in an average loudspeaker. Usually it is asymmetrical about the force axis, and as in § 4.130 there is then a unidirectional displacement of the diaphragm. During the reproduction of speech or music a myriad of frequencies is present in the current which flows in the driving coil. However, to simplify the analysis, we shall consider only two frequencies, namely, a powerful† low audio frequency $\omega_1/2\pi$, and a comparatively weak† high audio frequency $\omega_2/2\pi$, e.g. 100 c.p.s. and

---

† These adjectives refer to amplitude of motion, not to the aural sensation, which varies considerably with change in frequency at normal sound levels.

2,500 c.p.s., say. The latter will execute 25 oscillations in the same time as the former executes 1. We may visualize the higher component in action while the operating point on the characteristic of Fig. 12 B moves relatively slowly from O to N. On the approximately straight portion OM, the 2,500 c.p.s. oscillation of the diaphragm will be nearly sinusoidal, but as the operating point traverses the curved part

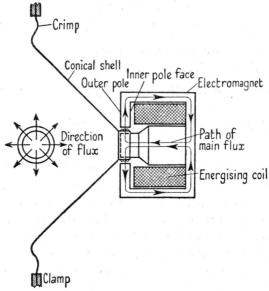

Fig. 22. Schematic diagram for moving-coil loudspeaker.

of the characteristic the wave form gets distorted. It follows that alien frequencies are created, so the sound output is affected accordingly. In the terminology of radio-acoustics, one frequency modulates the other, and the effect known as intermodulation occurs. The result in practice, if many audio frequencies in a wide band are present, may be aurally distressing. It is then imperative to reduce the input to the loudspeaker to bring the *distortion* below the limit of audibility. An effect of this type may occur in a much more marked degree with a certain class of thermionic valve, since the characteristic curve turns over at each end of the linear part much more abruptly than is indicated by the term by^3.

4.21. Simple analysis of intermodulation. We deal with a loss-free system whose differential equation may be written in the form

$$\ddot{y}+\omega_0^2 y+by^3 = f_1 \cos \psi_1 + f_2 \cos \psi_2, \tag{1}$$

with $\psi_1 = \omega_1 t$, $\psi_2 = \omega_2 t$, $\omega_2^2 \gg \omega_1^2$, $f_1 \gg f_2$. As in § 4.140, we assume (i) that the conditions for subharmonic oscillations are not satisfied, (ii) that the damping is small enough to be neglected, although it ultimately extinguishes the initial transient.

In (1) $\omega_0/2\pi$ is approximately equal to the natural frequency of the effective diaphragm mass and the axial constraint, so b is small. In a *well-designed* speaker having a diaphragm 10 in. in diameter, ω_0 *should* be less than $2\pi \times 20$. Thus we take $\omega_2^2 \gg \omega_1^2 \gg \omega_0^2$, and seek a solution whose individual terms are periodic. The nature of the system contemplated is such that there will be components having angular frequencies ω_1, ω_2. If f_1, f_2 and the term by^3 are not too large, we may assume as a first approximation that

$$y = A_1 \cos\psi_1 + A_2 \cos\psi_2, \tag{2}$$

which is the form of solution if $b = 0$. Inserting (2) into the term by^3 in (1), we obtain the equation

$$\ddot{y} + \omega_0^2 y = f_1 \cos\psi_1 + f_2 \cos\psi_2 + h(\cos\psi_1, \cos\psi_2), \tag{3}$$

where

$$h(\cos\psi_1, \cos\psi_2) = -\tfrac{1}{4}b\{(3A_1^3 + 6A_1 A_2^2)\cos\psi_1 +$$
$$+ (3A_2^3 + 6A_1^2 A_2)\cos\psi_2 + 3A_1^2 A_2[\cos(\psi_2 + 2\psi_1) + \cos(\psi_2 - 2\psi_1)] +$$
$$+ 3A_1 A_2^2[\cos(2\psi_2 + \psi_1) + \cos(2\psi_2 - \psi_1)] +$$
$$+ A_1^3 \cos 3\psi_1 + A_2^3 \cos 3\psi_2\}. \tag{4}$$

Using the inequalities given above, we find that a number of terms in that part of the particular integral of (3), which corresponds to (4), may be neglected. The approximate representation of this function (P.I.) is given by

$$y_p = -\tfrac{1}{4}b\left[\frac{3A_1^3}{(\omega_0^2 - \omega_1^2)}\cos\psi_1 + \frac{A_1^3}{(\omega_0^2 - 9\omega_1^2)}\cos 3\psi_1 +\right.$$
$$+ \frac{3A_1^2 A_2}{[\omega_0^2 - (\omega_2 + 2\omega_1)^2]}\cos(\psi_2 + 2\psi_1) + \frac{6A_1^2 A_2 \cos\psi_2}{(\omega_0^2 - \omega_2^2)} +$$
$$\left. + \frac{3A_1^2 A_2}{[\omega_0^2 - (\omega_2 - 2\omega_1)^2]}\cos(\psi_2 - 2\psi_1)\right]. \tag{5}†$$

Omitting the question of initial conditions which do not affect the point under discussion, (5) shows that there is a third harmonic $3\omega_1$, also two additional components having angular frequencies

---

† We omit consideration of the complementary function of (3) and the P.I. of the terms in f_1, f_2 therein, as they are irrelevant to the point at issue.

$(\omega_2+2\omega_1)$ and $(\omega_2-2\omega_1)$. These are classes of sum and difference frequencies, respectively. If $\omega_1/2\pi = 100$, $\omega_2/2\pi = 2{,}500$ cycles per second, the first frequency is 2,700 and the second 2,300 c.p.s. The coefficient $3A_1^2 A_2/[\ ]$ is called a modulation product since it involves A_1, A_2. The solution also contains components of 4,900, 5,100, 7,500 c.p.s., but their amplitudes are relatively small. Higher approximations to the solution would reveal the presence of other components.

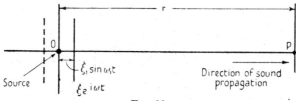

Source $-\xi_1 \sin \omega_1 t$ Direction of sound propagation
$\xi_2 e^{i\omega t}$

FIG. 23.

4.22. Additional example of intermodulation.

The reader may find it interesting to confirm that an approximate solution of

$$\ddot{y}+\omega_0^2 y+by^2 = f_1 \cos \omega_1 t+f_2 \cos \omega_2 t, \qquad (1)$$

is given by

$$y = -\frac{b}{2\omega_0^2}(A_1^2+A_2^2)+A_1 \cos \omega_1 t+A_2 \cos \omega_2 t+$$

$$+\frac{bA_1^2 \cos 2\omega_1 t}{2(4\omega_1^2-\omega_0^2)} + \frac{bA_2^2 \cos 2\omega_2 t}{2(4\omega_2^2-\omega_0^2)} + \frac{bA_1 A_2 \cos(\omega_1-\omega_2)t}{[(\omega_1-\omega_2)^2-\omega_0^2]}+$$

$$+\frac{bA_1 A_2 \cos(\omega_1+\omega_2)t}{[(\omega_1+\omega_2)^2-\omega_0^2]}. \qquad (2)$$

Here $A_1 = f_1/(\omega_0^2-\omega_1^2)$, $A_2 = f_2/(\omega_0^2-\omega_2^2)$, $|y_{\min}| < \omega_0^2/b = a/b$ in Fig. 11 A, and it is assumed that the conditions for the existence of a subharmonic are not satisfied. There is a constant term as in § 4.130, which represents a unidirectional displacement of the diaphragm. Also there are double, sum, and difference frequencies. The above case is akin to the creation of alien tones in the ear, by virtue of its asymmetrical characteristic curve. This property of the ear was discussed many years ago by Helmholtz [169].

4.23. Amplitude and frequency modulation in loudspeaker reproduction.†

Referring to Fig. 23, O represents a very small

---

† This is a *linear* problem, but has been included as a matter of interest. If ξ_1 were large enough, the curvature of the adiabatic characteristic for air would have to be taken into account as in [100, 101], § 4.199, Appendix I.

sound source which oscillates bodily with frequency $\omega_1/2\pi$ along the line OP, the amplitude of the motion being ξ_1. Simultaneously the source executes a motion along OP of frequency $\omega/2\pi$ and amplitude ξ, such that $\omega \gg \omega_1$, but $\xi \ll \xi_1$. Apart from the size of the source, this scheme corresponds to the case of a loudspeaker diaphragm. Since $\xi \ll \xi_1$, the distance of the source from P at any instant, is

$$r_1 = r - \xi_1 \sin \omega_1 t = r(1 - \epsilon \sin \omega_1 t), \tag{1}$$

with $\epsilon = \xi_1/r \ll 1$, provided $r \gg \xi_1$, as it would be in practice. The instantaneous velocity potential at P due to a simple source of strength $4\pi S$ and frequency $\omega/2\pi$ is [183]

$$\phi = \frac{Se^{-i(kr_1 - \omega t)}}{r_1} = \frac{Se^{-i(kr - k\xi_1 \sin \omega_1 t - \omega t)}}{r(1 - \epsilon \sin \omega_1 t)} \tag{2}$$

$$\simeq \frac{Se^{-ikr}}{r}[(1 + \epsilon \sin \omega_1 t)e^{i(z \sin \omega_1 t + \omega t)}], \tag{3}$$

where $z \doteq k\xi_1$, $k = \omega/c$, c the velocity of sound. Then if ρ is the air density, the pressure at P is (assuming S to be unity for convenience)

$$p = \rho \frac{\partial \phi}{\partial t}$$

$$= \rho \frac{e^{-ikr}}{r}[i(1 + \epsilon \sin \omega_1 t)(z\omega_1 \cos \omega_1 t + \omega) + \omega_1 \epsilon \cos \omega_1 t]e^{i(z \sin \omega_1 t + \omega t)} \tag{4}$$

$$= \frac{\rho}{r}e^{-i(kr - z \sin \omega_1 t - \omega t)}[\omega_1 \epsilon \cos \omega_1 t + i(1 + \epsilon \sin \omega_1 t)(z\omega_1 \cos \omega_1 t + \omega)]. \tag{5}$$

Taking the real part of (5), we obtain

$$p = \frac{\rho}{r}[\omega_1 \epsilon \cos \omega_1 t \cos(kr - z \sin \omega_1 t - \omega t) +$$

$$+ (1 + \epsilon \sin \omega_1 t)(z\omega_1 \cos \omega_1 t + \omega)\sin(kr - z \sin \omega_1 t - \omega t)]. \tag{6}$$

Now $|\omega_1 \epsilon \cos \omega_1 t| \ll |(1 + \epsilon \sin \omega_1 t)(z\omega_1 \cos \omega_1 t + \omega)|$, so to a close approximation we get

$$p \simeq -\frac{\rho}{r}[(1 + \epsilon \sin \omega_1 t)(z\omega_1 \cos \omega_1 t + \omega)\sin(\omega t + z \sin \omega_1 t - kr)]. \tag{7}$$

But $\omega \gg z\omega_1$, so (7) may be written

$$p \simeq -\frac{\rho\omega}{r}[1 + \epsilon \sin \omega_1 t + (z\omega_1/\omega)\cos \omega_1 t]\sin(\omega t + z \sin \omega_1 t - kr). \tag{8}$$

Putting $\epsilon = \xi_1/r$, $z\omega_1/\omega = k_1\xi_1 \ll 1$, $k_1 = \omega_1/c$ the [ ] in (8) becomes

$$A(t) = \{1 + k_1\xi_1(1 + 1/k_1^2 r^2)^{\frac{1}{2}} \cos[\omega_1 t - \tan^{-1}(1/k_1 r)]\}, \tag{9}$$

so amplitude modulation (fluctuation with time) occurs at P, having a frequency $\omega_1/2\pi$. Using the formula in [184, p. 52, ex. 16], we obtain

$$\sin(\omega t - kr + k\xi_1 \sin \omega_1 t) = \sum_{n=-\infty}^{\infty} J_n(k\xi_1)\sin[(\omega + n\omega_1)t - kr]. \quad (10)$$

Hence the sound pressure at P (apart from that due to $\omega_1/2\pi$) is given

by
$$p = -\frac{\rho\omega}{r}A(t) \sum_{n=-\infty}^{\infty} J_n(k\xi_1)\sin[(\omega + n\omega_1)t - kr]. \quad (11)$$

Consequently it comprises an infinite line spectrum of discrete frequencies extending indefinitely in the range above $\omega/2\pi$, but finitely below it, since $\omega \not< 0$.

Frequency	Amplitude (fluctuation at $\omega_1/2\pi$)
$\omega/2\pi$ the fundamental	$A(t)J_0(k\xi_1)$
$(\omega \pm \omega_1)/2$ two side frequencies	$A(t)J_1(k\xi_1)$
$(\omega \pm 2\omega_1)/2$,, ,, ,,	$A(t)J_2(k\xi_1)$
. . . . . .	. . . . . .
$(\omega \pm n\omega_1)/2$,, ,, ,,	$A(t)J_n(k\xi_1)$ $(n < \omega/\omega_1)$.

When $n > 0$, $\omega + n\omega_1 > \omega$, and there is an unlimited series of frequencies $\omega_1/2\pi$, $2\omega_1/2\pi$,..., which occur at equal intervals $\omega_1/2\pi$ above $\omega/2\pi$. When $n < 0$, there is a similar series terminating at $m\omega_1/2\pi$, where m is the largest integer making $(\omega - m\omega_1) > 0$. For other n, there is an unlimited series of frequencies interlaced with those mentioned above. The reader should plot a diagram showing the frequency spectrum, taking $\omega/2\pi = 2,560$ c.p.s., $\omega_1/2\pi = 50$ c.p.s., $\xi_1 = 0\cdot25$ cm., $c = 3\cdot43 \times 10^4$ cm. sec.$^{-1}$ For the value of $k\xi_1$ obtained from these data it is accurate enough to take $J_n(z) \simeq (\tfrac{1}{2}z)^n/n!$.

4.310. Forced oscillation in self-oscillatory thermionic valve circuit [9, 119]. The arrangement is shown schematically in Fig. 9 A, the differential equation being (3), § 4.10, with $E_0 \cos(\omega t + \varphi)$ on the right-hand side. Thus corresponding to (4), § 4.10, we have

$$\ddot{u} - b\dot{u} + c\frac{d(u^3)}{dt} + au = F_0 \cos(\omega t + \varphi), \quad (1)$$

with $F_0 = a(E_0/E_s)$, and a, b, $c > 0$. There are two possible main oscillations, (1) free in virtue of the negative resistance property of the valve, (2) forced due to the applied potential difference

$$E_0 \cos(\omega t + \varphi).$$

4.311. Solution of (1), § 4.310. To find an approximation adequate to explain salient experimental results, during the steady state, we assume that†

$$u = A_0 \cos\psi_0 + A \cos\psi, \qquad (1)$$

with $\psi_0 = \omega_0 t$, $\psi = \omega t$, ω_0, ω being the angular frequencies of the free and forced oscillations, respectively. Substituting from (1) into (1), § 4.310, yields:

$$
\left.
\begin{aligned}
\ddot{u} &= -\omega_0^2 A_0 \cos\psi_0 - \omega^2 A \cos\psi \\
-b\dot{u} &= b[\omega_0 A_0 \sin\psi_0 + \omega A \sin\psi] \\
c\frac{d(u^3)}{dt} &= -c[(\tfrac{3}{4}A_0^3\omega_0 + \tfrac{3}{2}A_0 A^2\omega_0)\sin\psi_0 + \\
&\qquad\qquad + (\tfrac{3}{4}A^3\omega + \tfrac{3}{2}A_0^2 A)\sin\psi] \\
au &= a[A_0 \cos\psi_0 + A \cos\psi] \\
F_0\cos(\psi+\varphi) &= F_0(\cos\psi\cos\varphi - \sin\psi\sin\varphi),
\end{aligned}
\right\} \qquad (2)
$$

terms involving $2\psi_0$, $3\psi_0$, etc., being omitted.

Equating coefficients of $\cos\psi$, $\sin\psi$, $\cos\psi_0$, $\sin\psi_0$ to zero independently, we get

$\cos\psi$:
$$-\omega^2 A + aA = F_0\cos\varphi, \qquad (3)$$

$\sin\psi$:
$$b\omega A - \frac{3A^3\omega c}{4} - \tfrac{3}{2}A_0^2 A\omega c = -F_0\sin\varphi, \qquad (4)$$

$\cos\psi_0$:
$$-\omega_0^2 A_0 + aA_0 = 0, \qquad (5)$$

$\sin\psi_0$:
$$b\omega_0 A_0 - \tfrac{3}{4}A_0^3\omega_0 c - \tfrac{3}{2}A_0 A^2\omega_0 c = 0. \qquad (6)$$

From (6) we obtain

$$|A_0| = \left(\frac{4b}{3c} - 2A^2\right)^{\frac{1}{2}}, \quad\text{or}\quad A_0 = 0. \qquad (7)$$

In absence of an applied potential difference, $A = 0$, and if $b > 0$, $CR/\sigma M \ll 1$, the amplitude of the free oscillation is given by

$$|\bar{A}_0| = \left(\frac{4b}{3c}\right)^{\frac{1}{2}} = 2\left(1 - \frac{CR}{\sigma M}\right)^{\frac{1}{2}}, \quad\text{by § 4.10.} \qquad (8)$$

The free oscillation vanishes when $A_0 = 0$, so by (7) the amplitude of the forced oscillation is then

$$|A| = |\bar{A}_0|/\sqrt{2}. \qquad (9)$$

In (7) since A_0 must be real, the forced oscillation exists alone if

$$|A| \geqslant |\bar{A}_0|/\sqrt{2}.$$

From (5),
$$\omega_0^2 = a = 1/LC, \qquad (10)$$

and by (3), (4) if the free oscillation is suppressed $A_0 = 0$, so

$$(\omega^2 - \omega_0^2)^2 + \omega^2(b - 3A^2 c/4)^2 = (F_0/A)^2, \qquad (11)$$

† It can be shown that no phase angle is required for the free oscillation.

G

or $$(\omega^2-\omega_0^2)^2/\omega^2 b^2+(1-3A^2c/4b)^2 = (F_0/Ab\omega)^2. \qquad (12)$$

Writing $(\omega^2-\omega_0^2)/\omega b = x$, $3A^2c/4b = y$, $3F_0^2c/4b^3\omega^2 = E$, (12) takes the form

$$x^2y+(1-y)^2y = E, \qquad (13)$$

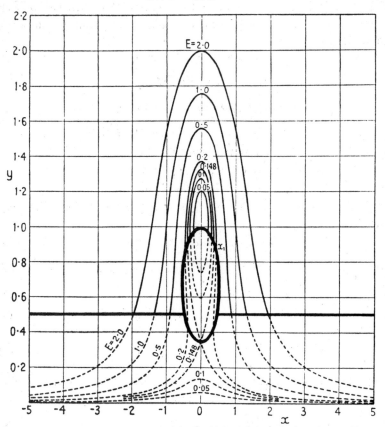

FIG. 24. Amplitude-frequency curves for 'driven' thermionic valve oscillator.

which is valid when there is no free oscillation. With the above substitution (6) yields

$$y_0 = 3A_0^2c/4b = (1-2y), \qquad y_0, y > 0. \qquad (14)$$

Taking $|\omega-\omega_0| \ll \omega_0$, then $|x| \simeq 2|\omega-\omega_0|/b$, so if ω_0 is the central frequency or tune point, x is nearly proportional to the amount of detuning. Since $3c/4b$ is constant, $y \propto A^2$, the square of the amplitude of the *forced* oscillation.

4.312. The amplitude-frequency curves when $A_0 = 0$. These are shown in Fig. 24, being obtained by plotting (13), § 4.311, for various values of E. They resemble the tuning curves of an LCR circuit, but from a physical viewpoint the broken line parts have no significance here. Imagine the curve marked $E = 0·2$ to be followed for x increasing from zero. A value x_1 is reached where the tangent

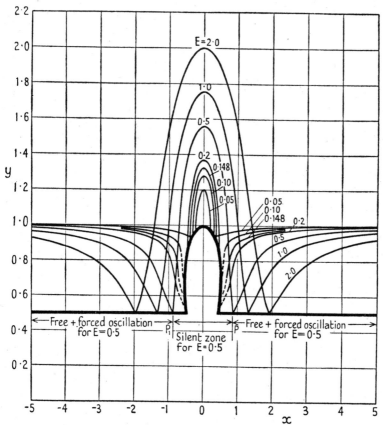

FIG. 25. Amplitude-frequency curves for 'driven' thermionic valve oscillator, illustrating the phenomenon of 'entrainment', and depicting the 'silent zone'.

is vertical. The locus of the vertical tangents to the family of E curves represents a transition stage known from experiment to be that where the free oscillation sets in. When $|x| > |x_1|$, there are both free and forced oscillations in the circuit, so $\bar{y} \propto (A_0^2 + A^2)$. The corresponding x–$\bar{y}$ curves veer away from the x-axis as illustrated in Fig. 25 [119].

Since $|A_0|$ is now > 0, the term $-\frac{3}{2}A_0^2 A\omega c$ in (4), § 4.311, must be incorporated in (11), § 4.311, so, using (7), § 4.311, we have

$$(\omega^2 - \omega_0^2)^2 + \omega^2(b - 9A^2c/4)^2 = (F_0/A)^2, \tag{1}$$

which is (11), §4.311, with 9 written for 3 in the second member. Thus corresponding to (13), § 4.311, we get

$$x^2y+(1-3y)^2y = E. \tag{2}$$

When $y = 0{\cdot}5$, $(1-y)^2 = (1-3y)^2$, so the curves corresponding to (13), § 4.311, and (2) above, meet at this point, provided $|x|$ is outside the locus of the vertical tangents. The two curves do not meet on the locus, since our approximate solution of (1), § 4.310, is not accurate enough for this to happen. Nevertheless the diagram of Fig. 25 agrees with experiment. Additional information on this topic is given in [28].

Suppose the circuit of Fig. 9 A were loosely coupled to a detector valve followed by an audio-frequency amplifier with loudspeaker. Starting at $\omega = \omega_0$, i.e. $x = 0$, on the curve $E = 0{\cdot}5$, if ω and, therefore, x were increased, silence would ensue up to the point P. Thereafter, there would be a beat tone of frequency $(\omega-\omega_0)/2\pi$ in the loudspeaker circuit. This would be heard if it were in the range of audibility of the human ear. PP_1 is known as the silent zone corresponding to $E = 0{\cdot}5$, where the free oscillation is suppressed by the forced one [9, 119].

4.313. Locus of vertical tangents.

The ovals in Fig. 24 are given by (13), § 4.311. Differentiating with respect to y, we get

$$2xy(dx/dy)+x^2+(1-y)^2-2y(1-y) = 0, \tag{1}$$

so if $dx/dy = 0$, we must have

$$x^2+(1-y)(1-3y) = 0, \quad \text{or} \quad 3x^2+9(y-\tfrac{2}{3})^2 = 1. \tag{2}$$

This is an ellipse, centre $(0, \tfrac{2}{3})$, semi-axes $1/\sqrt{3}$, $\tfrac{1}{3}$ which represents the locus of the vertical tangents as shown in Figs. 24, 25. Using (13), § 4.311, and (2) above, we find that y is triple-valued when $E < 8/27$. For $E = 8/27$, $y = \tfrac{2}{3}$, $x = \pm 1/\sqrt{3}$.

The parts of the curves in Fig. 25 corresponding to

$$\bar{y} = (y_0+y) \propto (A_0^2+A^2) \quad \text{(mean square basis)}$$

may be computed by aid of (2), § 4.312, and (14), § 4.311. The latter gives $(y_0+y) = (1-y)$, and by the former y decreases with increase in $|x|$, so (y_0+y) cannot exceed unity.

4.40. Subharmonics and relaxation oscillations.

A study of (1), § 4.310, taken in the form

$$\ddot{y}-\epsilon(1-y^2)\dot{y}+y = F\sin \omega t, \tag{1}$$

has been made using a differential analyser [53], and curves are reproduced in Figs. 26, 27. The parameters are given in the captions; y is proportional to the potential difference across the capacitance in Fig. 9 A, and the time scale is arbitrary. The phenomenon of resonance is almost absent in the case of a circuit executing relaxation oscilla-

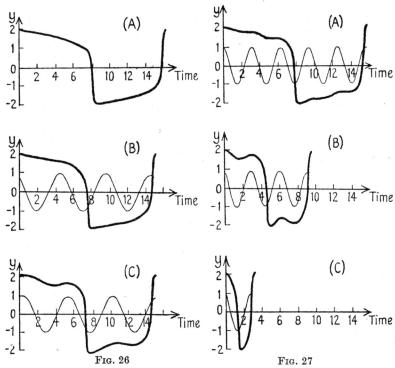

FIG. 26

FIG. 27

FIG. 26. A. Free relaxation oscillation with $\epsilon = 8$, $F = 0$. B. $\epsilon = 8$, $F = 25/32$, $\omega = 1\cdot25$: oscillation of drifting type. C. $\epsilon = 8$, $F = 25/8$, $\omega = 1\cdot25$: oscillation is $\frac{1}{3}$ harmonic of driving force.

FIG. 27. A. $\epsilon = 8$, $F = 2$, $\omega = 2$; oscillation is $\frac{1}{2}$ harmonic of driving force. B. $\epsilon = 8$, $F = 80$, $\omega = 2$; oscillation is $\frac{1}{2}$ harmonic of driving force. C. $\epsilon = 8$, $F = 160$, $\omega = 2$; oscillation has same period as driving force.

tions, to which a potential difference $F \sin \omega t$ is applied. The main influence of the latter is to alter the time period of the circuital relaxation oscillation. Thus a subharmonic† of very high order may

† Since the oscillator wave form is far from sinusoidal, the term subharmonic merely signifies that the periodic time of the oscillation is an integral multiple of that of the applied potential difference $F \sin \omega t$. In experiments described in [120, 123], by increasing the frequency of the driving potential difference, all subharmonics as far as the 200th were obtained, i.e. the periodic time of the relaxation oscillation was 200 times that of the driving potential difference.

occur. An increase in the driving potential difference reduces the order of the harmonic, but has little effect on the amplitude of the relaxation oscillation (Fig. 27). Some of the 'driven' oscillations are of the 'drifting type' (Fig. 26 B) and never attain the periodic synchronized state. Both the amplitude and the time interval between alternate zeros fluctuates (see [28, 29]).

A relaxation oscillation for which $\epsilon = 8$, $F = 0$ is depicted in Fig. 26 A. The result of applying a sinusoidal potential difference having a frequency three times that of the relaxation oscillation is shown in Fig. 26 C. The main component of the latter is a synchronized $\frac{1}{3}$ harmonic. The original paper should be consulted for curves obtained by making a large number and variety of parametric changes.

CHAPTER V

METHOD OF SLOWLY VARYING AMPLITUDE AND PHASE

5.10. Introduction. The approximate method to be described may be applied to non-linear equations when the solution takes the form

$$y = A(t)\sin[\omega t + \varphi(t)], \tag{1}$$

where the amplitude A and the phase angle φ† are functions of t whose rate of variation is small compared with the angular frequency ω. In some cases $A(t)$ may be variable but $\varphi(t)$ constant, and vice versa. Also, after a short time interval, $A(t)$ may be sensibly constant, i.e. $A(t) \to$ a constant, or to zero asymptotically when $t \to +\infty$. As an example of the latter we cite the familiar case of the free oscillation of a *linear* electrical LCR circuit in which the current is given by

$$I = I_0 e^{-\kappa t}\sin(\omega t + \varphi). \tag{2}$$

Here $A(t) = I_0 e^{-\kappa t} \to 0$ as $t \to +\infty$, while φ is a constant phase angle.

Consider a differential equation of the form

$$\ddot{y} + \epsilon g(y, \dot{y}) + \omega^2 y = 0, \tag{3}$$

in which the non-linear term $\epsilon g(y, \dot{y})$ is relatively small, and g is a function‡ of both the displacement y (or its equivalent) and its first time derivative $\dot{y}$. Neglecting this term, the equation reduces to the linear one

$$\ddot{y} + \omega^2 y = 0, \tag{4}$$

of which the complete solution is

$$y = A_1 \cos \omega t + B_1 \sin \omega t, \tag{5}$$

A_1, B_1 being arbitrary constants. In a sense this may be regarded as a first approximation, although it possesses no non-linear characteristics. (5) is expressible in the form (1), with $A = (A_1^2 + B_1^2)^{\frac{1}{2}}$, and $\varphi = \tan^{-1}(A_1/B_1)$, these being constants.

Writing $(\omega t + \varphi) = \chi$, the solution takes the form

$$y = A \sin \chi; \tag{6}$$

so

$$\dot{y} = A\omega \cos \chi. \tag{7}$$

---

† Strictly 'phase' pertains to sine waves, but it is convenient to use it here.
‡ If terms of the form by^3 occur, they are to be included in g, i.e. g comprises damping and non-linear control terms.

We now suppose that A and φ vary slowly with t, so by differentiating (6) we get [77, 175]

$$\dot{y} = \dot{A}\sin\chi + A(\omega+\dot{\varphi})\cos\chi. \tag{8}$$

Substituting for $\dot{y}$ from (7) into (8) leads to

$$\dot{A}\sin\chi + A\dot{\varphi}\cos\chi = 0. \tag{9}$$

Differentiating (7), we have

$$\ddot{y} = \dot{A}\omega\cos\chi - A\omega(\omega+\dot{\varphi})\sin\chi. \tag{10}$$

Substituting from (6), (7), (10) into (3) yields

$$\dot{A}\cos\chi - A\dot{\varphi}\sin\chi = -\frac{\epsilon}{\omega}g(A\sin\chi, A\omega\cos\chi). \tag{11}$$

Multiplying (9) by $\sin\chi$, (11) by $\cos\chi$ and adding, gives

$$\dot{A} = -\frac{\epsilon}{\omega}g(A\sin\chi, A\omega\cos\chi)\cos\chi. \tag{12}$$

Multiplying (9) by $\cos\chi$, (11) by $-\sin\chi$ and adding, we get

$$\dot{\varphi} = \frac{\epsilon}{\omega A}g(A\sin\chi, A\omega\cos\chi)\sin\chi. \tag{13}$$

By hypothesis $\dot{A}$ and $\dot{\varphi}$ vary but little in a period $2\pi/\omega$, which latter corresponds to a period 2π in $\psi = \omega t$. We shall assume, therefore, that to the degree of approximation contemplated, the mean values of $\dot{A}$ and $\dot{\varphi}$ over a period 2π in ψ are adequately accurate. Then using (12), the mean value of

$$\dot{A} = -\frac{\epsilon}{2\pi\omega}\int_0^{2\pi} g(A\sin\psi, A\omega\cos\psi)\cos\psi\,d\psi, \tag{14}$$

while by (13), the mean value of

$$\dot{\varphi} = \frac{\epsilon}{2\pi\omega A}\int_0^{2\pi} g(A\sin\psi, A\omega\cos\psi)\sin\psi\,d\psi. \tag{15}$$

Since $\chi = \omega t + \varphi$, it follows that

$$\dot{\chi} = \omega + \frac{\epsilon}{2\pi\omega A}\int_0^{2\pi} g(A\sin\psi, A\omega\cos\psi)\sin\psi\,d\psi. \tag{16}$$

When the restoring or spring control force (or its equivalent) contains terms of the form $y^2, y^3, \ldots$, A is unaffected, because the integrals corresponding to (14) vanish. These terms affect φ, however, since the corresponding integrals do not vanish. For a similar reason the damping terms $\dot{y}$, $\dot{y}^2$ affect A but not φ. Hence in the *first approximation*, non-linear control terms affect the frequency but not the amplitude, whereas damping terms affect the amplitude but not the frequency. In higher approximations either type of term influences both frequency and amplitude.

5.11. Solve

$$\ddot{y} - \epsilon(1-y^2)\dot{y} + y = 0 \quad (0 < \epsilon \ll 1). \tag{1}$$

This is the equation for a thermionic valve oscillator (see § 4.10). Here

$$g(y, \dot{y}) = -(1-y^2)\dot{y} = -(1-A^2\sin^2\chi)A\omega\cos\chi. \tag{2}$$

Substituting (2) into (14), § 5.10, with ψ for χ, gives

$$A = \frac{\epsilon A}{2\pi} \int_0^{2\pi} (1-A^2\sin^2\psi)\cos^2\psi \, d\psi \tag{3}$$

$$= \tfrac{1}{2}\epsilon A(1-\tfrac{1}{4}A^2). \tag{4}$$

When the steady state prevails, $\dot{A} = 0$, so $A = 2$, as in §§ 4.10, 4.110, with $0 < \epsilon \ll 1$. To determine A as a function of t during the growth of the oscillation, we have from (4)

$$2A\dot{A} = \tfrac{1}{4}\epsilon(4A^2 - A^4) = \tfrac{1}{4}\epsilon[4 - (A^2-2)^2]. \tag{5}$$

Thus

$$4\int \frac{d(A^2-2)}{4-(A^2-2)^2} = \epsilon\int dt + B_1, \tag{6}$$

so

$$\log[A^2/(4-A^2)] = \epsilon t + B_1, \tag{7}$$

or

$$\frac{A^2}{(4-A^2)} = Be^{\epsilon t}, \tag{8}$$

giving

$$A^2 = 4Be^{\epsilon t}/(1+Be^{\epsilon t}). \tag{9}$$

If $A = A_0$ when $t = 0$, $B = A_0^2/(4-A_0^2)$, so from this and (9), we obtain

$$A^2 = A_0^2 e^{\epsilon t}/[1+\tfrac{1}{4}A_0^2(e^{\epsilon t}-1)], \tag{10}$$

and, therefore, $\quad A = A_0 e^{\frac{1}{2}\epsilon t}/[1+\tfrac{1}{4}A_0^2(e^{\epsilon t}-1)]^{\frac{1}{2}}. \tag{11}$

It should be observed that if $A_0 = 0$ at $t = 0$, $A = 0$, which means that there is no oscillation. Hence it is necessary to start the oscillation by external means, so that $A_0 > 0$. From (11) it follows that A increases monotonically with increase in t, and tends to the ultimate value 2 as $t \to +\infty$. If we suppose that $A_0 > 2$, the amplitude will decay and $\to 2$ as $t \to +\infty$.

By (2) above, with ψ for χ, and (15), § 5.10,

$$\dot{\varphi} = -\frac{\epsilon}{2\pi} \int_0^{2\pi} (1-A^2\sin^2\psi)\cos\psi \sin\psi \, d\psi = 0. \tag{12}$$

Since $\omega = 1$, $$\chi = t+\varphi_0, \tag{13}$$

where φ_0 is an arbitrary value of χ when $t = 0$. Hence by (1), § 5.10, (11), (13) above, the solution of (1) to the degree of approximation envisaged is

$$y = A(t)\sin(t+\varphi_0) \tag{14}$$

$$= \frac{A_0 e^{\frac{1}{2}\epsilon t}\sin(t+\varphi_0)}{[1+\frac{1}{4}A_0^2(e^{\epsilon t}-1)]^{\frac{1}{4}}} \to 2\sin(t+\varphi_0) \tag{15}$$

as $t \to +\infty$.

The graphical representation of (15) is akin to the curve in Fig. 59. The foregoing is inapplicable when $\epsilon > 0.25$. It is then necessary to resort to a graphical method as exemplified in § 8.12.

5.12. Solve $$\ddot{y}-2\kappa\dot{y}+c\dot{y}^3+ay = 0, \tag{1}$$

a, c, κ being positive non-zero constants. See problems 42, 43 on p. 254

This is the equation for an electrically (not electronically) driven tuning-fork. The term $-2\kappa\dot{y}$ may be regarded as introducing a negative resistance, equivalent to a driving force. After the initial (starting) transient has ceased, the motion is periodic. As in §§ 5.10, 5.11 we assume that

$$\epsilon g(y, \dot{y}) = -2\kappa\dot{y}+c\dot{y}^3 \tag{2}$$

is relatively small. Then by (14), § 5.10, with $a = \omega^2$,

$$\dot{A} = \frac{2\kappa}{2\pi\omega} \int_0^{2\pi} A\omega\cos^2\psi \, d\psi - \frac{c}{2\pi\omega} \int_0^{2\pi} A^3\omega^3\cos^4\psi \, d\psi \tag{3}$$

$$= \kappa A - \tfrac{3}{8}c\omega^2 A^3 = A(\kappa - \tfrac{3}{8}c\omega^2 A^2). \tag{4}$$

When the motion is periodic $\dot{A} = 0$, so the ultimate amplitude is given by $\kappa - \tfrac{3}{8}c\omega^2 A^2 = 0$,

i.e. $$A = \frac{2}{\omega}\left(\frac{2\kappa}{3c}\right)^{\frac{1}{2}}. \tag{5}$$

To determine $A(t)$ we have to solve (4) as a differential equation. Thus

$$A\dot{A} = \frac{\kappa}{2p}[p^2-(A^2-p)^2], \tag{6}$$

where $p = 4\kappa/3c\omega^2$, so

$$2p \int \frac{d(A^2-p)}{[p^2-(A^2-p)^2]} = 2\kappa \int dt + B_1 \tag{7}$$

and, therefore, $\qquad \log[A^2/(2p-A^2)] = 2\kappa t + B_1.$ $\qquad\qquad$ (8)

Hence $\qquad\qquad\qquad A^2/(2p-A^2) = Be^{2\kappa t}.$ $\qquad\qquad\qquad$ (9)

If $A = A_0$ when $t = 0$, $B = A_0^2/(2p-A_0^2)$. Expressing (9) in the form

$$A^2 = 2pBe^{2\kappa t}/(1+Be^{2\kappa t}),$$ (10)

and substituting into (10) for B, p, yields

$$A^2 = A_0^2 e^{2\kappa t}/[1+(3c/8\kappa)\omega^2 A_0^2(e^{2\kappa t}-1)],$$ (11)

so $\qquad A(t) = A_0 e^{\kappa t}/[1+(3c/8\kappa)\omega^2 A_0^2(e^{2\kappa t}-1)]^{\frac{1}{2}}.$ (12)

If $A_0 = 0$ at $t = 0$, there is absence of motion, so the fork must be started initially. By (5) the ultimate amplitude is $A_s = (2/\omega)(2\kappa/3c)^{\frac{1}{2}}$. If $A_0 < A_s$ the amplitude grows, whereas if $A_0 > A_s$, the amplitude decays to the value A_s in a manner defined by (12). The growth stage is similar to that portrayed in Fig. 59.

By (15), § 5.10,

$$\dot{\varphi} = -\frac{2\kappa}{2\pi\omega A}\int_0^{2\pi} A\omega\cos\psi\sin\psi\,d\psi + \frac{c}{2\pi\omega A}\int_0^{2\pi} A^3\omega^3\cos^3\psi\sin\psi\,d\psi$$ (13)

$$= 0,$$ (14)

so $\qquad\qquad\qquad \varphi = \varphi_0, \text{ a constant},$ (15)

which is an arbitrary value of χ at $t = 0$. Thus

$$\chi = \omega t + \varphi_0.$$ (16)

Hence by (1), § 5.10, (12), (16) above, an approximate solution of (1) is

$$y = \frac{A_0 e^{\kappa t}\sin(\omega t + \varphi_0)}{[1+(3c\omega^2/8\kappa)A_0^2(e^{2\kappa t}-1)]^{\frac{1}{2}}}.$$ (17)

When the supply of electrical energy is discontinued, $\kappa = 0$ and (17) reduces to the form

$$y = \frac{A_0\sin(\omega t + \varphi_0)}{(1+\frac{3}{4}c\omega^2 A_0^2 t)^{\frac{1}{2}}} \to 0 \text{ as } t \to +\infty,$$ (18)

so the tuning-fork comes to rest.

5.13. Solve $\qquad\qquad \ddot{y}+2\kappa\dot{y}+ay+by^3 = 0,$ $\qquad\qquad$ (1)

$a, b, \kappa > 0$, $a > \kappa^2$, the terms $2\kappa\dot{y}$, by^3 being relatively small.

This is the equation for the system mentioned in § 3.10, but having viscous damping represented by $2\kappa\dot{y}$. Then from (14), § 5.10, with $\omega = a^{\frac{1}{2}}$,

$$A = -\frac{2\kappa}{2\pi\omega} \int_0^{2\pi} A\omega \cos^2\psi \, d\psi - \frac{b}{2\pi\omega} \int_0^{2\pi} A^3 \sin^3\psi \cos\psi \, d\psi \qquad (2)$$

$$= -\kappa A. \qquad (3)$$

Thus $\qquad \displaystyle\int \frac{dA}{A} = -\kappa t + B_1, \quad \text{or} \quad \log A = -\kappa t + B_1, \qquad (4)$

so $\qquad\qquad\qquad\qquad A = A_0 e^{-\kappa t}, \qquad (5)$

where A_0 is the value of A at $t = 0$.

Also by (15), § 5.10,

$$\dot{\varphi} = \frac{2\kappa}{2\pi\omega A} \int_0^{2\pi} A\omega \cos\psi \sin\psi \, d\psi + \frac{b}{2\pi\omega A} \int_0^{2\pi} A^3 \sin^4\psi \, d\psi \qquad (6)$$

$$= \frac{3bA^2}{8\omega}. \qquad (7)$$

Thus, on the *assumption* that A is constant,

$$\varphi = \frac{3bA^2 t}{8\omega} + \varphi_0, \qquad (8)$$

and, therefore, by (16), § 5.10,

$$\chi = \left(\omega + \frac{3bA^2}{8\omega}\right)t + \varphi_0. \qquad (9)$$

Hence by (1), § 5.10, the approximate solution of (1) above with $\varphi_0 = \frac{1}{2}\pi$, is

$$y = A_0 e^{-\kappa t} \cos[\omega + (3bA^2/8\omega)]t \qquad (10)$$

$$= A_0 e^{-\kappa t} \cos[a^{\frac{1}{2}} + 3bA_0^2 e^{-2\kappa t}/8a^{\frac{1}{2}}]t, \qquad (11)$$

so the motion once started dies away exponentially. By virtue of $e^{-2\kappa t}$ in the formula for the angular frequency, the latter decreases with increase in t. This corresponds to reduction in amplitude. The reader may find it interesting to compare (11) with (6), (7), § 3.17. As shown in 2°, § 9.23, the only singularity of equation (1) is a stable spiral point at $y = v = 0$.

5.14. Solve

$$\ddot{\theta} + [-2\kappa\dot{\theta} + (\alpha|\dot{\theta}|\dot{\theta} + \beta\dot{\theta}^3 - \gamma\theta^3)] + \omega^2\theta = 0, \qquad (1)$$

where α, β, γ, κ are real positive constants such that the part in [ ] is relatively small. This differential equation occurs in the problem of the rolling of a ship fitted with a stabilizing equipment, and it applies when the phase of the control is reversed [108]. After reversal, the amplitude of the motion increases, reaching an ultimate value, the oscillation then being periodic. This occurs only if $\kappa > 0$. The term $2\kappa\dot\theta$ may be written $\beta_1\dot\theta - \alpha_1\dot\theta$, the first part being due to the stabilizer with reversed phase, and the second to rolling resistance, i.e. in the language of electronics to negative and positive damping, respectively. If $\beta_1 > \alpha_1$, then $\kappa > 0$, so the damping is negative, and the stabilizer supplies the energy necessary to maintain the periodic oscillation.

By (14), § 5.10,

$$A = \frac{2\kappa}{2\pi\omega}\int_0^{2\pi} A\omega\cos^2\psi\,d\psi - \frac{\alpha}{2\pi\omega}\int_0^{2\pi} A^2\omega^2|\cos\psi|\cos^2\psi\,d\psi -$$

$$-\frac{\beta}{2\pi\omega}\int_0^{2\pi} A^3\omega^3\cos^4\psi\,d\psi + \frac{\gamma}{2\pi\omega}\int_0^{2\pi} A^3\sin^3\psi\cos\psi\,d\psi \qquad (2)$$

$$= A\left(\kappa - \frac{4\alpha\omega A}{3\pi} - \tfrac{3}{8}\beta\omega^2 A^2\right). \qquad (3)$$

When the motion is periodic $\dot A = 0$, so by (3)

$$\tfrac{3}{8}\beta\omega^2 A^2 + \frac{4\alpha\omega A}{3\pi} - \kappa = 0. \qquad (4)$$

Solving (4), and choosing the positive root, yields

$$A = \frac{16\alpha}{9\pi\beta\omega}\left[\left(1 + \frac{27\pi^2\beta\kappa}{32\alpha^2}\right)^{\frac12} - 1\right]. \qquad (5)$$

If $\dfrac{27\pi^2\beta\kappa}{32\alpha^2} \ll 1$, (5) is approximately

$$A \simeq \frac{16\alpha}{9\pi\beta\omega}\left[1 + \frac{27\pi^2\beta\kappa}{64\alpha^2} - 1\right] = 3\pi\kappa/4\alpha\omega. \qquad (6)$$

By (15), § 5.10,

$$\dot\varphi = -\frac{\gamma}{2\pi\omega A}\int_0^{2\pi} A^3\sin^4\psi\,d\psi = -\frac{3\gamma A^2}{8\omega}, \qquad (7)$$

since the other three integrals corresponding to [ ] in (1) vanish. Thus during the steady state

$$\varphi = -\frac{3\gamma A^2 t}{8\omega} + \varphi_0, \qquad (8)$$

since A is constant, having the value at (6), and φ_0 is an arbitrary phase angle.

Hence
$$\chi = \omega t + \varphi = \left(\omega - \frac{3\gamma A^2}{8\omega}\right)t + \varphi_0, \qquad (9)$$

and by aid of (6) the periodic solution is

$$\theta = (3\pi\kappa/4\alpha\omega)\sin[\omega(1-27\pi^2\kappa^2\gamma/128\alpha^2\omega^4)t+\varphi_0]. \tag{10}$$

The angular frequency of the oscillation $\omega_0 = [\omega-(3\gamma A^2/8\omega)]$ decreases with increase in A.

5.15. Solution of (3), § 5.14. To simplify the analysis we shall take the case when $\kappa = 0$, and find the law of amplitude decay for the positively damped system. We have to solve

$$\frac{dA}{dt} = -A^2\left(\frac{4\alpha\omega}{3\pi}+\tfrac{3}{8}\beta\omega^2 A\right) \tag{1}$$

$$= -\tfrac{3}{8}\beta\omega^2 A^2(A+2\delta), \tag{2}$$

where $\delta = 16\alpha/9\pi\beta\omega$. Then

$$\int \frac{dA}{A^2(A+2\delta)} = -\tfrac{3}{8}\beta\omega^2 t+B_1. \tag{3}$$

Now the integral may be written

$$\frac{1}{4\delta^2}\int \frac{dA}{(A+2\delta)}-\frac{1}{4\delta^2}\int \frac{dA}{A}+\frac{1}{2\delta}\int \frac{dA}{A^2} = \frac{1}{4\delta^2}\log\left(\frac{A+2\delta}{A}\right)-\frac{1}{2\delta A}. \tag{4}$$

At the beginning of the decay, if $2\delta/A \ll 1$, we have approximately

$$\frac{1}{4\delta^2}\log(1+2\delta/A)-\frac{1}{2\delta A} = \frac{1}{4\delta^2}\left(\frac{2\delta}{A}-\frac{2\delta^2}{A^2}\right)-\frac{1}{2\delta A} = -1/2A^2. \tag{5}$$

Substituting (5) into (3) yields

$$\frac{1}{A^2} = \tfrac{3}{4}\beta\omega^2 t+B. \tag{6}$$

If $A = A_0$ when $t = 0$, $B = 1/A_0^2$ and, therefore,

$$A(t) \simeq A_0/(1+\tfrac{3}{4}A_0^2\beta\omega^2 t)^{\frac{1}{2}}, \tag{7}$$

so the oscillation decays according to this law if κ is made zero† during the steady state. (7) shows that the greater A_0, the more rapid the decay in amplitude. By (9), § 5.14, the rate of oscillation increases with decrease in A. Apart from the damping terms, the behaviour is akin to that of a simple pendulum, the restoring force in both cases being due to gravity. The 'stiffness', or derivative of the force with respect to angular displacement, decreases with increase in amplitude.

5.16. Solve the simultaneous differential equations [107]

$$\ddot{\phi}-b\dot{\phi}+c\dot{\phi}^3+a\phi = 0, \tag{1}$$

and

$$\ddot{\theta}+b_1\dot{\theta}+a_1\theta = -\kappa_1\dot{\phi}+\kappa_2\dot{\phi}^3, \tag{2}$$

† This means that the driving force due to reversal of phase of the stabilizer is neutralized by the resistance to rolling.

all constants being positive and non-zero. These equations occur in the theory of ship stabilization, and the problem is to investigate the motion. First we remark that if $b = 2\kappa$, and $\phi = y$, (1) is identical with (1), § 5.12, the equation for an electrically maintained tuning-fork. The periodic solution may be obtained from (17), § 5.12, by letting $t \to +\infty$ taking $a = \omega^2$, $b = 2\kappa$, $\varphi_0 = \frac{1}{2}\pi$ (arbitrary). Then

$$\phi = A \cos\psi, \tag{3}$$

where $A = (4b/3\omega^2 c)^{\frac{1}{2}}$, $\psi = \omega t$.

Since $\kappa_2/\kappa_1 \ll 1$ usually, we omit the last term in (2), and substitute for $\dot\phi$ from (3) into (2). Thus the latter becomes

$$\ddot\theta + b_1 \dot\theta + a_1 \theta = B \sin\psi, \tag{4}$$

where $B = A\kappa_1 \omega$. In the solution of (4) we omit the complementary function, since it is an exponentially damped circular function which tends to zero as $t \to +\infty$. Then the particular integral of (4) is

$$\theta = -\frac{A\omega\kappa_1 \cos(\psi+\epsilon)}{[(\omega_1^2-\omega^2)^2+\omega^2 b_1^2]^{\frac{1}{2}}}, \tag{5}$$

with $a_1 = \omega_1^2$, $\epsilon = \tan^{-1}[(\omega_1^2-\omega^2)/b_1 \omega]$. Thus the ultimate motion is periodic with period $2\pi/\omega$ and amplitude

$$|\theta_0| = A\omega\kappa_1/[(\omega_1^2-\omega^2)+\omega^2 b_1^2]^{\frac{1}{2}}. \tag{6}$$

In the self-oscillatory mechanical system to which (1), (2) refer, the term $-b\dot\phi$ in (1) represents the driving force entailed by energy supplied from an external source (the stabilizer); and in electronic language it is equivalent to a negative resistance. If $b < 0$, the resistance is positive and the solution of (1) will then represent a damped oscillation of decreasing amplitude. Using the expression for this in (2) with $\kappa_2 = 0$, we obtain the equation of a dissipative system driven by an oscillatory force of gradually decreasing amplitude. Hence an oscillation once started will die away with increase in time. This is the desired practical result in the anti-rolling of ships.

5.170. Surges in hydro-electric installation [30]. The general arrangement of a simple surge tank for a hydro-electric power plant is shown schematically in Fig. 28. Water is supplied from a reservoir via a tunnel and pipe-line to turbines which drive electrical generators. The rate of flow of water to the turbines is controlled by valves at the lower end of the pipe-line, and they may be opened or closed as desired. In order to avoid a large pressure rise in the system due to change in

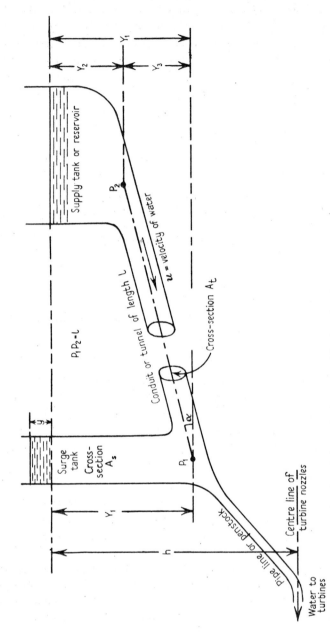

Fig. 28. Schematic diagram of hydro-electric supply system with surge tank.

momentum of the surplus water when valves are closed, the surge tank is situated at the lower end of the tunnel. The water level in the tank rises above that during steady flow, and the pressure is restricted to a safe value. When valves are opened, water flows out of the tank, thereby augmenting the supply from the reservoir. In either case, u, the velocity of the water in the tunnel, attains a steady value ultimately. Any change in the rate of flow of water to the turbines is accompanied by a surge in the tank, tunnel, and reservoir, which combination may be regarded as a form of enormous U-tube having a non-uniform cross-section.

Remarks on friction. When water flows in a tunnel or pipe, the whole cross-section being utilized, the friction force has been shown experimentally to be proportional to some power of the velocity u. In an iron or steel pipe this power may be rather less than 2, and in a concrete pipe nearly 2. The loss of water head due to friction, i.e. the height of a column of water to cause the same pressure, varies as u^ν. There is also a loss of head at the tunnel entrance, which varies as u^2, and this may be represented by $ku^2/2g$. If $\nu = 2$, the loss in a tunnel of length l is $lu^2/r_m C^2$, r_m being the hydraulic mean radius of the tunnel, and C the Chézy constant. Thus the total loss of head due to friction is fu^2, where the friction coefficient $f = (k/2g)+(l/r_m C^2)$. Since friction always opposes motion of the water (irrespective of its direction), in a differential equation we must write $\mp fu^2$, or its equivalent form $-f|u|u$.

5.171. Derivation of differential equation [30]. We make the following assumptions:

(i)   the cross-section of the reservoir is much greater than that of the surge tank,

(ii) the tunnel, tank, and pipe-line each has a uniform cross-section,

(iii) inertia of the water and friction in the surge tank are negligible,

(iv) $(h+y)$ in Fig. 28 is substantially constant, i.e. $y \ll h$, so that the rate of water flow in the pipe-line is independent of y.

The force relationship is:

mass $\times$ acceleration = (force due to water pressure at tunnel entrance)+(component of weight of water in tunnel)−(force due to pressure at lower end of tunnel)−(frictional force).

Thus if w is the weight of a cubic foot of water (62·4 lb.), and g the acceleration due to gravity (32·2 ft. sec.$^{-2}$), we have

$$\frac{wlA_t}{g}\frac{du}{dt} = A_t P_2 + wlA_t \sin\alpha - A_t P_1 \mp wlA_t u^2/r_m C^2, \tag{1}$$

or

$$(l/g)\frac{du}{dt} = \frac{1}{w}(P_2 - P_1) + Y_3 \mp lu^2/r_m C^2, \tag{2}$$

where $Y_3 = l\sin\alpha$. Now $P_2/w = (Y_2 \mp ku^2/2g)$, $P_1/w = (Y_1 + y)$. Substituting these into (2) gives

$$(l/g)\frac{du}{dt} = (Y_2 + Y_3 - Y_1) - y \mp [(k/2g) + (l/r_m C^2)]u^2 \tag{3}$$

$$= -y \mp fu^2, \tag{4}$$

since $(Y_2 + Y_3 - Y_1) = 0$. The rate of flow of water into the surge tank is the difference between the respective rates for tunnel and pipe-line. Hence if Q is the rate of flow in the latter,

$$A_s \frac{dy}{dt} = A_t u - Q. \tag{5}$$

Eliminating y between (4), (5) leads to the equation for the *velocity*, namely,

$$(l/g)\frac{d^2u}{dt^2} + 2f|u|\frac{du}{dt} + \frac{A_t}{A_s}u = \frac{Q}{A_s}. \tag{6}$$

This may be written in the form

$$\ddot{u} + 2\kappa|u|\dot{u} + au = d, \tag{7}$$

with

$$\kappa = fg/l, \quad a = A_t g/A_s l, \quad \text{and} \quad d = Qg/A_s l. \tag{8}$$

5.172. Singular point of (7), § 5.171 [243]. If the supply of water to the turbines is discontinued, $d = 0$, and with $v = du/dt$, we get $\ddot{u} = v\,dv/du$, so the equation may be written

$$v\frac{dv}{du} + 2\kappa|u|v + au = 0, \tag{1}$$

or

$$\frac{dv}{du} = \frac{-(au + 2\kappa|u|v)}{v}. \tag{2}$$

When $u = v = 0$, the right-hand side of (2) has the indeterminate form $0/0$, so the origin is a singular point, and by § 9.22 it is either a centre or a spiral point. Application of theorem 1, 1°, § 9.50, shows that $u, \dot{u} \to 0$ as $t \to +\infty$, so the origin is a stable spiral point. Consequently, if $d = 0$, the water in the tank, tunnel, and reservoir combination executes a damped oscillation whatever the value of $\kappa > 0$. This conclusion may be understood more readily if it is realized that the damping *coefficient* $2\kappa|u| \to 0$ as $u \to 0$. Moreover, the motion is ultimately quasi-periodic with approximate period $2\pi/a^{\frac{1}{2}}$.

When $d > 0$, water flows to the turbines, and in (7), § 5.171, we write $u = (x+c)$, where $c = d/a$, which gives

$$\ddot{x}+2\kappa|x+c|\dot{x}+ax = 0. \tag{3}$$

Putting $\dfrac{dx}{dt} = v_x$, $\ddot{x} = v_x\dfrac{dv_x}{dx}$, (3) becomes

$$\frac{dv_x}{dx} = \frac{-(ax+2\kappa|x+c|v_x)}{v_x}. \tag{4}$$

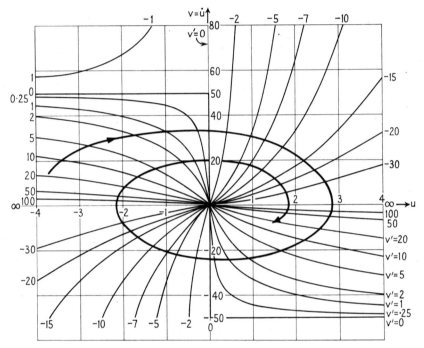

Fig. 28 A. Integral curve $(u,\ \dot{u} = v)$ for $\ddot{u}+2|u|\dot{u}+100u = 0$. Oscillatory case with $d = 0$. The origin is a stable spiral point.

By theorem 1, 1°, § 9.50, x and $\dot{x} \to 0$ as $t \to +\infty$, so it follows that at some time $t = t_1 > 0$, $c > |x|$. Then in $t_1 < t < \infty$, $|x+c|$ may be replaced by $(x+c)$.† Applying the criteria in §§ 9.20, 9.22, we find that if $\kappa^2c^2 < a$, the point $x = v = 0$, that is $u = c$, $v = 0$, is a stable spiral point, while if $\kappa^2c^2 \geqslant a$, it is a stable node. In the first case the water executes a damped oscillation, whereas in the second it is damped but non-oscillatory (aperiodic).

The *general forms* of the v–y curves, obtained by the method of

† For certain initial conditions, $c > |x|$ when $t_1 = 0$.

isoclines (see Chap. VIII) for three cases are depicted in Figs. 28 A, B, C. The numbers on the thin curves indicate the slope of the v–y curve at the crossing points. In connexion with Fig. 28 A, it may be remarked that if the initial conditions are $|u_0| > 0$, $|v_0| = a/2\kappa$, then over the range ($|u_0|$, 0), we have $|\dot{u}| = |v| = a/2\kappa$, so that $|v|$ is constant, and

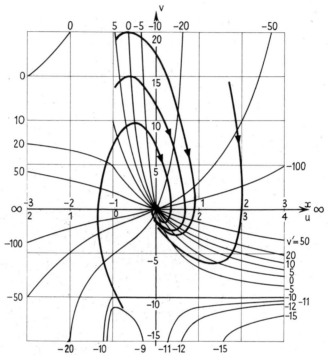

FIG. 28 B. Integral curves $(u, \dot{u} = v)$ for $\ddot{u} + 10|u|\dot{u} + 100u = 100$, that is, $\ddot{x} + 10|x+1|\dot{x} + 100x = 0$, where $u = (x+1)$. Oscillatory case with $d = 100$ and $\kappa^2 c^2 < a$. $u = 1$, $v = 0$ is a stable spiral point.

the relationship between water velocity u and time is linear. When u changes sign, the u–t relationship ceases to be linear.

5.173. Solution of (3), § 5.172 [243]. If κ is not too large and $\kappa^2 c^2 < a$, the u–t curve is a lowly damped oscillation, and the method in § 5.10 may be used. Thus in the first approximation, we assume that

$$x = A(t)\sin\{\omega t + \varphi(t)\}, \tag{1}$$

where $\omega^2 = a$. Then with $\omega t = \psi$, by (14), § 5.10, and (3), § 5.172,

$$\dot{A} = -\frac{\kappa A}{\pi} \int_0^{2\pi} |A \sin\psi + c|\cos^2\psi \, d\psi. \tag{2}$$

Two cases may arise: $1°$, $c = d/a \geqslant |A|$ for all $t \geqslant 0$; $2°$, $c = d/a < |A|$ for all $t \geqslant 0$, or for $0 \leqslant t < t_1$. These are illustrated by the curves in Figs. 28 D, E.

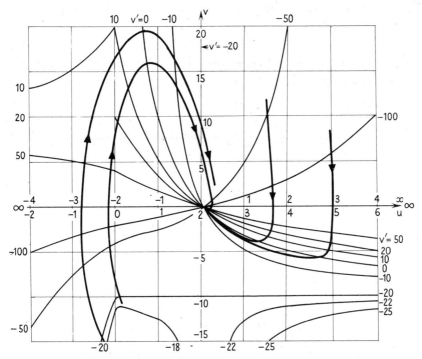

Fig. 28 C. Integral curves (u, v) for $\ddot{u} + 10|u|\dot{u} + 100u = 200$, that is $\ddot{x} + 10|x + 2|\dot{x} + 100x = 0$, where $u = x + 2$. Non-oscillatory case with $d = 200$ and $\kappa^2 c^2 = a$. $u = 2$, $v = 0$, is a stable node.

Case 1°. Here $|A\sin\psi + c|$ may be replaced by $(A\sin\psi + c)$—see Fig. 28 D—and since the integral corresponding to $A\sin\psi$ in (2) is zero, we obtain

$$\dot{A} = \frac{-\kappa c A}{\pi} \int_0^{2\pi} \cos^2\psi \, d\psi = -\kappa c A, \tag{3}$$

so

$$A(t) = A_0 e^{-\kappa ct}, \tag{4}$$

where A_0 is the amplitude at $t = 0$. Also by (15), § 5.10, we have

$$\dot{\varphi} = \frac{\kappa}{\pi} \int_0^{2\pi} (A\sin\psi + c)\cos\psi \sin\psi \, d\psi = 0, \tag{5}$$

so that

$$\varphi = \varphi_0, \text{ an } arbitrary \text{ phase angle.} \tag{6}$$

Writing $\varphi_0 = (\tfrac{1}{2}\pi - \phi_0)$, and substituting from (4), (6), into (1), the formal solution of (3), § 5.172, is

$$x = A_0 e^{-\kappa ct} \sin(\omega t + \varphi_0) = A_0 e^{-\kappa ct} \cos(\omega t - \phi_0). \qquad (7)$$

Hence, finally, in the first approximation, the velocity of the water in the tunnel is

$$u = \dot{x} + c = A_0 e^{-\kappa ct} \cos(\omega t - \phi_0) + d/a, \qquad (8)$$

A_0 and ϕ_0 being determinable from the initial conditions, i.e. those which obtain at the beginning of a surge after d has been altered.

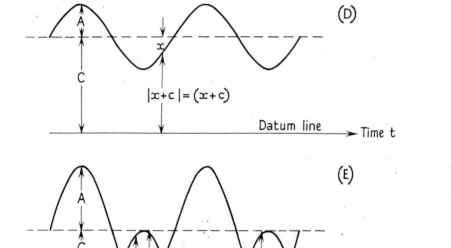

FIG. 28 D, E.   D. Illustrating case $1°$ in text, where the mean velocity of water in the tunnel either exceeds, or is equal to, the amplitude of the velocity oscillation due to the surge, i.e. $c = d/a \geqslant A$.   E. Illustrating case $2°$ in text, where the amplitude exceeds the mean velocity, i.e. $c = d/a < A$.

5.174. Initial conditions. Suppose that the steady rate of flow of water to the turbines is *reduced* from Q_1 to Q_2 by closing valves. To effect simplification, we assume that the time taken for the change in flow rate to be established is small compared with $2\pi/\omega$, the quasi-period of the surge. When $t \to -0$, $u = c = d_1/a$, but for $t > 0$, $c = d_2/a$, as illustrated in Fig. 28 F. Thus the initial conditions are $u(0) = d_1/a$, $\dot{u}(0) = 0$, and in (8), § 5.173, we take $c = d_2/a$. Accordingly,

$$[A_0 e^{-\kappa d_2 t/a} \cos(\omega t - \phi_0)]_{t=0} + d_2/a = d_1/a, \qquad (1)$$

so that $\qquad\qquad A_0\cos\phi_0 = (d_1-d_2)/a.$ $\qquad\qquad$ (2)

Differentiating (8), § 5.173, and putting $t = 0$, $\dot{u}(0) = 0$, $c = d_2/a$, gives,

$$\tan\phi_0 = \frac{\kappa d_2}{\omega a}, \quad\text{and}\quad \cos\phi_0 = \{1+(\kappa d_2/\omega a)^2\}^{\frac{1}{2}}. \qquad (3)$$

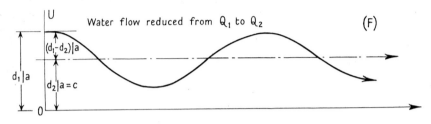

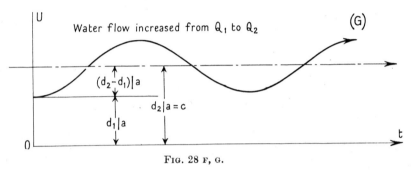

Fig. 28 f, g.

Substituting for $\cos\phi_0$ into (2) yields

$$A_0 = \{(d_1-d_2)/a\}\{1+(\kappa d_2/\omega a)^2\}^{\frac{1}{2}}. \qquad (4)$$

Hence from (8), § 5.173, and (4), the water velocity in the tunnel during the surge is

$$u = \{(d_1-d_2)/a\}\{1+(\kappa d_2/\omega a)^2\}^{\frac{1}{2}}e^{-\kappa d_2 t/a}\cos(\omega t-\phi_0)+d_2/a, \qquad (5)$$

where $\phi_0 = \tan^{-1}(\kappa d_2/\omega a)$. From (5) it is seen that as $t \to +\infty$, $u \to d_2/a$, the steady velocity after subsidence of the surge. By hypothesis, $c = d_2/a \geqslant A$, so we must have

$$d_1/\{1+[1+(\kappa d_2/\omega a)^2]^{\frac{1}{2}}\} < d_2 < d_1.$$

Suppose that the steady rate of water flow to the turbines is *increased* from Q_1 to Q_2 by opening valves (see Fig. 28 g). Then $d_1 < d_2$, and if $d_2/a \geqslant A_0$, (5) is valid and we have

$$u = -\{(d_2-d_1)/a\}\{1+(\kappa d_2/\omega a)^2\}^{\frac{1}{2}}e^{-\kappa d_2 t/a}\cos(\omega t-\phi_0)+d_2/a. \qquad (6)$$

As before, when $t \to +\infty$, $u \to d_2/a$, the final unidirectional velocity of the water in the tunnel.

5.175. *Case* 2°. $|A| > c = d/a$, $0 \leqslant t < t_1$ [243]. In this instance evaluation of the integral in (2), § 5.173, yields (assuming κ is not too large)

$$A = -\frac{\kappa A}{\pi}\left[\left\{\frac{2(A^2-c^2)^{\frac{1}{2}}(2A^2+c^2)}{3A}\right\} + 2c\sin^{-1}(c/A)\right]. \tag{1}$$

If $c/|A| \leqslant 0.2$, as a first approximation (1) gives

$$A = -(4\kappa/3\pi)A^2, \tag{2}$$

so that $A^{-1} = (4\kappa t/3\pi) + B$, a constant.   (3)

If $A = A_0$ when $t = 0$, then $B = 1/A_0$ and

$$A(t) = \frac{A_0}{1+(4A_0\kappa t/3\pi)}. \tag{4}$$

We find also that $\varphi = \varphi_0$, an arbitrary phase angle. Hence by (4) and (1), § 5.173, with $\varphi_0 = (\frac{1}{2}\pi - \phi_0)$, we get

$$u = x+c = \frac{A_0}{(1+\gamma t)}\cos(\omega t - \phi_0) + c, \tag{5}$$

where $\gamma = 4A_0\kappa/3\pi$, and provided that $A_0/(1+\gamma t) > c = d/a$, $0 \leqslant t < t_1$.

When the water supply to the turbines is reduced to a comparatively small value so that $d_1 \gg d_2$, the initial conditions are $u(0) = d_1/a$, $\dot{u}(0) = 0$, and we take $c = d_2/a$. Thus

$$A_0 = \frac{(d_1-d_2)/a}{\{1-[4\kappa(d_1-d_2)/3\pi\omega a]^2\}^{\frac{1}{2}}}, \tag{6}$$

and if $\theta = \tan^{-1}(\gamma/\omega)$,

$$u = \frac{A_0}{(1+\gamma t)}\cos(\omega t - \theta) + d_2/a, \tag{7}$$

provided that

$$A_0/(1+\gamma t) > d_2/a, \quad \text{and} \quad 0 \leqslant t < t_1 = (3\pi/4\kappa)(a/d_2 - 1/A_0).$$

When $t > t_1$, the solution has the form at (8), § 5.173, namely,

$$u = A_1 e^{-\kappa c t}\cos(\omega t - \phi_1) + c, \tag{8}$$

where A_1 and ϕ_1 may be determined from the values of u and $\dot{u}$ at $t = t_1$. Then by (5)

$$u(t_1) = \frac{A_0}{(1+\gamma t_1)}\cos(\omega t_1 - \phi_0) + c, \tag{9}$$

and $\dot{u}(t_1) = -\frac{A_0}{(1+\gamma t_1)}\left[\frac{\gamma\cos(\omega t_1 - \phi_0)}{(1+\gamma t_1)} + \omega\sin(\omega t_1 - \phi_0)\right]. \tag{10}$

From (8)–(10), we find that

$$A_1 = \frac{A_0 e^{\kappa c t_1} \cos(\omega t_1 - \phi_0)}{(1+\gamma t_1) \cos(\omega t_1 - \phi_1)},$$ (11)

and $\quad \phi_1 = \omega t_1 + \tan^{-1}\left[\dfrac{\kappa c}{\omega} - \dfrac{\gamma}{\omega(1+\gamma t_1)} - \tan(\omega t_1 - \phi_0)\right].$ (12)

$|A| > c = 0$, $t \geqslant 0$. Suppose that when the velocity is d_1/a, the water supply to the turbines is stopped completely. The initial conditions are now $u(0) = d_1/a$, $\dot{u}(0) = 0$, with $c = 0$, and the required results may be obtained from (5), (6), by putting $d_2 = 0$. Thus

$$A_0 = (d_1/a)/[1-(4\kappa d_1/3\pi\omega a)^2]^{\frac{1}{2}},$$ (13)

and the velocity of the water in the tunnel is

$$u = \frac{A_0}{(1+\gamma t)} \cos(\omega t - \theta).$$ (14)

Comparison of (14) and (5), § 5.174, shows that the decay of the oscillation is more rapid in the latter case, owing to the respective damping factors being $1/(1+\gamma t)$ and $e^{-\kappa d_2 t/a}$. A flow of water entails $d_2 > 0$, so that in (3), § 5.172, the respective damping coefficients for $d_2 > 0$ and $d_2 = 0$ are $2\kappa|x+c|$ and $2\kappa|x|$, the former entailing greater energy loss than the latter.

5.176. Water level in surge tank. This is given by (4), § 5.171, namely,

$$y = -(l/g)\frac{du}{dt} - f|u|u.$$ (1)

For a shut-down $d = 0$, and in case 2° we use (14), § 5.175. Accordingly

$$y = (l/g)\left\{\frac{\omega A_0 \sin(\omega t - \theta)}{(1+\gamma t)} - \frac{\gamma A_0 \cos(\omega t - \theta)}{(1+\gamma t)^2}\right\} -$$
$$-\frac{fA_0^2}{(1+\gamma t)^2}|\cos(\omega t - \theta)|\cos(\omega t - \theta)$$ (2)

$$= \frac{A_0 l}{g(1+\gamma t)}\left\{\omega \sin(\omega t - \theta) - \frac{\gamma \cos(\omega t - \theta)}{(1+\gamma t)}\right\} -$$
$$-\frac{fA_0^2}{(1+\gamma t)^2}|\cos(\omega t - \theta)|\cos(\omega t - \theta).$$ (3)

When $t = 0$,

$$y = -fA_0^2\omega^2/(\omega^2+\gamma^2) = -f(d_1/a)^2 = -f[u(0)]^2,$$ (4)

which is the loss of head between the reservoir and the surge tank, due to friction.

5.18. Coulomb damping. In this case the damping is presumed to be independent of the velocity (magnitude and direction) when it is greater than zero, but vanishes with the velocity. The corresponding force always resists the motion independent of its direction. These points are illustrated by Fig. 29.

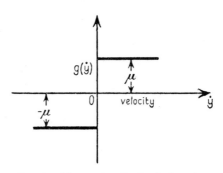

FIG. 29. Illustrating Coulomb damping.

EXAMPLE. Solve $\quad \ddot{y}+g(\dot{y})-\omega^2 y = 0,$ $\qquad\qquad$ (1)

where $g(\dot{y}) = \pm\mu$, a constant when $\dot{y} > 0, \dot{y} < 0$, but $g(\dot{y}) = 0$ when $\dot{y} = 0$ as in Fig. 29 [187]. By (14), § 5.10, dividing the interval $(0, 2\pi)$ in accordance with Fig. 29,

$$\dot{A} = -\frac{\mu}{2\pi\omega}\int_0^{\frac{1}{2}\pi}\cos\psi\,d\psi+\frac{\mu}{2\pi\omega}\int_{+\frac{1}{2}\pi}^{\frac{3}{2}\pi}\cos\psi\,d\psi-\frac{\mu}{2\pi\omega}\int_{\frac{3}{2}\pi}^{2\pi}\cos\psi\,d\psi \qquad (2)$$

$$= -2\mu/\pi\omega. \qquad\qquad (3)$$

Hence $\qquad\qquad |A| = A_0-2\mu t/\pi\omega,$ $\qquad\qquad$ (4)

A_0 being the initial displacement.

Now $|A|$ cannot be negative, so the motion ceases when $|A|$ vanishes, i.e. $t = \pi\omega A_0/2\mu$. Thus the solution is given by

$$y = A(t)\sin(\omega t+\varphi_0) \quad (0 \leqslant t \leqslant \pi\omega A_0/2\mu). \qquad (5)$$

Since $\dot{\varphi} = 0$, $\varphi = \varphi_0$, which in our case is $\frac{1}{2}\pi$. The larger A_0, the longer the motion persists.

CHAPTER VI

THE EQUIVALENT LINEAR EQUATION

6.10. Theoretical considerations. The approximate solutions of non-linear equations obtained in Chap. V may be shown to satisfy *linear* differential equations of the type [175]

$$\ddot{y}+p(t)\dot{y}+q(t)y = 0, \tag{1}$$

where $p(t)$, $q(t)$ are either constants or continuous functions of t. The form of solution used in connexion with the approximations in Chap. V is

$$y = A(t)\sin \chi, \qquad \chi = \omega t+\varphi(t), \tag{2}$$

where $A(t)$ and $\varphi(t)$ are slowly varying functions of t. Differentiating the first part of (2) with respect to t, we have

$$\dot{y} = \dot{A}\sin\chi \quad +A\dot{\chi}\cos\chi. \tag{3}$$

Also

$$\left.\begin{array}{l} \ddot{y} = \ddot{A}\sin\chi \quad +2\dot{A}\dot{\chi}\cos\chi-A\dot{\chi}^2\sin\chi+A\ddot{\chi}\cos\chi \\[2mm] -\left(\dfrac{2\dot{A}}{A}\right)\dot{y} = -\dfrac{2\dot{A}^2}{A}\sin\chi-2\dot{A}\dot{\chi}\cos\chi \\[2mm] \dot{\chi}^2 y = \qquad\qquad\qquad A\dot{\chi}^2\sin\chi. \end{array}\right\} \tag{4}$$

and

By addition (4) yields

$$\ddot{y}-\left(\frac{2\dot{A}}{A}\right)\dot{y}+\dot{\chi}^2 y = \left(\ddot{A}-\frac{2\dot{A}^2}{A}\right)\sin\chi, \tag{5}$$

provided we neglect $\ddot{\chi}$, which is zero in all cases examined in Chap. V, except § 5.13, where it is $O(\epsilon^2)$. By (14), § 5.10, $\ddot{A}$, $\dot{A}^2/A$ are both $O(\epsilon^2)$, so the right-hand side of (5) may be neglected in an approximation of order ϵ. Under this condition, the linear equation

$$\ddot{y}-(2\dot{A}/A)\dot{y}+\dot{\chi}^2 y = 0 \tag{6}$$

is the equivalent of the non-linear equation

$$\ddot{y}+\epsilon g(y,\dot{y})+\omega^2 y = 0. \tag{7}$$

In a general sense the coefficients $2\dot{A}/A$ and $\dot{\chi}^2$ are functions of t,† and we assume that g does not have terms with fractional indices. (6) may be put in the convenient form

$$\ddot{y}+2\bar{\kappa}\dot{y}+\bar{\omega}^2 y = 0, \tag{8}$$

† This does not introduce non-linearity in y.

where $\bar{\kappa} = -\dot{A}/A$, $\bar{\omega} = \dot{\chi}$. By aid of (14), § 5.10, we have

$$\bar{\kappa} = \frac{\epsilon}{2\pi\omega A} \int_0^{2\pi} g(A\sin\psi,\, A\omega\cos\psi)\cos\psi \; d\psi, \tag{9}$$

while $\bar{\omega}$ is given by the right-hand side of (16), § 5.10.

6.11. Principle of energy equality [77]. Since (6), (7), § 6.10, are equivalent, the work per cycle calculated from each must be equal (to the degree of approximation envisaged). In some cases the equations may refer to a damped oscillation, so a 'cycle' is defined to be the time interval $\tau_0 = 2\pi/\omega$, or $\bar{\tau}_0 = 2\pi/\bar{\omega}$, as the case may be. Putting $v = \dot{y}$, (7), § 6.10, may be written

$$\frac{v\,dv}{dy} + \epsilon g(y, \dot{y}) + \omega^2 y = 0. \tag{1}$$

Multiplying (1) by $dy = \dot{y}\,dt$ and integrating over a cycle τ_0, gives

$$\int_0^{2\pi/\omega} v\,dv + \int_0^{2\pi/\omega} \omega^2 y\,dy + \epsilon \int_0^{2\pi/\omega} g(y, \dot{y})\dot{y}\,dt = \text{a constant } C, \tag{2}$$

so
$$\tfrac{1}{2}[v^2 + \omega^2 y^2]_{t=0}^{2\pi/\omega} + \epsilon \int_0^{2\pi/\omega} g(y, \dot{y})\dot{y}\,dt = C. \tag{3}$$

By virtue of periodicity† [ ] $= 0$, so we obtain

$$\epsilon \int_0^{2\pi/\omega} g(y, \dot{y})\dot{y}\,dt = C, \tag{4}$$

which is the energy dissipated in heat during the cycle. In like manner from (6), § 6.10, we obtain

$$2\bar{\kappa} \int_0^{2\pi/\omega} \dot{y}^2\,dt = C_1, \tag{5‡}$$

where $\bar{\kappa} = -\dot{A}/A$. Substituting in (4) for y, $\dot{y}$ from (6), (7), § 5.10, gives

$$C = \epsilon \int_0^{2\pi/\omega} g(A\sin\chi,\, A\omega\cos\chi)A\omega\cos\chi\,dt \tag{6}$$

$$= \epsilon A \int_0^{2\pi} g(A\sin\chi,\, A\omega\cos\chi)\cos\chi\,d\chi. \tag{7}$$

---

† A damped oscillation is not periodic, but if the damping is small enough, this term will be correspondingly small.

‡ Strictly, the upper limit should be $2\pi/\bar{\omega}$, but in view of the degree of approximation contemplated, $2\pi/\omega$ has been used.

Substituting $\dot{y} = A\omega \cos \chi$ into (5), yields

$$C_1 = 2\bar{\kappa}A^2\omega^2 \int_0^{2\pi/\omega} \cos^2\chi \, dt = 2\bar{\kappa}A^2\omega \int_0^{2\pi} \cos^2\chi \, d\chi \qquad (8)$$

$$= 2\pi\omega\bar{\kappa}A^2. \qquad (9)$$

If we equate C, C_1, the value of $\bar{\kappa}$ from (7), (9) is the same as that in (9), § 6.10. It follows that, to the degree of approximation envisaged, the energy dissipated per cycle is equal in the non-linear and the equivalent linear systems. We selected the cycle $(0, 2\pi/\omega)$ for simplicity. The same principle applies, however, to *any* cycle

$$(2\pi n/\omega, 2\pi(n+1)/\omega),$$

provided the appropriate value of A is used. With a damped oscillation, A would decrease with increase in time, so C, C_1 would do likewise.

6.20. Example. Find the linear equation equivalent to

$$\ddot{y} + 2\kappa\dot{y} + \omega^2 y + by^3 = 0 \qquad (\omega^2 \gg \kappa^2 > 0). \qquad (1)$$

From (9), § 6.10,

$$\bar{\kappa} = \frac{1}{2\pi\omega A} \int_0^{2\pi} (2\kappa A\omega \cos \psi + bA^3 \sin^3\psi)\cos \psi \, d\psi \qquad (2)$$

$$= \frac{1}{2\pi\omega A} 2\pi\kappa\omega A = \kappa. \qquad (3)$$

By (16), § 5.10

$$\bar{\omega} = \dot{\chi} = \omega + \frac{1}{2\pi\omega A} \int_0^{2\pi} (2\kappa A\omega \cos \psi + bA^3 \sin^3\psi)\sin \psi \, d\psi \qquad (4)$$

$$= \omega + \frac{bA^2}{2\pi\omega} \frac{3}{4}\pi = \omega + \frac{3bA^2}{8\omega}. \qquad (5)$$

Substituting from (3), (5) into (8), § 6.10, the linear equation equivalent to (1) is

$$\ddot{y} + 2\kappa\dot{y} + \left(\omega + \frac{3bA^2}{8\omega}\right)^2 y = 0. \qquad (6)$$

Here the coefficient of $\dot{y}$ is constant, but that of y is a function of t, and it has the value $\left(\omega + \dfrac{3bA_0^2}{8\omega}\right)^2$ at $t = 0$, since by (5), § 5.13,

$$A(t) = A_0 e^{-\kappa t}.$$

Thus as y (see (10), § 5.13) decreases with increase in t, $\left(\omega + \dfrac{3bA^2}{8\omega}\right) \to \omega$.

6.21. Linearization of

$$\ddot{y}+h(y) = 0, \tag{1}$$

$h(y)$ being an odd function of y. We consider a periodic solution representable with adequate approximation (depending, of course, upon the nature of the function $h(y)$), by

$$y = A \sin \bar{\omega}t, \tag{2}$$

this being the dominant term of a Fourier series, with A constant. Multiplying (1) by $y\, dt$ and integrating over a period, we have

$$\int_0^{2\pi/\bar{\omega}} y\, d\dot{y} + \int_0^{2\pi/\bar{\omega}} h(y)y\, dt = 0, \tag{3}$$

since there is no loss and the motion is periodic. Taking the first integral by parts

$$[y\dot{y}]_0^{t=2\pi/\bar{\omega}} = 0, \tag{4}$$

so

$$\int_0^{2\pi/\bar{\omega}} \dot{y}^2\, dt = \int_0^{2\pi/\bar{\omega}} h(y)y\, dt. \tag{5}$$

Substituting from (2) into (5) gives, with $\psi = \bar{\omega}t$,

$$\bar{\omega}^2 A^2 \int_0^{2\pi} \cos^2\psi\, d\psi = A \int_0^{2\pi} h(A \sin \psi)\sin \psi\, d\psi, \tag{6}$$

so

$$\bar{\omega}^2 = \frac{1}{\pi A} \int_0^{2\pi} h(A \sin \psi)\sin \psi\, d\psi. \tag{7}$$

Thus the linear equivalent of (1) is

$$\ddot{y}+\bar{\omega}^2 y = 0. \tag{8}$$

6.22. Example. Find the linear equivalent of

$$\ddot{y}+ay+by^3 = 0. \tag{1}$$

Applying (7), § 6.21,

$$\bar{\omega}^2 = \frac{1}{\pi A} \int_0^{2\pi} (aA \sin \psi+bA^3 \sin^3\psi)\sin \psi\, d\psi \tag{2}$$

$$= a+\tfrac{3}{4}bA^2, \tag{3}$$

where A is the *constant* amplitude of motion of the loss-free system. Then the equivalent linear equation for (1) is

$$\ddot{y}+\bar{\omega}^2 y = 0, \tag{4}$$

this being satisfied by (2), § 6.21, $\bar{\omega}$ being given by (3) above.

Suppose now we take the equation

$$\ddot{y}+ay+by^3 = f\cos \omega t, \tag{5}$$

a, b, f, ω being such as to preclude a subharmonic. Then the equivalent linear equation is

$$\ddot{y} + \bar{\omega}^2 y = f \cos \omega t, \tag{6}$$

of which the periodic solution corresponding to the forced oscillation is

$$y = f \cos \omega t / (\bar{\omega}^2 - \omega^2) = \frac{f \cos \omega t}{(a + \frac{3}{4} b A^2 - \omega^2)}. \tag{7}$$

This agrees with the first approximation $y = A_1 \cos \omega t$ in § 4.140, if A is written for A_1 obtained from (9), § 4.140.

6.310. Linearization of electrical circuits with non-linear resistance [175]. Here we use the principle of energy equality in § 6.11, and assume that as a first approximation the current is sinusoidal. Referring to Fig. 30 suppose the potential difference across resistance R is $f(I)$, a function of I the current. Then we calculate the value of the constant equivalent resistance R_e such that if $I = I_0 \sin \omega t$, the energy loss in R over a period is $\frac{1}{2} I_0^2 R_e$. This is reminiscent of measurement of the effective resistance of an iron-cored coil by a bridge method using sinusoidal current and a tuned detector selective to the frequency $\omega/2\pi$, but not to the higher harmonics.

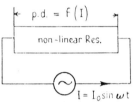

FIG. 30. Electrical circuit with non-linear resistance which is a function of the current.

We have

$$\tfrac{1}{2} I_0^2 R_e = (\omega/2\pi) \int_0^{2\pi/\omega} f(I) I \, dt = \frac{I_0}{2\pi} \int_0^{2\pi} f(I_0 \sin \psi) \sin \psi \, d\psi, \tag{1}$$

with $I = I_0 \sin \omega t$, and $\psi = \omega t$. Thus

$$R_e = \frac{1}{\pi I_0} \int_0^{2\pi} f(I_0 \sin \psi) \sin \psi \, d\psi. \tag{2}$$

We remark that in a thermionic valve circuit, R_e may be negative.

Suppose $\qquad E = f(I) = R_0 I + b I^3, \tag{3}$

$R_0, b > 0$, then (2) gives for the equivalent resistance

$$R_e = R_0 + \tfrac{3}{4} b I_0^2. \tag{4}$$

6.311. Equivalent linear inductance. The relationship between total magnetic flux interlinkage Φ and unidirectional current I in an iron-cored coil takes the form of the well-known B–H curve, provided the iron is demagnetized initially. During magnetization by a sinu‐soidal current $I = I_0 \sin \omega t$, the relationship per cycle between Φ and I takes the form of the familiar hysteresis loop of Fig. 31. The use of a suitable mathematical expression for this would complicate the

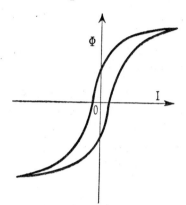

FIG. 31. Magnetic hysteresis loop.

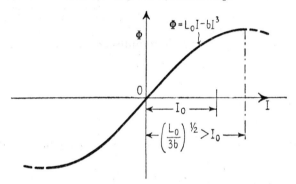

FIG. 32. Assumed relationship between total magnetic flux interlinkage and current in coil with ferromagnetic core. The maximum current in circuit during operation must be less than $(L_0/3b)^{\frac{1}{2}}$.

analysis, so for simplicity we assume absence of hysteresis and take the approximate relationship

$$f(I) = \Phi = L_0 I - b I^3, \tag{1}$$

L_0 being the inductance when I is small, and $I < (L_0/3b)^{\frac{1}{2}}$, $b > 0$. The physical significance of this relationship (see Fig. 32) will be more readily grasped when we remember that inductance is total flux interlinkages per unit current, i.e. the inductance

$$L = \Phi/I = L_0 - b I^2. \tag{2}$$

L_0 is the constant, and $-bI^2$ the variable part of the inductance, which latter introduces non-linearity. By (2), § 6.310, the equivalent linear inductance is given by

$$L_e = \frac{1}{\pi I_0} \int_0^{2\pi} f(I_0 \sin \psi) \sin \psi \, d\psi \tag{3}$$

$$= \frac{1}{\pi I_0} \int_0^{2\pi} (L_0 I_0 \sin \psi - b I_0^3 \sin^3 \psi) \sin \psi \, d\psi \tag{4}$$

$$= L_0 - \tfrac{3}{4} b I_0^2. \tag{5}$$

EXAMPLE. The circuit shown schematically in Fig. 33 contains an iron-cored coil. If L_e, R_e are the equivalent linear inductance and resistance, respectively, the current amplitude is given by

$$I_0 \simeq E_0 \Big/ \Big[R_e^2 + \Big(\omega L_e - \frac{1}{\omega C} \Big)^2 \Big]^{\frac{1}{2}}. \tag{6}$$

Assuming for simplicity that R_e is constant, by substituting for L_e from (5) into (6), we see that I_0 is not a single-valued function of ω. Thus if ω is varied, the jump phenomenon described in § 4.170 will be exhibited. Moreover, the relation between ω and I_0 will take a form such that over a restricted range of ω, I_0 is multivalued (see Fig. 16 B).

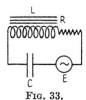

FIG. 33.

6.312. Inductive tuning. A circuit comprising an iron-cored inductance L, capacitance C, resistance R, and a supply source

$$E = E_0 \sin \omega t,$$

may be brought to resonance by increasing E_0 from zero. The effect of so doing is to increase I, thereby decreasing L, until when $E_0 = \bar{E}$ the reactance vanishes. The current now rises precipitately to many times its former value. With further increase in E_0, the current rises gradually. If E_0 is reduced, the falling current exceeds the rising one, and when $E_0 < \bar{E}$, the current drops suddenly to a low value. This series of events (form of hysteresis) is illustrated by the part in Fig. 34 marked $R = 29.7$ ohms. When $R \geqslant 67$, there is no loop, but the I–E_0 curve has a point of inflexion (maximum slope), where 'resonance' may be considered to occur. Additional information will be found in reference [140], while the matter is treated analytically in [64, 65].

6.313. Transconductance of thermionic valve.

In § 6.310 the analysis was based upon the circuital *current* being sinusoidal. Here we take the potential difference across the resistance to be sinusoidal, i.e. $E = E_0 \sin \omega t$. The non-linearity of the resistance entails a non-sinusoidal current, and we have the relationship $I = f(E)$, a function

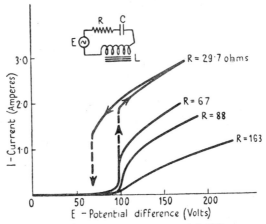

FIG. 34. Relationship between potential difference and current in circuit having capacitance, resistance, and coil with ferromagnetic core.

of E. Accordingly it is expedient to deal with an equivalent linear conductance σ_e, which is the reciprocal of the equivalent resistance R_e. Thus by (2), § 6.310,

$$\sigma_e = 1/R_e = \frac{1}{\pi E_0} \int_0^{2\pi} f(E_0 \sin \psi) \sin \psi \, d\psi. \tag{1}$$

For a thermionic valve, the relationship between anode current I_a and grid potential may be expressed to an adequate approximation by

$$f(E_g) = I_a = I_0 + \alpha_1 E_g + \alpha_2 E_g^2 + \alpha_3 E_g^3 + \alpha_4 E_g^4 + \alpha_5 E_g^5, \tag{2}$$

where I_0 is the current when $E_g = 0$ (cathode and grid at the same potential) and $\alpha_1, ..., \alpha_5$ are constants. Usually the first four terms of (2) suffice, so if we apply (1) with $E_g = E_0 \sin \omega t$,

$$\sigma_e = \frac{1}{\pi E_0} \int_0^{2\pi} (I_0 + \alpha_1 E_0 \sin \psi + \alpha_2 E_0^2 \sin^2 \psi + \alpha_3 E_0^3 \sin^3 \psi) \sin \psi \, d\psi \tag{3}$$

$$= \alpha_1 + \tfrac{3}{4} \alpha_3 E_0^2. \tag{4}$$

Now $\alpha_3 < 0$, so σ_e decreases with increase in grid swing $2E_0$. It should be observed that terms of even order in E_0 do not contribute to (4), since they cancel out (individually) over an interval $(0, 2\pi)$.

6.314. Thermionic valve circuit.

Referring to Fig. 35† we consider only the oscillatory component of the anode current. Then we have

$$I_a = I + I_1 + I_2, \tag{1}$$

and

$$\frac{L\,dI}{dt} = RI_1 = \frac{1}{C}\int I_2\,dt. \tag{2}$$

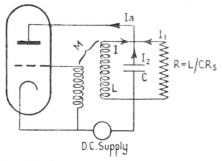

FIG. 35. Schematic diagram of triode with oscillatory circuit. R_s, the series resistance of L is shown as an equivalent parallel resistance of value $R = L/CR_s$, for sinusoidal current.

Also from (2)
$$I_1 = \frac{L}{R}\frac{dI}{dt}, \qquad I_2 = LC\frac{d^2I}{dt^2}. \tag{3}$$

Substituting from (3) into (1) leads to

$$LC\frac{d^2I}{dt^2} + \frac{L}{R}\frac{dI}{dt} + I = I_a. \tag{4}$$

The relationship between anode current I_a, and the grid and anode potentials E_g, E_a, respectively, is

$$I_a = \sigma_e(E_g + E_a/\mu), \tag{5}$$

$\mu \gg 1$ being the amplification factor of the valve, and σ_e its equivalent linear transconductance.‡ The oscillatory part of the anode potential is $-L\,dI/dt$, while $E_g = M\,dI/dt$, so (5) may be written

$$I_a = \sigma_e(M - L/\mu)\frac{dI}{dt}. \tag{6}$$

† For convenience, R_s the series resistance of L, has been represented by a parallel resistance $R = L/CR_s$, it being assumed that the oscillatory current is sensibly sinusoidal, and R_s small enough for the potential drop across it due to unidirectional current to be negligible. Also grid current is assumed negligible.

‡ Or equivalent linear mutual conductance.

Substituting from (6) into (4) yields the equivalent linear equation

$$LC\frac{d^2I}{dt^2}+\left[\frac{L}{R}-\sigma_e(M-L/\mu)\right]\frac{dI}{dt}+I=0. \tag{7}$$

For a periodic oscillation the damping coefficient in [ ] must vanish, so

$$L/R-\sigma_e(M-L/\mu)=0, \tag{8}$$

or
$$\sigma_e=L/R(M-L/\mu). \tag{9}$$

Thus the critical value of M, to maintain a steady oscillation is

$$M=L/R\sigma_e+L/\mu. \tag{10}$$

In terms of the series coil resistance $R_s=L/CR$, and the internal resistance of the valve $R_a=\mu/\sigma_e$, (10) becomes

$$\mu M=L(R_a/R+1)=CR_s R_a+L. \tag{11}$$

In practice M would exceed the value at (10), (11). From (10) we see that, for a given coil, the greater the amplification factor and the transconductance of the valve, the more easily will oscillation be obtained.

Using the expression for σ_e from (4), § 6.313, and $R=L/CR_s$ in (9), we find that the amplitude of the potential difference between grid and cathode is given by

$$E_0=\left\{\frac{4}{3\alpha_3}\left[\alpha_1-\frac{\mu CR_s}{\mu M-L}\right]\right\}^{\frac{1}{2}}, \tag{12}$$

where α_3 is expressed as a positive number (see below (4), § 6.313).

CHAPTER VII

EQUATIONS HAVING PERIODIC COEFFICIENTS

7.10. Mathieu's equation. We commence with this *linear* type, since it constitutes a suitable introduction to our later consideration of a non-linear modification thereof. The canonical form, i.e. ruled by general usage, is

$$y'' + (a - 2q\cos 2z)y = 0, \tag{1}$$

where for our particular purpose a, q are real parameters. The co-efficient of y is the single-valued periodic function $(a - 2q\cos 2z)$ having period π in z. With $\omega t = z$, (1) may be regarded as the equation for a loss-free dynamical system having a variable spring control $(a - 2q\cos 2z)$, the variation being caused by a driving agent. For a damped system, the term $2\kappa y'$ must be added to the left-hand side of (1). Alternatively (1) may be written in the form

$$y'' + ay = (2q\cos 2z)y. \tag{2}$$

Then with ωt for z, (2) applies to a simple mass-spring dynamical system *driven* by a force $(2q\cos 2z)y$, which depends upon the displacement y. Absence of damping means that the mechanical impedances of the elements of the system are entirely 'reactive' in type, and one's curiosity is aroused, therefore, as to the possibility of resonance. If $a = 4$ and y on the right-hand side is replaced by a constant f, the equation becomes

$$y'' + 4y = 2fq\cos 2z, \tag{3}$$

the particular integral being

$$y_p = (\tfrac{1}{2}fq)z\sin 2z. \tag{4}$$

Thus the amplitude $\to \pm\infty$ as $z \to +\infty$, so the motion is unstable and non-periodic. If a damping term $2\kappa y'$ is introduced into equation (3), the particular integral is

$$y_p = (fq/2\kappa)\sin(2z + \varphi_0). \tag{5}$$

The system operates at resonance, the amplitude of motion being $(fq/2\kappa)$. The condition for resonance, namely, that $a = 4$, is *independent of* q. Although we shall encounter the form of solution at (4) later on, it is not possible to deduce results pertaining to (2) from either

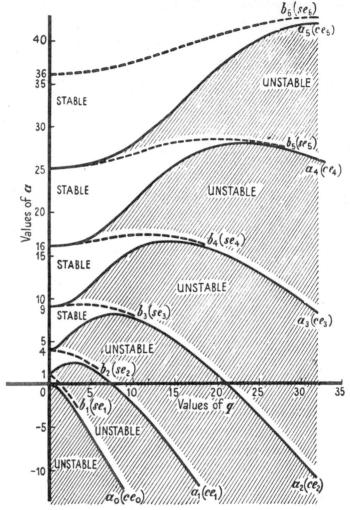

FIG. 36. Stability chart for the Mathieu equation $y'' + (a - 2q\cos 2z)y = 0$.

(4) or (5). The theory of Mathieu's equation has been treated in detail elsewhere [185], and the reader should consult this reference for additional information. For present purposes we shall merely state established forms of solution of (1).

7.11. Forms of solution of Mathieu's equation. The particular form depends upon the values of a, q. To effect discrimination we use the stability chart of Fig. 36, where the (a, q) plane is divided by the curves into regions of stability and instability. Herein we restrict ourselves to the range $q \geqslant 0$.

1°. When (a, q) lies *within* a stable region, the two linearly independent solutions take the respective forms

$$y_1 = \sum_{r=-\infty}^{\infty} c_m \cos(m+\beta)z, \tag{1}$$

and
$$y_2 = \sum_{r=-\infty}^{\infty} c_m \sin(m+\beta)z, \tag{2}$$

the c_m being real constants dependent upon a and q [185].

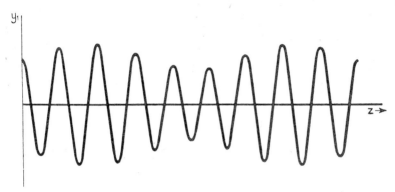

Fig. 37. Graph showing *form* of solution of Mathieu's equation when (a, q) lies in a stable region of the plane. In conducting experimental work with (a, q) in a stable region, it is necessary to start the oscillation by external means. The damping should be very small; eventually the system will come to rest [see 185, (2), (3), p. 97].

(1) is an even and (2) an odd function of z. In (1), (2), $0 < \beta < 1$, $m = 2r, (2r+1)$, when (a, q) lies between (a_{2n}, b_{2n+1}) or (a_{2n+1}, b_{2n+2}), respectively. If $\beta = p/s$ (in its lowest terms) is a rational fraction, $0 < p/s < 1$, y_1, y_2 are periodic, the period being given on p. 144. If β is irrational, the solution is non-periodic, i.e. it does not repeat itself *exactly* at any interval. In practice where β is calculated to a limited number of decimal places, the solution will be periodic. All solutions of above type are bounded, this feature being illustrated by the graph in Fig. 37. Some $\beta =$ constant curves for certain ranges of a, q are plotted in Fig. 38.

2°. When (a, q) lies *within* an unstable region of the (a, q) plane, the two linearly independent solutions take the respective non-periodic forms

$$y_1 = e^{\mu z} \sum_{r=0}^{\infty} p_m \cos(mz+\phi_m), \tag{1}$$

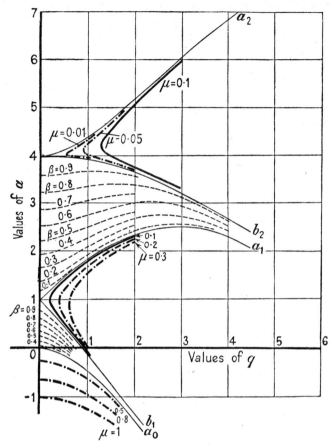

FIG. 38. Iso-β (solution stable) and iso-μ (solution unstable) curves for the Mathieu equation $y'' + (a - 2q \cos 2z)y = 0$. Formulae for a_1 and b_1 are given on p. 144.

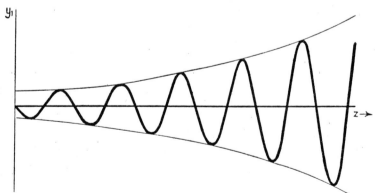

FIG. 39. Graph showing form of solution corresponding to (1), 2°, § 7.11.

and
$$y_2 = e^{-\mu z} \sum_{r=0}^{\infty} p_m \cos(mz - \phi_m),\qquad(2)$$

p_m, ϕ_m being real constants, dependent upon a, q. Here μ real > 0, and when $m = 0$, $\phi_0 = 0$. $m = 2r$, $(2r+1)$ according as (a, q) lies between (b_{2n}, a_{2n}) or (b_{2n+1}, a_{2n+1}), respectively. The solutions are neither odd nor even. They may be interchanged by writing $-z$ for z in either of them. $y_1 \to \pm\infty$, and $y_2 \to 0$ as $z \to +\infty$, so y_1 is defined to be unstable, but y_2 is stable in $0 < z < \infty$. In the range

$$-\infty < z < \infty,$$

both solutions are unstable.

3°. When (a, q) lies *upon* one of the curves of Fig. 36, the linearly independent solutions have the following forms:

$$y_1 = \sum_{r=0}^{\infty} A_m \cos mz, \quad m = 2r \text{ or } (2r+1) \text{ according as } (a, q) \text{ is on}$$
$$a_{2n} \text{ or } a_{2n+1},\qquad(1)$$

$$y_2 = C(q)zy_1 + f(z), \quad C(q) \text{ a function of } q;\qquad(2)$$

$$y_1 = \sum_{r=0}^{\infty} B_m \sin mz, \quad m = (2r+1) \text{ or } (2r+2) \text{ according as } (a, q) \text{ is}$$
$$\text{on } b_{2n+1} \text{ or } b_{2n+2},\qquad(3)$$

$$y_2 = S(q)zy_1 + g(z), \quad S(q) \text{ a function of } q.\qquad(4)$$

A_m, B_m are real constants dependent upon a and q, while $f(z)$, $g(z)$ are periodic functions of z, whose period is that of y_1. When (a, q) lies upon $\left.\begin{matrix} a_{2n}, b_{2n+2} \\ a_{2n+1}, b_{2n+1} \end{matrix}\right\}$, the first solutions have period $\left.\begin{matrix} \pi \\ 2\pi \end{matrix}\right\}$. Being neither stable nor unstable, such solutions may be classed as neutral. All the second solutions are non-periodic by virtue of the factor z in their first members. Also they are unstable and tend to $\pm\infty$ as $z \to +\infty$. If the first solution is odd in z, the second is even, and vice versa. The complexity of the matter needs no comment.

7.12. Experimental illustration of instability. In an apparatus which obeys Mathieu's equation (1), § 7.10, suppose the parameters a, q are adjusted to lie in an unstable region of Fig. 36, e.g. between the curves b_1 and a_1. In the absence of energy loss, the amplitude of the motion, or its equivalent, would increase exponentially with time in accordance with the solution†

$$y_1 = e^{\mu z} \sum_{r=0}^{\infty} \rho_{2r+1} \cos[(2r+1)z+\phi_{2r+1}] \quad (\mu \text{ real} > 0), \qquad (1)$$

until it was curbed by virtue of some limiting property of the system. The limit is set either by an element exhibiting non-linearity at large amplitudes, or by rupture of some member (!).

For a dissipative system, the linear differential equation has the form

$$y''+2\kappa y'+(\bar{a}-2q\cos 2z)y = 0. \qquad (2)$$

Writing $y = e^{-\kappa z}u(z)$, where $u(z)$ is a twice differentiable function of z, (2) is transformed to the Mathieu equation

$$u''+(a-2q\cos 2z)u = 0, \qquad (3)$$

with $a = (\bar{a}-\kappa^2)$. By aid of (1), the appropriate solution of (3) has the form

$$u_1 = e^{\mu z} \sum_{r=0}^{\infty} \rho_{2r+1} \cos[(2r+1)z+\phi_{2r+1}], \qquad (4)$$

μ, the ρ and ϕ differing from those in (1), in virtue of the value

$$a = (\bar{a}-\kappa^2).$$

Thus if $\kappa > \mu$, the motion will be stable in $0 < z < \infty$, since it tends to zero as $z \to +\infty$. On the other hand, if $\kappa < \mu$, the motion will be unstable in $0 < z < \infty$. Accordingly in the first case, the amplitude of the motion (once started) will decay exponentially to zero as z, and, therefore, as $t \to +\infty$, whereas in the second case it will increase exponentially without limit. When $\mu = \kappa$, the motion will be neutral.

The second case, with $\kappa < \mu$, has been investigated experimentally as described below [95]. A set of eight equally spaced laminated iron-cored coils are arranged in circular fashion and connected in series. Another set of similar coils is placed coaxially with the first set. In the intervening gap there is a coaxial aluminium disk having eight equally spaced teeth. The two sets of coils are connected in series with a variable capacitance, as illustrated schematically in Fig. 40. Since there is some residual magnetism in the iron cores, motion of the teeth on the disk past the coils causes a fluctuation in the circuital inductance. Suppose the rate of variation to be 1,900 c.p.s., then if C in Fig. 40 is adjusted to make $1/(LC)^{\frac{1}{2}} \simeq 950$ c.p.s., a subharmonic current having this frequency flows in the circuit. Despite the absence

† The second solution of the form (2) 2°, § 7.11, is omitted, since it would tend to zero in accordance with the factor $e^{-\mu z}$. It would of course be of relative importance at the start. To introduce the time element we may consider that $z = \omega t$.

of a source of electrical power in circuit, the voltage amplitude grows with increase in time. In the experiments described in reference [95], without a non-linear element in circuit, the voltage reached the range $1·2 \times 10^4$ to $1·5 \times 10^4$ (12 to 15 kV), which was sufficient to rupture the insulation of the capacitance. This method of transforming mechanical energy from a rotating toothed disk to electrical energy in an electrical circuit has been called 'parametric excitation', because

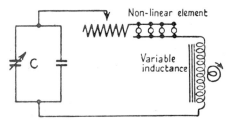

Fig. 40. Circuit diagram for experiments with periodically varying inductance, including a non-linear element.

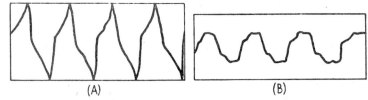

Fig. 41 A, B. Oscillograms of current in circuit of Fig. 40 under different conditions.

the building-up process depends upon variation of a parameter (L in this case) in the differential equation for the electrical oscillation.

7.13. Influence of non-linear element in circuit. The voltage amplitude is now found to attain a limiting value after a short time interval from the start. The desired result may be obtained by connecting a bank of lamps in series with the capacitance and variable inductance, or by using a unidirectional current in auxiliary windings on the coils, thereby causing magnetic saturation of the cores. The effect in either case resembles that in a valve oscillator where the ultimate amplitude of the periodic oscillation is determined by curvature of the valve characteristic curves.

The oscillograms of Figs. 41 A, B show two types of wave form obtained during the steady state when $\mu > \kappa$, limitation being due to a non-linear element [95]. The non-sinusoidal form of the oscillations is probably caused by the iron cores of the coils (see § 6.311). Fig. 42 is an oscillogram of a decay transient following a steady oscillation with $\mu > \kappa$, the condition being changed to make $\mu < \kappa$, so that damping preponderates.

There is an essential difference between the maintenance of these oscillations and those in a triode circuit. In the parametric case, mechanical energy is supplied from an external source at frequency ω/π, and converted into electrical energy in the circuit at half this frequency, there being no internal negative damping. With the triode,

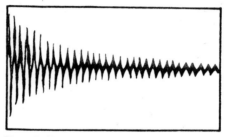

FIG. 42. Decay transient for circuit of Fig. 40
when damping is increased suddenly.

electrical energy is supplied directly to the valve from a unidirectional source (zero frequency), and converted into electrical energy at frequency $\omega/2\pi$ (apart from harmonics), by virtue of the negative resistance property of the valve.

7.14. Capacitive excitation. The results described in § 7.12 were obtained with fixed C, but varying L. It is obvious, however, that fixed L and varying C will yield similar effects. Experiments were conducted with C varying at a frequency of the order 900 c.p.s., the inherent circuital frequency being 450 c.p.s., i.e. half the parametric frequency. The insulation broke down unless the voltage amplitude was limited by inserting six 220-volt neon tubes in series with the circuit [95].

7.20. Melde's experiment. One end of a horizontal thread is fixed, the other being attached to a prong of a massive low-frequency tuning-fork. When the fork moves along the thread and the tension is suitably adjusted, the thread vibrates perpendicularly to its length, i.e. transversely, *at a frequency one-half that of the fork.* If A, the amplitude of the prong is less than a certain value A_0, say, the oscillation dies away. When $A > A_0$, the oscillation builds up to an ultimate value, and the motion is periodic to all intents and purposes, so long as A is sensibly constant. If the motion were described symbolically by Mathieu's equation with a viscous damping term, e.g. (2), § 7.12, the amplitude would either increase until the thread broke or die away (all or nothing!). Since the amplitude is limited in practice, a non-linear effect must be present. The tension of the thread at any point increases with increase in amplitude, and the equation of motion becomes non-linear. We shall assume the presence of the non-linear term by^3, and in § 7.232 show how it causes amplitude limitation. The equation for the vibrating thread then has the *form*

$$y'' + 2\kappa y' + (a + by^2 - 2q \cos 2z)y = 0 \quad (b > 0, z = \omega t) \qquad (1)$$

which is (2), § 7.12, with the non-linear term by^3 added thereto. This cannot be regarded as a non-linear Mathieu equation, since the latter is linear! It is a non-linear equation of the second order having a periodic coefficient.

7.21. Numerical example. Consider the linear equation

$$y'' + 0 \cdot 16y' + (1 \cdot 0064 - 0 \cdot 32 \cos 2z)y = 0. \qquad (1)$$

If we write $y = e^{-0 \cdot 08z}u(z)$ therein, it becomes

$$u'' + (1 - 0 \cdot 32 \cos 2z)u = 0, \qquad (2)$$

whose parametric point $(1, 0 \cdot 16)$ lies in an unstable region of Fig. 38, between b_1 and a_1. From reference [185, p. 122] the solution of (2) which $\to \pm\infty$ as $z \to +\infty$, is

$$u_1 = ce^{0 \cdot 08z}(\cos z - 0 \cdot 021 \cos 3z + \ldots + 0 \cdot 94 \sin z - 0 \cdot 0175 \sin 3z + \ldots), \qquad (3)$$

c being any non-zero real constant. From above and (3),

$$y_1 = e^{-0 \cdot 08z}u_1(z) \simeq c(\cos z + 0 \cdot 94 \sin z) \simeq 1 \cdot 37c \cos(z - 43 \cdot 25°). \qquad (4)$$

The period of the oscillation represented by (4) is 2π, whereas that of the variation in tension of the thread due to the reed (driving force) is π,† so a subharmonic of half-frequency occurs.

Suppose we keep $a = 1$, but increase q from $0 \cdot 16$ to $0 \cdot 162$. Then by [185, p. 103, (4)], $\mu = 0 \cdot 081$, so $(\mu - \kappa) = 0 \cdot 001$ and, therefore, we obtain the unstable solution

$$y_1 \simeq 1 \cdot 37ce^{0 \cdot 001z} \cos(z - 43 \cdot 25°). \qquad (5)$$

† The actual period is, of course, π/ω.

Thus if $z = 10^3$, the amplitude will be increased in the ratio

$$e = 2 \cdot 718...,$$

with reference to its value at $z = 0$. Now $z = \omega t$, so if $\omega = 2\pi \times 50$, the time taken for this amplitude change to occur is

$$t = 10^3/100\pi \simeq 3 \cdot 18 \text{ sec.}$$

On the other hand, if $a = 1$, and q is reduced from $0 \cdot 16$ to $0 \cdot 158$, $\mu = 0 \cdot 079$, $(\mu - \kappa) = -0 \cdot 001$ and

$$y_1 \simeq 1 \cdot 37 c e^{-0 \cdot 001 z} \cos(z - 43 \cdot 25), \tag{6}$$

so the solution is stable. The oscillation will be extinguished ultimately by virtue of the factor $e^{-0 \cdot 001 z}$.

From [185, p. 97] it may be deduced that the motion corresponding to (1) with 2κ for $0 \cdot 16$, can take one of the following forms:

(i) $\kappa = \mu = 0 \cdot 08$, neutral having period 2π, (a, q) being on the curve $\mu = 0 \cdot 08$;

(ii) $\kappa < 0 \cdot 08$, unstable $\to \pm\infty$ as $z \to +\infty$, (a, q) on the right-hand side of the curve $\mu = 0 \cdot 08$;

(iii) $\kappa > 0 \cdot 08$, stable $\to 0$ as $z \to +\infty$, (a, q) on the left-hand side of the curve $\mu = 0 \cdot 08$.

7.22. Improved experimental procedure.

A more versatile version of Melde's experiment is as follows: Attach one end of a length of thin white nylon thread to a steel reed operated electromagnetically from the 50 c.p.s. electric supply mains. To the other end attach a small weight (variable in steps), and pass the thread over a pulley, the arrangement permitting variation in length. Make adjustments so that the thread (about 1 metre long) vibrates in its second mode (centre-point nodal) at 100 c.p.s. when driven *transversely*. By turning the reed through 90° about a vertical axis, the thread will be driven along its length, so the tension will vary at 100 c.p.s. The thread will now vibrate, without a central node, at half the reed frequency, i.e. 50 c.p.s. It then appears to the eye as a symmetrical lens-shaped section, and the motion seems to be periodic with constant amplitude. The 50 c.p.s. tone can be heard by placing the ear in a suitable position relative to the thread. Comparison may be made with the octave above, which is the fundamental tone of the reed. A more elaborate investigation may, of course, be made by means of a microphone, amplifier, and frequency analyser, but this is not justifiable unless the driving agent is devoid of harmonics.

Now connect a variac in series with the magnet winding of the reed, and reduce the current below that required at the threshold of oscillation. Increase the current slowly up to and just beyond the threshold, when the amplitude of motion will build up to an ultimate value.

The length of the thread may be increased or decreased by a fraction of the original before oscillation stops. In [239] it is shown that the length may be varied between $(3^{\frac{1}{2}}/2)l$ and $(5^{\frac{1}{2}}/2)l$, where l corresponds to $a = 1$ in (1), § 7.20. The thread may be viewed by aid of a stroboscope, and the 'visual motion' slowed down to any desired extent. If the frequency variation of both reed and stroboscope is small enough, the shape at the instant may be 'frozen', i.e. it appears to be stationary.

7.230. Approximate solution of $y'' + (a - 2q \cos 2z)y + by^3 = 0$

$(a, b, q > 0)$. This is (1), § 7.20, with $\kappa = 0$. We shall obtain a periodic solution whose period is twice that of $\cos 2z$. This entails a subharmonic of order 2. During the experiment described in § 7.22, the following salient features were observed:

(i) The motion was periodic, the main component having half the frequency of the driving reed;

(ii) The displacement was symmetrical about the equilibrium position of the thread.

Accordingly—in point of time—the displacement may be represented by Fourier series of the types ($b > $ or < 0)

$$y = \sum_{r=0}^{\infty} \frac{A_{2r+1} \cos}{B_{2r+1} \sin} (2r+1)z \quad (z = \omega t). \tag{1}$$

To comply with (ii) we shall *assume* that non-linearity may be represented by the odd function $\quad by^3 + cy^5 + ..., \tag{2}$

where $b > 0$ for the vibrating thread.

Case 1°, $b > 0$. To obtain a first approximation when (a, q) lies in the unstable region of Fig. 38 between b_1 and a_1, b small, $0 < q < 0.25$, say, we take

$$y = A_1 \cos z + A_3 \cos 3z. \tag{3}$$

Substituting (3) into the differential equation, we get

$$
\left.
\begin{aligned}
y'' &= -(A_1 \cos z + 9A_3 \cos 3z) \\
ay &= a(A_1 \cos z + A_3 \cos 3z) \\
-(2q \cos 2z)y &= -q[A_1(\cos z + \cos 3z) + A_3(\cos z + \cos 5z)] \\
by^3 &= \tfrac{1}{4}b[A_1^3(3\cos z + \cos 3z) + A_3^3(3\cos 3z + \cos 9z) + \\
&\quad + A_1^2 A_3(3\cos z + 6\cos 3z + 3\cos 5z) + \\
&\quad + A_1 A_3^2(6\cos z + 3\cos 5z + 3\cos 7z)].
\end{aligned}
\right\} \tag{4}
$$

Equating the coefficients of $\cos z$, $\cos 3z$ to zero:

$$(a-1-q)A_1 + \tfrac{3}{4}bA_1(A_1^2 + A_1 A_3 + 2A_3^2) - qA_3 = 0, \tag{5}$$

$$(a-9)A_3 + \tfrac{1}{4}b(A_1^3 + 6A_1^2 A_3 + 3A_3^3) - qA_1 = 0. \tag{6}$$

Since the observed motion is sensibly harmonic, we assume *pro tem.* that $|A_3/A_1| \ll 1$. Thus in (5) we neglect terms in A_3, and obtain

$$A_1^2 \simeq \frac{4}{3b}(1+q-a), \tag{7}$$

while from (6), we get the approximation

$$(a-9)A_3 + \tfrac{1}{4}bA_1^3 + \tfrac{3}{2}b\,A_1^2 A_3 - qA_1 = 0. \tag{8}$$

Substituting from (7) into (8) yields

$$A_3/A_1 \simeq (2q+a-1)/3(2q-a-7). \tag{9}$$

With $a = 1$, $q = 0\cdot25$, $|A_3/A_1| \simeq 1/45$, so in this case the assumption $|A_3/A_1| \ll 1$ is justifiable. It will be realized that, if q is large enough, A_1 may not be the dominant coefficient in (1).

The value of A_1 may be improved by using (9) in (5). Thus dividing out by A_1, and neglecting $2(A_3/A_1)^2$, we get

$$\tfrac{3}{4}bA_1^2(1+A_3/A_1) = 1+q-a+qA_3/A_1, \tag{10}$$

so

$$A_1^2 = \frac{4}{3b}[1+q(1+A_3/A_1)-a]/(1+A_3/A_1) \tag{11}$$

$$\simeq \frac{4}{3b}[1+q-a+(a-1)A_3/A_1]. \tag{12}$$

Substituting from (9) into (12) gives

$$A_1^2 \simeq \frac{4}{3b}[1+q-a+(a-1)(2q+a-1)/3(2q-a-7)], \tag{13}$$

which is a better approximation than (7). If $a = 1-2q$, and $A_1 = \pm 2(q/b)^{\frac{1}{2}}$, $A_1 \cos z$ are *exact* solutions of the equation, stable if $0 < q < 0\cdot5$, as shown in § 2, Appendix II, where $q = 2\gamma$.

Case 2°, $b < 0$, q small > 0. Here we use the second series in (1), and with $-b$ for b in the D.E. ($b > 0$), we take

$$y = B_1 \sin z + B_3 \sin 3z. \tag{14}$$

Proceeding as before leads to

$$(a-1+q)B_1 - \tfrac{3}{4}bB_1(B_1^2 - B_1 B_3 + 2B_3^2) - qB_3 = 0, \tag{15}$$

$$(a-9)B_3 + \tfrac{1}{4}b(-B_1^3 + 6B_1^2 B_3 + 3B_3^3) - qB_1 = 0. \tag{16}$$

From (15), neglecting terms in B_3, we get

$$B_1^2 \simeq \frac{4}{3b}(a-1+q), \tag{17}$$

and from (16), (17)

$$'B_3/B_1 \simeq -(2q+1-a)/3(2q+a+7). \tag{18}$$

The improved value of B_1^2 corresponding to (13) 1°, is

$$B_1^2 \simeq \frac{4}{3b}[a-1+q-(a-1)(2q+1-a)/3(2q+a+7)]. \tag{19}$$

Formulae (7), (13) in 1°, show that the amplitude of motion of the thread is limited by virtue of the factor b^{-1}.

7.231. Additional considerations.

The equation in § 7.230 may be written

$$y'' + [(a+by^2) - 2q \cos 2z]y = 0. \tag{1}$$

Taking $y = A_1 \cos z$ as a *first* approximation, (1) gives

$$y'' + [(a+bA_1^2 \cos^2 z) - 2q \cos 2z]y = 0, \tag{2}$$

or
$$y'' + [(a+\tfrac{1}{2}bA_1^2) - 2(q - \tfrac{1}{4}bA_1^2)\cos 2z]y = 0, \tag{3}$$

which is a Mathieu equation with parametric point $(a+\tfrac{1}{2}bA_1^2)$, $(q-\tfrac{1}{4}bA_1^2)$. Since the motion of the thread (see § 7.22) has period 2π in $z = \omega t$, it seems *probable* that the parametric point of (3) will lie on the curve a_1 in Fig. 38, so we shall investigate this. Using (7), § 7.230, we have

$$a+\tfrac{1}{2}bA_1^2 = \tfrac{1}{3}(2q+2+a), \tag{4}$$

and
$$q-\tfrac{1}{4}bA_1^2 = \tfrac{1}{3}(2q-1+a). \tag{5}$$

If $|q| \ll 2$, on curve a_1 in Fig. 38,

$$a_1 \simeq 1+q_1 = \tfrac{1}{3}(2q+2+a), \tag{6}$$

by substituting for q_1 from (5). Then (6) is the a_1 value at (4). Hence for $b > 0$, *in the first approximation* we have shown that stabilization occurs because the ultimate motion is such that (1) becomes the Mathieu equation (3), whose parametric point lies on a_1. Moreover, for any (a, q) between b_1 and a_1, b small > 0, $0 < q \leqslant 0.25$, say, the parametric point starts there when $y = 0$. As the amplitude builds up, by virtue of inherent instability, the a value increases while the q value decreases, so the parametric point moves from (a, q) towards the curve a_1, on which the a, q values are given by (4), (5). In a higher approximation, using additional terms of the Fourier series (assuming periodic motion), the ultimate parametric point would lie upon the characteristic curve for a Hill equation whose solution had period 2π in z [185, p. 127].

When $b < 0$, similar analysis leads to the conclusion that in the first approximation the ultimate parametric point corresponding to that in (3) lies on the curve b_1 in Fig. 38.

7.232. Influence of damping. The equation is now

$$y'' + 2\kappa y' + [(a + by^2) - 2q \cos 2z]y = 0. \tag{1}$$

With (a, q) between b_1 and a_1 in Fig. 38, we assume for a first approximation that

$$y = A_1 \cos z + B_1 \sin z = A \cos(z - \tan^{-1} B_1/A_1), \tag{2}$$

where $A = (A_1^2 + B_1^2)^{\frac{1}{2}}$. Proceeding as in § 7.230, we find that

$$(a - 1 - q + \tfrac{3}{4}bA^2)A_1 + 2\kappa B_1 = 0, \tag{3}$$

and
$$-2\kappa A_1 + (a - 1 + q + \tfrac{3}{4}bA^2)B_1 = 0. \tag{4}$$

For A_1, B_1 to be non-zero, we must have

$$(a - 1 + q + \tfrac{3}{4}bA^2)(a - 1 - q + \tfrac{3}{4}bA^2) + 4\kappa^2 = 0, \tag{5}$$

so
$$(a - 1 + \tfrac{3}{4}bA^2)^2 + (4\kappa^2 - q^2) = 0. \tag{6}$$

Solving (6), the square of the ultimate amplitude is

$$A^2 = \frac{4}{3b}[(1 - a) + (q^2 - 4\kappa^2)^{\frac{1}{2}}]. \tag{7}$$

The condition $[\quad] = 0$

corresponds to $A = 0$, so the oscillation once started will decay unless

$$(4/3b)[\quad] > 0. \tag{8}$$

Also for the reality of A we must have $|q| > 2\kappa$.

7.233. Numerical example. Using the data $a = 1$, $q = 0.25$, $\kappa = 0.03$, $b = 0.05$ in (7), § 7.232, we find that

$$|A| \simeq 2.54. \tag{1}$$

From (7), § 7.232, A^2 is imaginary or zero according as

$$q \leqslant 0\text{·}06 \tag{2}$$

so for maintenance of the oscillation, we must have $q > 0\text{·}06$.

From (4), § 7.232,

$$A_1/B_1 = \left(a-1+q+\frac{3b}{4}A^2\right)\Big/2\kappa \tag{3}$$

$$\simeq 8\text{·}22, \tag{4}$$

and $$\tan^{-1}B_1/A_1 \simeq 7°. \tag{5}$$

Thus by (2), § 7.232, and (1), (5) above, the displacement of the thread is

$$y \simeq 2\text{·}54\cos(z-7°). \tag{6}$$

Although the analysis in preceding sections has been associated specifically with a vibrating thread, it is applicable to any system which complies with (1) § 7.232 under the restrictions imposed, e.g. a long uniform column subjected to a constant axial load, having a superimposed sinusoidal ripple force due to unbalanced rotating machinery. There would need to be inherent non-linearity of adequate degree to prevent failure of the column, if with a linear constraint the motion were unstable.

7.234. Energy considerations. We deal with (1), § 7.232, on the same lines as in §§ 4.141, 4.18. Multiplying throughout by $dy = y'\,dz$, and integrating over a period $(0, 2\pi)$, the first, third, and fourth integrals vanish, leaving

$$2\kappa \int_0^{2\pi} (y')^2\,dz = 2q \int_0^{2\pi} (\cos 2z)yy'\,dz, \tag{1}$$

where the right-hand side represents (in effect) the product of force and velocity (power) integrated over the interval. Substituting into (1) for y from (2), § 7.232, leads to

$$2\kappa \int_0^{2\pi} (-A_1\sin z+B_1\cos z)^2\,dz$$

$$= 2q \int_0^{2\pi} \cos 2z(A_1\cos z+B_1\sin z)(-A_1\sin z+B_1\cos z)\,dz, \tag{2}$$

so $$2\kappa \int_0^{2\pi} (A_1^2\sin^2 z+B_1^2\cos^2 z)\,dz = 2q \int_0^{2\pi} \cos 2z(A_1 B_1\cos 2z)\,dz, \tag{3}$$

the other integrals vanishing by virtue of orthogonality of the circular functions. The left-hand side of (3) represents the energy loss per period due to viscous damping, while the right-hand side represents an equal amount supplied by the driving mechanism. If $z = \omega t$, the energy must, on physical grounds, be supplied at angular frequency 2ω. This is confirmed by the presence of $\cos 2z$ in the integrand of (3). Evaluating the integrals in (3) yields

$$2\kappa\pi(A_1^2 + B_1^2) = 2q\pi A_1 B_1. \tag{4}$$

The reader should confirm that (4) may be derived from (3), (4), § 7.232, also.

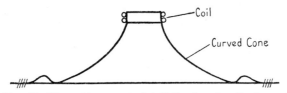

Fig. 43. Illustrating a conical shell (loudspeaker diaphragm) having a curved generator.

7.30. Subharmonics in loudspeaker diaphragms.

When a *free-edge* straight-sided conical shell—Fig. 22 with the cone severed at outer end of straight part—is driven axially, nodal radii occur at certain low frequencies. In the nth radial mode, there are $(2n+2)$ nodal radii. Stroboscopic examination reveals that the sectors of the cone vibrate at half the frequency of the driving coil. Alternate sectors move in opposite directions, thereby causing interference of the sound radiated. Since low-frequency waves are long, the interference may entail inaudibility of the sound.

When the edge of the cone is made rigid and clamped as in Fig. 22, it cannot bend readily, so that radial modes are not present at low frequencies. But if the driving force is increased sufficiently, radial modes occur at discrete frequencies, which are higher than those of the corresponding modes of a free edge cone. These modes are responsible for the subharmonics, a point which has been confirmed stroboscopically. For certain conical paper diaphragms 8 to 10 inches in outer diameter, subharmonics occur in the range 500 to 4,000 c.p.s., approximately. If the side of the cone is curved, as illustrated in Fig. 43, subharmonics are obtained less readily than they would be with the corresponding straight-sided cone [102].

When a subharmonic occurs in the above frequency range, two main frequencies are audible, (i) the fundamental, (ii) the subharmonic.

If the frequency is raised appropriately, the next mode with its corresponding subharmonic occurs, and so on.

The vibrational characteristics of loudspeaker diaphragms in relation to subharmonics are similar, in certain respects, to those of a vibrating thread discussed hitherto. In Fig. 44 the abscissa represents the root mean square value of a sinusoidal current in the coil.

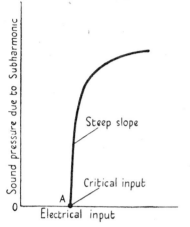

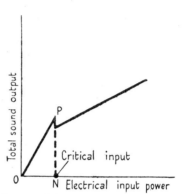

Fig. 44. Relation between electrical input (at constant frequency) to loudspeaker with straight-sided conical diaphragm, and the sound pressure due to subharmonic of half the input frequency.

Fig. 45. Relation between *total* sound output from and electrical power to loudspeaker, at constant frequency.

The current is increased from zero and when the value at A is reached, the subharmonic commences. If the current is increased very slowly as A is approached, the subharmonic may take as long as 20 seconds to attain its ultimate amplitude. Moreover, A corresponds to the threshold for the vibrating thread. As shown in Fig. 44 the curve at A rises very suddenly. For instance with a coil current of 0·4 ampere there was no subharmonic, but when increased by 0·5 per cent. (0·002A), a strong subharmonic occurred, being almost unaltered in strength when the current was 0·5 ampere.

The acoustical power output from the diaphragm is plotted against input in Fig. 45. Up to the value of output represented by NP, the relationship is linear, but when the subharmonic occurs and is almost at full strength, the output drops suddenly (a discontinuity), after which the relationship is linear again, but with reduced slope. The latter and the sudden drop are explained in § 7.32. If the current is reduced below the threshold at A in Fig. 44 the subharmonic disappears. The similarity between the behaviour of the loudspeaker diaphragm and the vibrating string will be evident.

7.31. Mechanism exhibiting subharmonic. This is shown schematically in Fig. 46. A mass m slides over a frictionless horizontal plane. The links and spring are massless; the pin-joints at A, O, B are frictionless. AB, OA, are long enough for motion parallel to BD to be negligible in comparison with that along the axis of the spring. The driving force $F_0 = lf_0 \cos 2\omega t$ is applied to the cross-head B. It

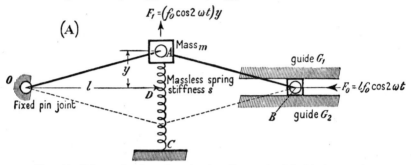

FIG. 46. Schematic plan of mechanism illustrating Mathieu's equation.

may be resolved into two components, one along AB, the other along DA. The latter is nearly $(f_0 \cos 2\omega t)y$, and it causes m to slide along the line CDA. There are three forces associated with m, namely, (i) the inertia force $m\ddot{y}$, (ii) the constraint sy due to the spring, (iii) the driving force $(f_0 \cos 2\omega t)y$. The equation of motion is

$$m\frac{d^2y}{dt^2} + sy = (f_0 \cos 2\omega t)y. \tag{1}$$

Substituting $z = \omega t$, $a = s/\omega^2 m$, $2q = f_0/\omega^2 m$, (1) becomes

$$\frac{d^2y}{dz^2} + (a - 2q \cos 2z)y = 0, \tag{2}$$

which is the canonical form of Mathieu's equation. If we suppose that viscous damping is present, we get an equation like (2), § 7.12. Then introducing a non-linear element (the range of linear extension and contraction of the spring is limited), the equation may take the form (1), § 7.20. The behaviour of this system follows the lines already given.

7.32. Simple alternative to mechanism in § 7.31. The arrangement depicted in Fig. 47 is a simplified version of the mechanism in

Fig. 46. The steel-strip-mass combination will execute a subharmonic oscillation of the driving force, the amplitude reaching a definite value, provided the proper conditions obtain. We now consider this device in its relation to a conical loudspeaker diaphragm. Imagine the straight-sided cone to be divided up into strips by a number of radial lines as illustrated in Fig. 48. Each of these strips may be regarded somewhat similarly to the steel strip in Fig. 47 if the central mass

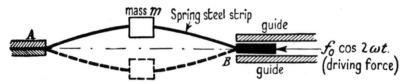

FIG. 47. Simple device for showing subharmonic of half-frequency.

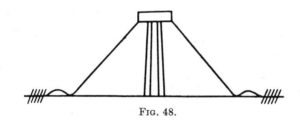

FIG. 48.

were removed.† A strip on the cone has relatively great rigidity, because it is supported along each side. Thus the driving force must be comparatively large in order to incite the sub-harmonic vibration. Since the motion of the cone in this mode is mainly radial, appreciable bending occurs, and the circumferential stress is large. This is concomitant with relatively large loss, to which the change of slope in Fig. 45 may be attributed.

7.410. Simple pendulum with oscillating support. This may be demonstrated using the apparatus shown schematically in Fig. 49. A simple pendulum comprising a bob of mass m attached to a thin nylon thread is suspended from a point O on a long flexible cantilever with a large mass m_1 at its free end; $m_1 \gg m$, and $m_1 V^2_{max} \gg m v^2_{max}$, where V^2_{max}, v^2_{max} are the respective maximum velocities. These conditions ensure that the reaction of the pendulum on the bar will be negligible. When the bar is set in vibration vertically, the motion of

† A subharmonic is obtainable with non-uniform strips of the type into which the cone may be divided.

the point O is almost simple harmonic. If the periodic time of the pendulum is twice that of the bar, the amplitude of the former builds up with increase in time, reaching an ultimate value. Thereafter, so far as can be judged with the aid of a stop-watch and a scale, the motion is periodic; and apart from a slow decay due to damping, it appears

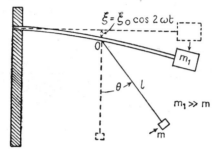

FIG. 49. Simple pendulum with oscillating support.

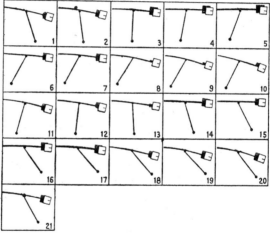

FIG. 50. Photographs of apparatus of Fig. 49 illustrating subharmonic of half-frequency.

probable that the amplitude would remain constant. The 2/1 period ratio is illustrated by the photographs reproduced in Fig. 50 [91], which depict instantaneous positions of the vibrating system. From squares 1 to 21 the bar has executed almost two complete oscillations, while the pendulum has completed nearly one. The amplitude (see square 19) is larger than that contemplated in the analysis which follows in § 7.411 et seq.

When the reaction of the pendulum at the point O on the bar is not negligible, i.e. the foregoing conditions are not fulfilled, the motion of the bar is affected by that of m, and vice versa. Moreover, the 'coupling' between the two oscillating members (two degrees of freedom) is too large for the independent motion of either. If m is at rest and m_1 is set in vibration, the amplitude of m grows while that of m_1 decays with increase in time, ultimate maximum and minimum values being reached. Thereafter the phenomenon occurs in reverse, and this cycle of events continues until the initial energy has been dissipated in inherent loss. Moreover, the amplitude of m is 'modulated', and a form of 'beats' occurs, as in the case of two coupled electrical oscillatory circuits. The periodic times of m and m_1 now differ from that for each vibrator independently.

7.411. Differential equation for § 7.410.

Referring to Fig. 49, if O is stationary the non-linear differential equation for a loss-free pendulum of mass m and length l is, by § 3.160,

$$ml\frac{d^2\theta}{dt^2}+mg\sin\theta = 0. \tag{1}$$

When O has a vertical motion defined by $\xi = \xi_0 \cos 2\omega t$, the corresponding acceleration is $\ddot{\xi} = -4\omega^2\xi_0 \cos 2\omega t$. Assuming the pendulum thread to keep taut always, the external force acting vertically on the bob is $m(g-4\omega^2\xi_0 \cos 2\omega t)$, so the equation of motion becomes

$$ml\ddot{\theta}+m(g-4\omega^2\xi_0 \cos 2\omega t)\sin\theta = 0, \tag{2}$$

θ being referred to the moving support as origin. Writing $g/l = \omega_0^2$, $a = (\omega_0/\omega)^2$, $q = 2\xi_0/l$, $\omega t = z$, and introducing a damping term, we obtain the non-linear equation

$$\theta''+2\kappa\theta'+(a-2q\cos 2z)\sin\theta = 0. \tag{3}$$

If $|\theta| < \frac{1}{6}\pi$, we may put $\sin\theta \simeq \theta-\frac{1}{6}\theta^3$, so (3) now takes the form

$$\theta''+2\kappa\theta'+(a-2q\cos 2z)(\theta-\frac{1}{6}\theta^3) = 0. \tag{4}$$

As in § 3.161 we remark that the derivative of the restoring force associated with $(\theta-\frac{1}{6}\theta^3)$ decreases with increase in θ.

7.412. Approximate solution of (4), § 7.411.

In accordance with § 7.410 we suppose the motion is periodic, and we assume as a first approximation that

$$\theta = A_1\sin z+B_1\cos z, \tag{1}$$

$B_1 \cos z$ being needed by virtue of damping loss. Substituting from (1) into (4), § 7.411, we obtain

$$
\left.\begin{aligned}
\theta'' &= -(A_1 \sin z + B_1 \cos z) \\
2\kappa\theta' &= 2\kappa(-B_1 \sin z + A_1 \cos z) \\
a\theta &= a(A_1 \sin z + B_1 \cos z) \\
-(2q \cos 2z)\theta &= q[A_1(\sin z - \sin 3z) - B_1(\cos z + \cos 3z)] \\
-\tfrac{1}{6}a\theta^3 &= -\tfrac{1}{24}a[A_1^3(3\sin z - \sin 3z) + \\
&\quad + 3A_1^2 B_1(\cos z - \cos 3z) + 3A_1 B_1^2(\sin z + \sin 3z) + \\
&\quad + B_1^3(3\cos z + \cos 3z)] \\
(\tfrac{1}{3}q \cos 2z)\theta^3 &= \tfrac{1}{24}q[3A_1^3(-\sin z + \sin 3z) - A_1^3(\sin z + \sin 5z) + \\
&\quad + 3A_1^2 B_1(\cos 3z - \cos 5z) + 3A_1 B_1^2(\sin 3z + \sin 5z) + \\
&\quad + 3B_1^3(\cos z + \cos 3z) + B_1^3(\cos z + \cos 5z)].
\end{aligned}\right\} \quad (2)
$$

Equating the coefficients of $\sin z$, $\cos z$ to zero independently, we get

$$\sin z: \qquad A_1(a-1+q) - \tfrac{1}{8}aA_1(A_1^2 + B_1^2) - \tfrac{1}{6}qA_1^3 - 2\kappa B_1 = 0, \qquad (3)$$

$$\cos z: \qquad B_1(a-1-q) - \tfrac{1}{8}aB_1(A_1^2 + B_1^2) + \tfrac{1}{6}qB_1^3 + 2\kappa A_1 = 0. \qquad (4)$$

If $\tfrac{1}{6}qA_1^2 \ll \tfrac{1}{8}a(A_1^2 + B_1^2)$, and $\tfrac{1}{6}qB_1^2 \ll \tfrac{1}{8}a(A_1^2 + B_1^2)$, the terms $-\tfrac{1}{6}qA_1^3$, $\tfrac{1}{6}qB_1^3$ may be neglected. Then with $A = (A_1^2 + B_1^2)^{\frac{1}{2}}$, this being the amplitude of vibration, (3), (4) reduce to

$$[(a-1-\tfrac{1}{8}aA^2) + q]A_1 - 2\kappa B_1 = 0, \qquad (5)$$

and
$$[(a-1-\tfrac{1}{8}aA^2) - q]B_1 + 2\kappa A_1 = 0. \qquad (6)$$

For A_1, B_1 to be non-zero, we must have

$$(a-1-\tfrac{1}{8}aA^2)^2 - q^2 + 4\kappa^2 = 0, \qquad (7)$$

so the ultimate amplitude is

$$|A| = \left[\frac{8}{a}\{(q^2 - 4\kappa^2)^{\frac{1}{2}} + (a-1)\}\right]^{\frac{1}{2}}. \qquad (8)$$

A is real provided $q > 2\kappa$ and

$$(q^2 - 4\kappa^2)^{\frac{1}{2}} + (a-1) > 0. \qquad (9)$$

For a sustained oscillation, $|A| > 0$, and this obtains if (9) is satisfied.

7.413. Stability considerations. For simplicity we take $\kappa = 0$, and (4), § 7.411, becomes

$$\theta'' + (a - 2q \cos 2z)(\theta - \tfrac{1}{6}\theta^3) = 0, \qquad (1)$$

which may be put in the form

$$\theta'' + [a(1 - \tfrac{1}{6}\theta^2) - 2q(1 - \tfrac{1}{6}\theta^2)\cos 2z]\theta = 0. \qquad (2)$$

We use the approximate solution $\theta = A \sin z$ with $A_1 = A$, (since $B_1 = 0$ when $\kappa = 0$), and proceed on the lines of § 7.231. By virtue of § 7.410, we have $a = (\omega_0/\omega)^2 = 1$, so (2) takes the form

$$\theta'' + [\{1 - \tfrac{1}{12}A^2(1+q)\} - 2\{q - \tfrac{1}{12}A^2(\tfrac{1}{2}+q)\}\cos 2z - \tfrac{1}{12}qA^2 \cos 4z]\theta = 0, \tag{3}$$

which is a Hill type of equation [185, p. 127]. By (8), § 7.412, with $\kappa = 0$, $a = 1$,

$$\tfrac{1}{12}A^2 = \tfrac{2}{3}q. \tag{4}$$

Substituting from (4) into (3), and neglecting terms in q^2, we obtain the approximate equation

$$\theta'' + [(1 - \tfrac{2}{3}q) - \tfrac{4}{3}q \cos 2z]\theta = 0. \tag{5}$$

This is a Mathieu type whose parametric point $(1 - \tfrac{2}{3}q)$, $\tfrac{2}{3}q$ lies on the characteristic curve b_1 in Fig. 38. Accordingly when q is small enough, the motion is periodic of period 2π in z.

In more accurate analytical work, it appears likely that stability of motion may ensue, by virtue of the parameters in the Hill type of equation corresponding to (3) having values such that the solution is periodic in z, with period 2π.

From a physical viewpoint the varying 'spring' control introduces an effect akin to progressive de-tuning as the amplitude of the pendulum increases. A phase change occurs between the driving force and the velocity, thereby limiting the amplitude ultimately. If $q >$ some value q_0, the motion is unstable.

7.420. Self-excited oscillations due to solid friction. One of the oldest examples occurs in the bowing of stringed musical instruments, e.g. violin. The oscillation of the string is caused by unidirectional motion of the bow, so a driving force at zero frequency causes vibration at an audible frequency. This effect may be explained by considering the variation in friction force between bow and string due to variation in the relative velocity of the two. The relationship between solid friction force and the *relative* velocity of a body moving over a rough horizontal surface has the form illustrated in Fig. 51. When the body is relatively at rest, the force to overcome static friction is represented by OA. As the relative velocity increases, the friction decreases. Thus from A to E the slope of the curve is negative. Now the electrical quantities analogous to force and velocity are potential difference and current, respectively. Over a

certain range of the anode potential–anode current curve for a four-electrode screened grid thermionic valve, the slope is negative, as illustrated in Fig. 52 A. If a suitable LCR circuit is connected between anode and cathode (Fig. 52 B), oscillation at approximately the natural frequency of the circuit occurs, by virtue of the negative resistance

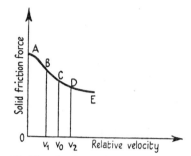

FIG. 51. Showing form of relationship between relative velocity and solid friction force.

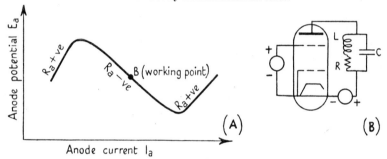

FIG. 52. A. Illustrating negative resistance characteristic of screened grid thermionic valve. The internal resistance is $dE_a/dI_a = R_a$. B. Screened grid valve with oscillatory circuit.

property of the valve. The amplitude of the oscillation is limited owing to curvature of the characteristic, the internal resistance becoming positive to the left of the maximum, and to the right of the minimum in Fig. 52 A. The negative resistance entails energy supply from the unidirectional source at zero frequency, which is converted into oscillations in the LCR circuit. During steady oscillation the energy supplied per cycle is equal to that dissipated per cycle in ohmic loss.

The case of a violin string resembles that above, inasmuch as oscillation depends upon the characteristic curve having a negative slope. Referring to Fig. 51, suppose the forward velocity of the bow is v_0.

If the string moves backwards with increasing velocity, the friction force decreases. It is least when the string has its maximum velocity $|v_3|$ at D, the relative velocity being $v_0 + |v_3| = v_2$. Thereafter the velocity of the string decreases until at the point of maximum backward displacement it is zero, with relative velocity v_0 at C. The string now moves forward with the bow, and attains a maximum velocity v_4 at B, with relative velocity $v_0 - v_4 = v_1 > 0$, if the bow moves faster than the string. The relative velocity then increases from v_1 to v_0, and BC is traversed. Thereafter the motion is along $CDCBC\ldots$.

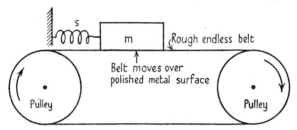

FIG. 53. Schematic diagram of apparatus for obtaining self-excited mechanical oscillations.

When the bow and string move in the same direction, energy is supplied to the latter, but it is dissipated when they move in opposite directions. The ultimate amplitude is reached when the two energies are equal.

7.421. Analytical considerations. For this purpose it is preferable to deal with a system having discrete parameters, rather than one like a violin string where mass and stiffness are distributed (a continuous system). Referring to Fig. 53, an endless belt travels at constant speed round two pulleys. A control spring is fixed to a mass m resting on the outer face of the upper side of the belt, whose inner face moves over a plane polished horizontal metal surface. Provided that the speed of the belt is suitable, m will execute oscillations along the direction of motion.

Let $y =$ displacement of m from the unstrained position of the spring,

$s =$ stiffness of spring, i.e. force per unit axial displacement,

and $f(v) =$ functional representation of the curve in Fig. 51.

There are three forces acting on m, namely, (a) accelerational $m\,d^2y/dt^2$, (b) restoring due to spring sy, and (c) $f(v_0 - \dot{y})$, the driving force of the belt due to solid friction. Then we must have

$$m\frac{d^2y}{dt^2} + sy = f(v_0 - \dot{y}).\tag{1}$$

Taking $|\dot{y}| \ll v_0$, by Taylor's theorem we get

$$f(v_0 - \dot{y}) \simeq f(v_0) - \dot{y}f'(v_0) + \tfrac{1}{2}\dot{y}^2f''(v_0) - \tfrac{1}{6}\dot{y}^3f'''(v_0),\tag{2}$$

differentiations being with respect to v. Thus, by (1), (2), we obtain the equation

$$m\frac{d^2y}{dt^2} + [f'(v_0) - \tfrac{1}{2}\dot{y}f''(v_0) + \tfrac{1}{6}\dot{y}^2f'''(v_0)]\dot{y} + sy = f(v_0).\tag{3}$$

Writing $x = y - f(v_0)/s$, and $\omega_0^2 = s/m$, (3) becomes

$$\ddot{x} + (1/m)[f'(v_0) - \tfrac{1}{2}\dot{x}f''(v_0) + \tfrac{1}{6}\dot{x}^2f'''(v_0)]\dot{x} + \omega_0^2 x = 0,\tag{4}$$

which is non-linear by virtue of the terms in $\dot{x}^2$, $\dot{x}^3$.

Initially when $\dot{x}$ is small, $(1/m)[\ ]$, the coefficient of $\dot{x}$, is negative since $f'(v_0) < 0$, so the oscillation grows with increase in time. But if $\dot{x}_{max} > \dot{x}_1$, say, the coefficient of $\dot{x}$ is alternately positive and negative. When it is such that the energy supplied from the belt, by virtue of the negative slope of the friction–relative velocity curve, is equal to that dissipated, the amplitude has its final value.

Under suitable conditions relaxation oscillations will occur, as explained in [187]. If in a mechanical system, to which (4) applies, the coefficient of $\dot{x}$ were always negative, the oscillation would—in theory—build up indefinitely. In practice this cannot happen, but mechanical failure may occur. As a matter of interest it may be mentioned that in conducting the experiment described in § 7.22, when the thread was removed (the vibrator functioning meanwhile), the small unlubricated pulley mounted on the same framework commenced to rotate, and attained a speed of several hundred r.p.m. A drop of oil on the bearings reduced the friction such that rotation ceased.

7.422. Froude's pendulum.

Fig. 54 represents a pendulum suspended from a dry horizontal shaft, of circular cross-section, by a ring or loop. It is well known that if the shaft rotates with suitable constant angular velocity ω_0, the pendulum oscillates with gradually increasing amplitude, which reaches an ultimate value. If the amplitude is not too large, the differential equation of motion with stationary support is the linear type (see § 3.160 with $\sin\theta \simeq \theta$)

$$\ddot\theta + 2\kappa\dot\theta + a\theta = 0, \tag{1}$$

where for generality the viscous damping term $2\kappa\dot\theta$ has been included. Moreover, once the motion is started, it will be extinguished ultimately by viscous damping. By virtue of §§ 7.420, 7.421, when the shaft rotates, a variable friction force at the suspension must be taken into account. Its value is a function of $(\omega_0 - \dot\theta)$, the difference in angular velocity of the shaft and pendulum. Representing the term for the frictional driving torque by

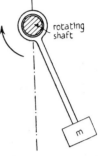

Fig. 54. Schematic diagram for Froude's pendulum.

$$\chi(\omega_0 - \dot\theta) \simeq \chi(\omega_0) - \dot\theta\chi'(\omega_0) + \tfrac{1}{2}\dot\theta^2\chi''(\omega_0) -$$
$$- \tfrac{1}{6}\dot\theta^3\chi'''(\omega_0) \quad (|\dot\theta| \ll \omega_0), \tag{2}$$

the equation for the pendulum is

$$\ddot\theta + 2\kappa\dot\theta + a\theta = \chi(\omega_0 - \dot\theta), \tag{3}$$

or $\quad \ddot\theta + [2\kappa + \chi'(\omega_0) - \tfrac{1}{2}\dot\theta\chi''(\omega_0) + \tfrac{1}{6}\dot\theta^2\chi'''(\omega_0)]\dot\theta + a\theta = \chi(\omega_0), \tag{4}$

which is non-linear owing to the terms in $\dot\theta^2$, $\dot\theta^3$. Putting

$$x = \theta - \chi(\omega_0)/a,$$

(4) becomes

$$\ddot x + [2\kappa + \chi'(\omega_0) - \tfrac{1}{2}\dot x\chi''(\omega_0) + \tfrac{1}{6}\dot x^2\chi'''(\omega_0)]\dot x + ax = 0, \tag{5}$$

which has the same form as (4), § 7.421. In (5), $\kappa > 0$, $\chi'(\omega_0) < 0$ (see Fig. 51). Initially [ ] < 0, but when the amplitude attains its ultimate value, [ ] is alternately positive and negative, such that the energy supplied per cycle by the rotating shaft is equal to that dissipated in heat.

When the amplitude of motion is large, $a\theta$ in (4) must be replaced by $a\sin\theta$, so the equation now takes the form

$$\ddot\theta + [2\kappa + \chi'(\omega_0) - \tfrac{1}{2}\dot\theta\chi''(\omega_0) + \tfrac{1}{6}\dot\theta^2\chi'''(\omega_0)]\dot\theta + a\sin\theta = \chi(\omega_0). \tag{6}$$

To ensure amplitude limitation, the differential equation of a self-excited system must be non-linear. Nevertheless all non-linear equations of the second order do not possess this property. For instance the equation for a pendulum with negative damping, namely, $\quad \ddot\theta - 2\kappa\dot\theta + a\sin\theta = 0 \quad (\kappa > 0) \tag{7}$

is non-linear. But it has a solution such that θ is not limited as in the

Froude pendulum. The point in question is illustrated vividly by the Tacoma suspension-bridge failure described in § 7.423. Another case is the vibration of electrical transmission lines when the cross-section is enlarged and non-circular due to the formation of ice. In both cases there is negative damping by virtue of aerodynamical forces.

7.423. Self-excited oscillations due to aerodynamical forces.

When a mechanical structure is subjected to an air stream, e.g. a steady wind, in addition to static forces, there are variable forces caused by the formation of eddies. In many cases the eddy or vortex motion is quasi-periodic, and if the quasi-period approximates to one of the natural periods of the structure, vibrations of large amplitude may occur. These are the ordinary forced oscillations. The motion is resisted by (a) frictional damping in the structure itself, (b) aerodynamical damping. Both (a), (b) are positive, so when the energy derived per cycle from the wind is equal to that lost due to (a)+(b), the amplitude has a constant value. If the motion of the structure is appreciable, alternating eddies may be created such that the amplitude of the motion *increases* steadily until the structure fails. These oscillations are self-excited, and the resulting effect is equivalent to negative damping. Moreover, the oscillating system is able to extract energy from a constant unidirectional air-stream ($\omega = 0$), as in the case of the thermionic valve mentioned in § 7.420.

The most interesting, and at the same time catastrophic, case on record is that of the Tacoma suspension bridge built across the Narrows at Paget Sound in the State of Washington, U.S.A. It had a central span of 2,800 feet between the two towers, and a width of 39 feet between the suspension cables. The torsional rigidity of the roadway was relatively low, owing to the high span/width ratio of 72/1. From the outset, the roadway was prone to oscillate *vertically* due to the aerodynamical action of the wind, the normal displacement of 50 inches being much greater than that in other large suspension bridges. From 1 July 1940 until about 10 a.m. on 7 November 1940, only vertical oscillations seem to have been observed. But on the latter date, a cable band connected to the centre ties slipped, and thereafter torsional oscillations of the roadway occurred in a wind of 42 m.p.h. There was a node at mid-span, the deformation resembling that when a flat strip is held at each end and twisted alternately in opposite directions. The maximum inclination of the roadway was $\pm45°$ to the horizontal, entailing a total vertical edge displacement of 28 feet (!), the frequency being about 14 cycles per minute. Computation indicates that to maintain the torsional vibration, the horse-power supplied by the wind must have been of order 5,000. Failure occurred about an hour after the torsional oscillations started.

An approximate differential equation for the above takes the form

$$\frac{d^2\theta}{dt^2}+[\kappa_2(v)+\kappa_1(\theta)]\frac{d\theta}{dt}+a\theta = 0, \tag{1}$$

where $\kappa_1(\theta) > 0$ is the damping coefficient for the mechanical structure and $\kappa_2(v)$ is the aerodynamical damping, being a function of the wind velocity v. If $v > v_0$, say, then $\kappa_2(v) < 0$, so with $|\kappa_2(v)| > \kappa_1(\theta)$, the oscillation will grow with increase in time. But $\kappa_1(\theta)$ increases with increase in amplitude, so a point is reached when the damping vanishes, and a steady oscillation occurs, provided v is not too large. When v exceeds a certain value, the damping is always negative, so the amplitude grows until the structure fails.

An account of the Tacoma bridge disaster appeared in *Engineering*, **150**, 481, 1940. On 28 March 1941 an exhaustive report entitled 'The Failure of the Tacoma Narrows Bridge' was published by the Federal Works Agency, Washington, D.C. Amongst other things it contains mathematical analysis and experimental results pertaining to vibrational modes and aerodynamical forces, together with data obtained from wind-tunnel tests on scale models. Curves are given illustrating the change from positive to negative aerodynamical damping due to altered conditions, e.g. higher wind velocity. See reference on p. 144.

7.43. Parametric oscillation.

A variation of Melde's experiment [95] may be performed by causing a cyclical alteration in the physical state of the vibrating element. A thin metal wire having a weight at its lower end is freely suspended, the arrangement being such that the lowest transverse mode of the wire is about 50 c.p.s. When a current of this frequency flows in the wire, its temperature varies at double this rate. Thus the wire extends and contracts at double the frequency of the transverse mode, thereby simulating the conditions in Melde's experiment. If the current is large enough, the wire vibrates at 50 c.p.s.

7.44. Oscillation due to non-linear coupling [187].

If a mass m is fixed to the lower end of a uniform massless helical spring of stiffness s, the periodic time of vibration in a vertical direction is $\tau_0 = 2\pi(m/s)^{\frac{1}{2}}$.

This motion constitutes one degree of freedom. If the mass is drawn aside and released, the system will oscillate as a simple pendulum. This signifies a second degree of freedom. Since the axial force on the spring varies with the angular displacement, there will be an axial oscillation also, and the two freedoms are simultaneous. There is a third freedom, namely, torsional oscillation about the axis, mentioned in 3°, § 7.45. Herein we shall consider the first two modes only. It is evident from what precedes that coupling exists between the two freedoms,† so that the modes may interact. For example, if the system were set in oscillation in one freedom, it might gradually pass over to the other, by virtue of the coupling effect.

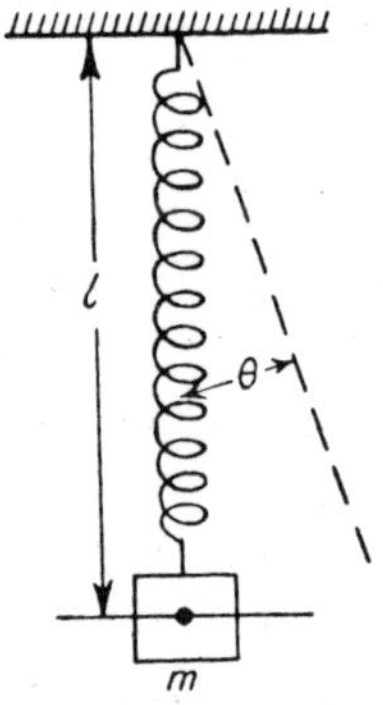

FIG. 55. Illustrating pendulum comprising mass and uniform massless coil-spring.

Analytical considerations. In Fig. 55, l is the length of the pendulum when vertical and stationary, ξ the displacement (extension or contraction) on either side of l, s the spring stiffness, m the mass of the bob, θ the angular displacement from the vertical. Assuming $|\theta| < \frac{1}{6}\pi$, we may write $\cos\theta \simeq 1 - \frac{1}{2}\theta^2$, and it can be shown that the equations of motion are

$$\ddot{\xi} + \omega_1^2 \xi = l(\dot{\theta}^2 - \tfrac{1}{2}\omega_0^2 \theta^2), \tag{1}$$

and

$$\ddot{\theta} + \omega_0^2 \theta = -\frac{1}{l}(2\xi\ddot{\theta} + 2\dot{\xi}\dot{\theta} + \omega_0^2 \xi\theta), \tag{2}$$

where $\omega_0^2 = l/g$, $\omega_1^2 = s/m$. When $\xi = \dot{\xi} = \ddot{\xi} = 0$, the right-hand side of (2) vanishes and

$$\ddot{\theta} + \omega_0^2 \theta = 0. \tag{3}$$

The system then behaves as a simple pendulum of constant length. This would happen if $\omega_1^2 = s/m$ were very large, i.e. a stiff spring. When $\theta = \dot{\theta} = \ddot{\theta} = 0$, the right-hand side of (1) vanishes and

$$\ddot{\xi} + \omega_1^2 \xi = 0. \tag{4}$$

The system then behaves as a simple mass-spring combination, and executes a simple harmonic motion in a vertical direction, there being no transverse motion. In practice one motion would incite the other by virtue of the non-linear terms on the right-hand side of (1), (2). We now extend the analysis to include these coupling terms.

† It follows, in a rigorous sense, that the modes are not entirely 'free'. The system described in § 7.410 when $mv_{\max}^2$ is comparable with $m_1 V_{\max}^2$ is somewhat similar to that described here.

7.45. Influence of non-linear coupling terms.

$1°$. Suppose that the pendulum, initially vertical and at rest, is drawn aside and released when $|\theta| = |\theta_0| < \tfrac{1}{6}\pi$, $t = 0$. Then *at the start*

$$\theta = \theta_0 \cos \omega_0 t. \tag{1}$$

Substituting this into (1), § 7.44, we get

$$\ddot{\xi} + \omega_1^2 \xi = \tfrac{1}{4}\omega_0^2 l \theta_0^2 (1 - 3 \cos 2\omega_0 t). \tag{2}$$

If $\omega_1 \neq 2\omega_0$ the complete solution of (2) is

$$\xi = A \sin \omega_1 t + B \cos \omega_1 t - \frac{3\omega_0^2 l \theta_0^2 \cos 2\omega_0 t}{4(\omega_1^2 - 4\omega_0^2)} + \frac{\omega_0^2 l \theta_0^2}{4\omega_1^2}. \tag{3}$$

It follows from (3) that the axial motion has two periodic components of frequency $\omega_1/2\pi$, $2\omega_0/2\pi$, respectively, while the spring has a constant extension $\omega_0^2 l\theta_0^2/4\omega_1^2$. When $\omega_1 = 2\omega_0$, the particular integral of (2) has the non-periodic form $t \sin 2\omega_0 t$, so the oscillation in the ξ mode builds up with increase in time. Since the energy of the system is constant, the oscillation in the θ mode must decay.

$2°$. Suppose m is pulled down an amount $\xi_0 \ll l$ when the pendulum is vertical, and released at $t = 0$. The subsequent motion in the ξ mode will be defined initially by

$$\xi = -\xi_0 \cos \omega_1 t. \tag{1}$$

Substituting this into the right-hand side of (2), § 7.44, leads to the equation

$$[1 - (2\xi_0/l)\cos \omega_1 t]\ddot{\theta} + [2\omega_1(\xi_0/l)\sin \omega_1 t]\dot{\theta} + $$
$$+ \omega_0^2[1 - (\xi_0/l)\cos \omega_1 t]\theta = 0. \tag{2}$$

By hypothesis $2\xi_0 \ll l$, so if we write $\omega_1 t = 2z$, $a = (2\omega_0/\omega_1)^2$, $q = 2\xi_0/l$, (2) becomes

$$\theta'' + (2q \sin 2z)\theta' + a\theta = 0. \tag{3}$$

Substituting $\theta = e^{\frac{1}{2}q \cos 2z}u(z)$, where $u(z)$ is a twice differentiable function of z, (3) is transformed to the Hill type of equation [185, p. 127]

$$u'' + [(a - \tfrac{1}{2}q^2) - 2q \cos 2z + \tfrac{1}{2}q^2 \cos 4z]u = 0. \tag{4}$$

By hypothesis $q \ll 1$, so (4) has the approximate form

$$u'' + (a - 2q \cos 2z)u = 0, \tag{5}$$

which is the standard Mathieu equation. If (a, q) lies between b_1 and a_1 in Fig. 38, the solution of (5) is unstable, so the oscillation of the pendulum in the θ mode will build up. Initially θ has the form

$$e^{\mu z + \frac{1}{2}q \cos 2z} \times \text{function with period } 2\pi \text{ in } z. \tag{6}$$

By virtue of energy constancy of the system, the ξ mode will decay. In practice, owing to damping, the oscillations in both modes will cease ultimately. From the above analysis it appears that, by virtue of non-linearity of coupling, the θ and ξ modes are mutually excitable.

3°. If a metal cylinder having a screwed cross-bar with adjustable masses is attached to the free end of the spring, the latter extends or contracts and twists simultaneously, when oscillating vertically. By screwing the masses on the cross-bar inwards or outwards (as required), the appropriate moment of inertia for the occurrence of torsional oscillations of large amplitude may be found. The energy of the system is transferred from one mode of oscillation to the other.

Supplementary notes

Formulae for a_1 and b_1 in Figs. 36, 38.

$$a_1 = 1 + q - \tfrac{1}{8}q^2 - \tfrac{1}{64}q^3 - \tfrac{1}{1536}q^4 + \tfrac{11}{36864}q^5 + O(q^6) ;$$

for b_1 write $-q$ for q in the formula for a_1.

Period of y_1 and y_2 in 1°, § 7.11. The period in z is either $s\pi$ or $2s\pi$ according as p or $s+p$ is even ($m = 2r$) or odd ($m = 2r+1$), $s \geqslant 2$.

Reference for § 7.423. An exhaustive analytical and experimental investigation will be found in Bulletin No. 116, parts I–V (1950–4), of the University of Washington Engineering Experiment Station, entitled Aerodynamic Stability of Suspension Bridges, with special reference to the Tacoma Narrows Bridge.

CHAPTER VIII

GRAPHICAL AND NUMERICAL SOLUTIONS

8.10. Introduction. The principal graphical method is that of isoclines, i.e. lines of equal slope. Like other graphical procedures for solving differential equations, the degree of accuracy may be enhanced (up to a point) by large-scale construction using paper sheets 2 or more feet square. Once the technique has been acquired, the solution in graphical form may be obtained fairly quickly in a particular case. Any graphical construction or numerical integration process is tedious compared with a purely analytical method, but unless a differential analyser or an electronic calculating machine is available (even then the time taken to set the machine may not be inconsiderable, although this is immaterial if a large number of similar equations are to be solved), we are faced with Hobson's choice!

To illustrate the isocline method, we commence with the simple linear equation
$$d^2y/dt^2 + y = 0. \tag{1}$$
Writing $v = dy/dt$, (1) becomes
$$v\frac{dv}{dy} + y = 0, \quad \text{or} \quad \frac{dv}{dy} = -\frac{y}{v}. \tag{2}$$
We take rectangular coordinates y, v, so that dv/dy is the slope of the curve depicting the relationship between y, v. Choose a value of dv/dy, say, *unity*, then (2) becomes
$$v = -y, \tag{3}$$
which is a straight line through the origin making an angle $\frac{3}{4}\pi^r = 135°$ with the y-axis. Draw a series of short lines whose slope dv/dy is *unity*, i.e. making $45°$ with the y-axis, to intersect the first line at equal intervals as shown in Fig. 56. Now choose $dv/dy = +\frac{3}{2}$, giving
$$v = -\tfrac{2}{3}y. \tag{4}$$
This represents a straight line through the origin with slope $-\frac{2}{3}$. As before, draw a series of short lines with slope $+\frac{3}{2}$ to intersect this line. Proceeding in this way for discrete values of dv/dy, the diagram of Fig. 56 is obtained. Suppose the initial conditions are $y = 5, v = 0$, when $t = 0$, then the starting-point is P on the y-axis. Here the slope of the v–y curve is infinite. Commencing at P, a curve is drawn which

crosses each line radiating from the origin at the same angle as the short intersecting lines. Under this condition the relationship at (2) is satisfied. If the drawing is accurate enough, the curve, in the present instance, will return to P, being theoretically a circle of radius OP.

Analytically from (2)

$$\int v \, dv + \int y \, dy = \text{a constant,} \tag{5}$$

so

$$v^2 + y^2 = c^2, \tag{6}$$

which represents a family of circles with centre O and radius c. In

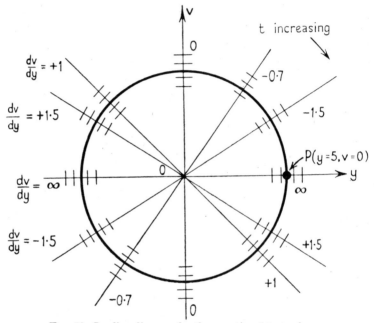

FIG. 56. Isocline diagram for the equation $\ddot{y} + y = 0$.

the case above, $c = OP$, but c may have any positive value. This is the first step in the graphical solution. It may be remarked in regard to curves of this type that through every point in the (y, v) plane there passes one, but *only one*, of them.

The next step is to find t. Now $v = dy/dt$, so $dy/v = dt$, and, therefore,

$$t = \int_{v_0}^{y} dy/v. \tag{7}$$

To evaluate this integral, divide the fourth quadrant into a number of parts by equally spaced ordinates, as shown in Fig. 57 A. The time taken for y to travel from P to P_1 is

$$t_1 = h/v_1, \tag{8}$$

v_1 being the average velocity in the interval (area PP_1N/h), and in general to travel from P to P_m,

$$t_m = h \sum_{r=1}^{m} 1/v_r. \tag{9}$$

To plot y and t, each t_m must be calculated. The smaller h (up to a point) the greater the accuracy of the result.

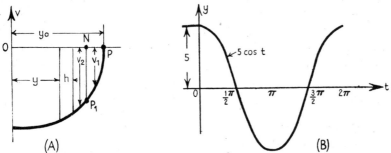

(A)   (B)

FIG. 57. A. Illustrating procedure to obtain $t = \int dy/v$. B. Solution curve for $\ddot{y}+y = 0$ obtained by aid of integral procedure in A.

8.11. Solution of (6), § 8.10. If the method of computing t outlined in § 8.10 is followed, the solution will be obtained as a curve. That in Fig. 57 B corresponds to one turn clockwise round the circle in Fig. 56. The curve is repeated each revolution, so the solution is periodic. By (4) below, the period is 2π.

Usually one resorts to a graphical construction under analytical duress! In general the symbolical form of the function represented by the solution curve will be unknown. The foregoing graphical construction has revealed the important fact that the solution is *periodic*.

Solving (6), § 8.10, and using the positive root,

$$dy/dt = (c^2-y^2)^{\frac{1}{2}}, \tag{1}$$

so $$\int dy/(c^2-y^2)^{\frac{1}{2}} = t+\varphi \text{ (a constant of integration).} \tag{2}$$

Hence $$\sin^{-1}(y/c) = t+\varphi, \tag{3}$$

or $$y = c\sin(t+\varphi) = A\sin t + B\cos t, \tag{4}$$

where A, B are arbitrary constants. This will be recognized as the formal solution of (1), § 8.10. If in the latter we write $\omega^2 y$ for y, it becomes

$$\frac{d^2y}{dt^2} + \omega^2 y = 0, \tag{5}$$

so
$$v\,dv/dy + \omega^2 y = 0. \tag{6}$$

Thus
$$v^2 + \omega^2 y^2 = c_1^2, \tag{7}$$

or
$$\frac{y^2}{(c_1/\omega)^2} + \frac{v^2}{c_1^2} = 1, \tag{8}$$

so the curves in the (y, v) plane are ellipses with centre O and semi-axes c_1/ω, c_1. Since these are closed curves, the solution of (5) is periodic, being
$$y = A_1 \sin \omega t + B_1 \cos \omega t. \tag{9}$$

It is evident that so long as the differential equation to be solved may be expressed in the form
$$v = f(y, v'), \tag{10}$$

where $f(y, v')$ is a function of y, v', the curves with v' a constant may be plotted, and the y–v curve obtained by the graphical construction of § 8.10. Other graphical methods are given in § 8.13 and in [133, 186]. The procedure in the two latter is well worth a trial.

8.12. Solve $\ddot{y} - \epsilon(1-y^2)\dot{y} + y = 0$, **for** $\epsilon = 0.1$, 1.0, 10.0. This equation was derived in § 4.10. It may be expressed in the forms
$$v\,dv/dy - \epsilon(1-y^2)v + y = 0, \tag{1}$$

or
$$dv/dy = \epsilon(1-y^2) - y/v, \tag{2}$$

or
$$v = y/[\epsilon(1-y^2) - dv/dy]. \tag{3}$$

Using (3), choose $dv/dy = -1$, then with $\epsilon = 0.1$ we get
$$v = y/[0.1(1-y^2)+1]. \tag{4}$$

The curve corresponding to (4) is marked -1 in Fig. 58. The short lines cutting the curve have slope -1. Putting $dv/dy = -2$ yields the curve so marked, the short lines having this slope. When $dv/dy \to \infty$, $v \to 0$, so we have the y-axis. Writing $y = 0$ in (2), we get
$$dv/dy = \epsilon = 0.1,$$

the value of dv/dy on the v-axis. With $dv/dy = 0$, (3) gives
$$v = 10y/(1-y^2), \tag{5}$$

and the curve has three parts, a common central one and those on each side of the asymptotes $y = \pm 1$. Proceeding in this way, the thin line curves of Fig. 58 are obtained. If we start at the origin where $y = v = t = 0$, and draw a curve parallel to the short intersecting lines, the radius vector increases with increase in angle. Beyond a certain point the rate of increase diminishes, and ultimately the curve spirals round with slowly increasing radius vector, being asymptotic (internally) to some closed curve. Consequently the solution of the equation is periodic.

On the other hand, if we start at A in the second quadrant, say, the curve will spiral inwards with decreasing radius vector until finally it is asymptotic (externally) to the same closed curve. So far as the

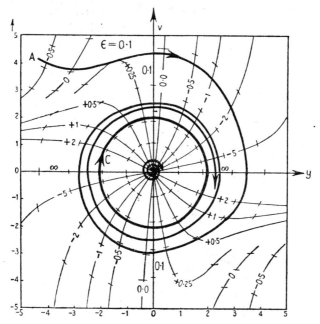

Fig. 58. y–v curves for the equation $\ddot{y}-\epsilon(1-y^2)\dot{y}+y=0$, with $\epsilon = 0.1$. The closed curve C towards which the inner and outer spirals gradually approach is the *limit cycle* [122].

accuracy of geometrical construction is concerned, a closed curve will usually be obtained in practice. When the v–y curves take the form of increasing or decreasing spirals which merge into a closed curve encircling the origin, the motion of the system represented by the differential equation is *stable and periodic*. In the present case, since $\epsilon = 0.1$, the equation does not differ appreciably from (1), § 8.10, so the closed y–v curve is almost circular. For (1), 8.10, the radius is arbitrary, as also are the constant A, B multipliers in the solution (4), § 8.11. In Chapter II it is pointed out that the constants in the solution of a non-linear equation although arbitrary, are functions of the initial conditions, while in § 4.111 the constant multiplier in the solution of the equation under discussion is shown to have a unique value. Hence any radius vector of the closed curve in Fig. 58 is unique.

If the integration indicated in § 8.10 is carried out, the y–t solution

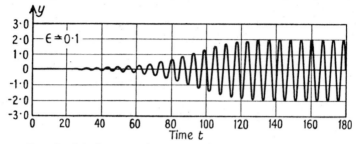

FIG. 59. Solution curve for $\ddot{y} - \epsilon(1 - y^2)\dot{y} + y = 0$, with $\epsilon = 0.1$.

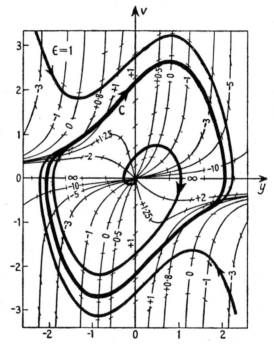

FIG. 60. y–v curves for $\ddot{y} - \epsilon(1 - y^2)\dot{y} + y = 0$, with $\epsilon = 1.0$.

curve results. It takes the form illustrated in Fig. 59, quickly attaining an approximately sinusoidal form with amplitude about 2. This is in accord with the analysis in §§ 4.10, 4.110.

The y–v curves and the corresponding solutions obtained in the above manner for $\epsilon = 1.0$, 10, are reproduced in Figs. 60, 61. When

$\epsilon = 1$, the closed v–y curve departs appreciably from a circular form. Consequently the y–t solution curve, although periodic, is not sinusoidal. When $\epsilon = 10$, the v–y curve in Fig. 61 begins to approach the limiting form for $\epsilon \to +\infty$. The y–t solution curves of Figs. 62, 63 are now far from sinusoidal, while the ultimate periodic wave form is attained after one oscillation. The curve in Fig. 63 is characterized by a sudden increase (or decrease) in displacement at the beginning and end of each half period, followed by a slow decrease (or increase) in the intermediate stages. Also as ϵ increases, the periodic time of the steady oscillation does likewise, as illustrated in Figs. 59, 62, 63. This type is termed a 'relaxation' oscillation, and it occurs only when ϵ is large enough [118, 120]. As shown in § 8.15, if ϵ is large enough the periodic time is approximately

$$\tau_0 = (3 - \log_e 4)\epsilon \simeq 1\cdot 614\epsilon, \qquad (6)$$

and increases with increase in ϵ.

The closed curve to which the increasing and decreasing spirals are asymptotic was called a *limit cycle* by Poincaré [116]. This is characteristic of all self-oscillatory systems whose motion is periodic. Another example is a watch or a clock. If the balance wheel (or pendulum) is given a small motion, it will build up to an ultimate value with increase in time. On the other hand, if the initial impulse is large enough, the balance wheel (or pendulum) will gradually settle down to a periodic motion as above. Thus the balance wheel of a watch or the pendulum of a clock may be regarded as a form of stable self-oscillator.

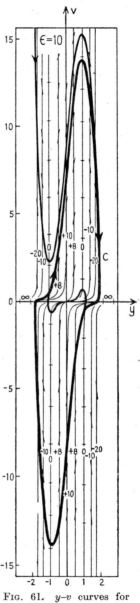

FIG. 61. y–v curves for $\ddot{y} - \epsilon(1 - y^2)\dot{y} + y = 0$, with $\epsilon = 10\cdot 0$ [122].

8.13. The Liénard graphical construction [88]. This is another method for solving certain types of differential equation which are reducible to an appropriate first-order form. Let the reduced form be

$$dv/dy = [F(v)-y]/v, \qquad (1)$$

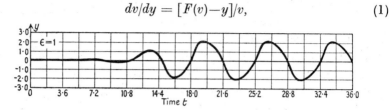

FIG. 62. Solution curve for $\ddot{y} - \epsilon(1-y^2)\dot{y} + y = 0$, with $\epsilon = 1\cdot0$.

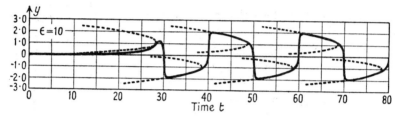

FIG. 63. Solution curve for $\ddot{y} - \epsilon(1-y^2)\dot{y} + y = 0$, with $\epsilon = 10\cdot0$.

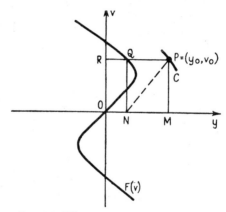

FIG. 64. Liénard graphical construction.

where we shall suppose that $F(v)$ is an odd function of v, i.e.

$$F(v) = -F(-v).$$

The first step is to plot the $F(v)$ curve as shown in Fig. 64, where an arbitrary one has been chosen. We use the initial conditions $y = y_0$, $v = v_0$, which define the point P on the y–v curve. Draw PR parallel to the y-axis, and PM, QN parallel to the v-axis. Then NP is the radius vector of the v–y curve C at the point P, where its tangent is perpendicular to PN. This is easily demonstrated: $PR = y$, $PM = v$, $-NM/PM = [F(v)-y]/v$; then (1) follows if $dv/dy = -NM/PM$. By continuing this graphical construction a curve is obtained which either (i) spirals inwards or outwards, ultimately being asymptotic to a closed curve; or (ii) spirals continually outwards. In (i) the solution of a differential equation of the second order is stable and periodic, and it may be shown that only one closed curve exists in the y–v plane. In (ii) the motion is unstable and increases without limit as $t \to +\infty$.

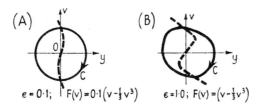

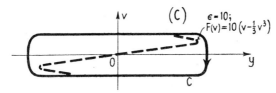

FIG. 65 A, B, C. v–y curves for thermionic valve oscillator
using Liénard graphical construction.

8.14. Relaxation oscillations.

The equation for oscillations of this type, which occur in a thermionic valve circuit, is usually taken in the form (see § 4.10)

$$\ddot{u} - \epsilon(1-u^2)\dot{u} + u = 0. \tag{1}$$

For present purposes it is more convenient to use

$$\ddot{y} - \epsilon(1-\tfrac{1}{3}\dot{y}^2)\dot{y} + y = 0. \tag{2}$$

(1) is derived from (2) by differentiating with respect to t and writing $\dot{y} = u$. Taking $v = dy/dt$, (2) becomes

$$v\,dv/dy - \epsilon(v-\tfrac{1}{3}v^3) + y = 0, \tag{3}$$

or $$dv/dy = [\epsilon(v-\tfrac{1}{3}v^3) - y]/v. \tag{4}$$

In accordance with § 8.13 we plot the curves $y = \epsilon(v-\tfrac{1}{3}v^3)$ for $\epsilon = 0.1$, 1·0, 10·0 and obtain the $F(v)$ depicted in Figs. 65 A, B, C. Next we use the graphical construction in § 8.13 and get the integral curves marked C. When $\epsilon = 0.1$, the curve is almost a circle. Theoretically the curve is approached asymptotically, but in each diagram it is shown closed. When $\epsilon = 1$, the curve is distinctly non-circular, while for $\epsilon = 10$, it is substantially a rectangle with rounded ends, but the shape depends upon the vertical scale, e.g. see the ultimate form in Fig. 66 as $\epsilon \to +\infty$. It consists of two straight lines BC, AD joined by arcs AB, CD. By increasing the width in the y-direction, this diagram would resemble Fig. 65 c in shape.

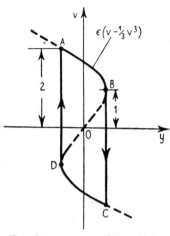

FIG. 66. *v–y* curve (Liénard) for relaxation oscillator, $\epsilon \to +\infty$.

8.15. Periodic time of relaxation oscillation [122, 123].

An oscillation corresponds to the movement of a variable point (y, v) once round the closed curve $ABCDA$ in Fig. 66. Now $v = dy/dt$, so $dt = dy/v$. Thus the periodic time is

$$\tau_0 = \int dy/v, \tag{1}$$

the integral being taken round the curve in Fig. 66. Since

$$y = \epsilon(v - \tfrac{1}{3}v^3), \qquad \frac{dy}{v} = \epsilon\left(\frac{1}{v} - v\right) dv, \tag{2}$$

so (1) becomes

$$\tau_0 = 2\epsilon \int_2^1 \left(\frac{1}{v} - v\right) dv. \tag{3}$$

The integration limits and the external 2 pertain to movement from A to B (twice) only, since BC and DA contribute nothing, by virtue of constancy of y. Thus

$$\tau_0 = 2\epsilon\left[\tfrac{1}{2}v^2 - \log_e v\right]_1^2 = \epsilon(3 - 2\log_e 2). \tag{4}$$

In deriving (1), § 8.14, t was written for ωt ($\omega^2 = 1/LC$), so in the appropriate units

$$\tau_0 = (\epsilon/\omega)(3 - 2\log_e 2) \simeq 1\cdot 614\epsilon/\omega, \tag{5}$$

which tends to infinity with ϵ. For an oscillatory circuit where $\epsilon \simeq 0$, $\bar{\tau}_0 \simeq 2\pi/\omega$, so the ratio of the periodic times of the relaxation and free oscillations is approximately

$$1\cdot 614\epsilon/2\pi \simeq 0\cdot 257\epsilon, \tag{6}$$

if ϵ is large enough. In a self-oscillatory thermionic valve circuit, to obtain relaxation oscillations ϵ would be increased by using a larger inductance of low resistance. Consequently the amplitude of the grid potential variation would increase, thereby causing a greater proportion of the curved part of the valve characteristic to be used than before. Thus the increase in ϵ would be accompanied by distortion of wave-form, as is demonstrated clearly by the curves in Figs. 62, 63.

8.20. Impulse tests of curved steel shells.

In certain heavy industries it is imperative that workers should wear boots having toe-

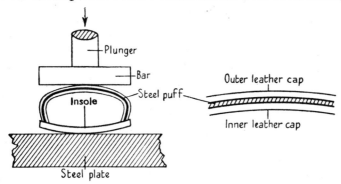

Fig. 67. Schematic diagram of apparatus for testing steel toe-puffs.
Sides of puff should be vertical.

caps reinforced by spring steel toe-puffs. This precaution reduces the possibility of serious injury to the toes if a heavy body should fall on the boot. The general scheme will be understood from Fig. 67, which is self-explanatory. The steel puff is situated between the inner lining and the outer leather toe-cap. To test the efficacy of this form of construction, a flat bar surmounted by a cylindrical plunger, free to move in a vertical bearing, rests on the upper side of the toe-cap. At a certain instant a heavy weight W is released from a specified height, and hits the top of the plunger. The toe-puff is depressed an amount depending upon the mass of the weight W/g, the height it falls, w/g the mass of the plunger and cross-bar, the restoring or spring force exerted by the puff, and the internal frictional loss. Having attained maximum depression, the weight is forced upwards by virtue of the potential energy of the deformed cap, being thrown off ultimately. The main problem is to find the maximum deflexion of the cap under given conditions, so that the clearance between it and the insole at that instant may be known. To avoid injury to the toes, the clearance must have a minimum value. The measurement in question is readily made by means of the simple yet efficacious device illustrated in Fig. 68. It consists of a piston fitting closely in an outer cylindrical cap. The latter has three longitudinal slots, so that a spring effect is obtained when the cap is squeezed radially. This is effected by tightening an outer clamp over a thick rubber ring which distributes the pressure. The air above the piston can escape through holes in the outer cylinder. A small hole is drilled through the sole of the boot at the proper testing-

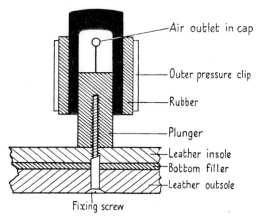

FIG. 68. Section through capsule for measuring maximum depression of toe-cap.

point, and the capsule fitted in position, as illustrated in Fig. 68. The outer cylinder is drawn upwards until it touches the inner surface of the toe-cap. The capsule is then removed and its length measured by a micrometer, after which it is replaced in the boot. Preferably, but not necessarily, the outer cylinder is moved away from the toe-cap by an amount determinable from experimental data. This reduces the initial acceleration of the outer cylinder. It can be shown analytically that if the frictional force between the piston and outer cylinder exceeds a certain value, the correct depression will be obtained.† The outer cylinder comes to rest at the same instant as the toe-puff, provided the pressure between the two is always positive. The accuracy of the capsule has been confirmed experimentally.

Tests conducted for general industrial purposes are such that the steel of the toe-puff is taken well beyond its elastic range, so there is appreciable permanent deformation. Under this condition, mathematical analysis must be discarded. Accordingly we shall limit our

† From 2 to 4 lb. gives an adequate margin of safety.

analysis to sensibly elastic deformation. A static load curve (elastic) for a boot having a carbon steel puff is shown in Fig. 69. The relationship between load P in lb. and the depression in inch units was found to be

$$P \simeq (21\!\cdot\!8y+2\!\cdot\!73)^3 - 21 = g(y). \quad (1)$$

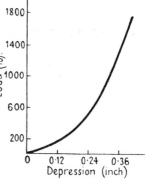

8.21. The differential equation. This has the form

$$m\frac{d^2y}{dt^2}+r\frac{dy}{dt}+g(y) = W+w. \quad (1)$$

Substituting for $g(y)$ from (1), § 8.20, and neglecting w,† we obtain

$$m\ddot{y}+r\dot{y}+(21\!\cdot\!8y+2\!\cdot\!73)^3 = W+21. \quad (2)$$

FIG. 69. Static load-depression curve for boot with steel toe-puff, obtained by loading plunger in Fig. 67 and using capsule of Fig. 68.

In (2) m is the mass of the moving parts, namely, W/g, while r is the resistance (per unit velocity) due to loss in the toe-cap, assumed to be a constant. With $W = 60$ lb., we have $m = 60/32\!\cdot\!2 \times 12$, so $m^{-1} = 6\!\cdot\!44$ in. lb.$^{-1}$ sec.$^{-2}$ units. Multiplying (2) throughout by m^{-1}, we obtain

$$\ddot{y}+2\kappa\dot{y}+(40\!\cdot\!6y+5\!\cdot\!09)^3 = 521, \quad (3)$$

with $2\kappa = r/m$, the viscous damping coefficient. Writing $v = dy/dt$, $v' = dv/dy$, (3) takes the form

$$v = [521-(40\!\cdot\!6y+5\!\cdot\!09)^3]/(v'+2\kappa). \quad (4)$$

We now assign a series of values to v', and proceed as in § 8.10. The isocline diagram is reproduced in Fig. 70. First we consider the case $\kappa = 0$. Suppose $\dot{W}$ falls a vertical distance of $6+y_{max}$ inches, so that v_0, its downward velocity, and that of the toe-cap at the instant of impact is 70 in. per sec. Then in (4) we take $\kappa = 0$, $v_0 = 70$, $y = 0$, and obtain $v'_0 = 5\!\cdot\!55$. This is the slope of the curve marked $\kappa = 0$, at $y = 0$. Again from (4), with $\kappa = 0$, $v' = 0$, we find that

$$521-(40\!\cdot\!6y+5\!\cdot\!09)^3 = 0, \quad \text{so} \quad y = 0\!\cdot\!073. \quad (5)$$

Also when $v' \to \infty$, $v \to 0$, i.e. on the y-axis. Performing the integration $\int_0^y dy/v$, as described in § 8.10, the curve marked $\kappa = 0$ in Fig. 71 may be plotted.

† $w \simeq 2$ lb. which may be neglected from a *practical* viewpoint. As an exercise the reader should solve (2) if w is included. m will be increased and v_0 decreased by about 3 per cent. The equivalent mass of the toe-cap is negligible.

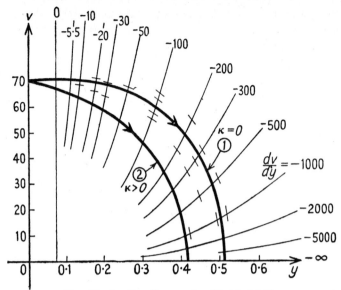

FIG. 70. Isocline diagram for (3), (4), § 8.21.

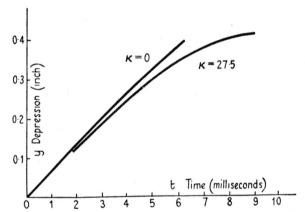

FIG. 71. Solution curves for (3), § 8.21, with $\kappa = 0$ and $\kappa = 27.5$.

8.22. Solution when $\kappa > 0$. Here we are faced with a difficulty, since κ is unknown. We have recourse, therefore, to experimental data. The measured value of $y_{\max}$ corresponding to the data in § 8.21 was 0·42 inch. Thus in Fig. 70 two points on the y–v curve are $y = 0$, $v = 70$, and $y = 0.42$, $v = 0$. When $v' \gg 2\kappa$ the curve for $\kappa > 0$ will cross those already plotted from (4) with $\kappa = 0$, substantially at the angles already marked off. Accordingly we draw a trial curve starting at $y = 0.42$, $v = 0$ and extending to $y = 0$, $v = 70$. Next we consider the energy relations by aid of (3), § 8.21, written in the form

$$v\frac{dv}{dy}+2\kappa v = 521-67000(y+0.1254)^3. \qquad (1)$$

Integrating (1) with respect to y yields

$$-\int_0^{v_0} v\,dv+2\kappa\int_0^{y_{max}} v\,dy$$

$$= 521y_m-16750(y_m+0.1254)^4+16750\times0.1254^4. \qquad (2)$$

Thus $\qquad 2\kappa\int_0^{y_{max}} v\,dy = \tfrac{1}{2}v_0^2+\text{the right-hand side of (2).} \qquad (3)$

Inserting $v_0 = 70$, $y_m = 0.42$, we obtain

$$2\kappa\int_0^{0.42} v\,dy \doteqdot 1185. \qquad (4)$$

Now $\int_0^{0.42} v\,dy$ is the area under the trial curve for $\kappa > 0$ in Fig. 70. By numerical integration this has the value 22. Thus to a first approximation $\qquad \kappa = 1185/44 \simeq 27. \qquad (5)$

Using this in (4), § 8.21, the slopes of the short crossing lines on the y–v curves of Fig. 70 may be corrected. Thus if $v' = -100$ for $\kappa = 0$, the new slope of the short lines will be such that $v'+2\kappa = -100$, i.e. $v' = -154$, and so on. In this way a new y–v curve for $\kappa > 0$ may be drawn, and usually it will be accurate enough for *practical* purposes. For the second or improved curve so found,

$$\int_0^{0.42} v\,dy = 21.5, \text{ giving } \kappa = 27.5. \qquad (6)$$

Performing the integration for t as in § 8.10, the curve marked $\kappa = 27.5$ in Fig. 71 was obtained.

In practice we are not concerned with events which follow the maximum depression, so the curve in Fig. 71 marked $\kappa = 27.5$ has not been continued beyond this value.

As a matter of interest, test data for a steel toe-puff stiffer than that considered hitherto are set out in Table 3. Since a single impulse caused permanent set, a new puff was used for each experiment.

TABLE 3

Data for carbon steel toe-puff

Initial clearance in boot 1·1 inch: distance W (60 lb.) falls $= (h+y_m)$ inch

Height h (inch)	Maximum depression y_m (inch)	Total energy expended (in. lb.)	Permanent set (inch)
2	0·15	129	0·014
6	0·25	375	0·028
12	0·34	740	0·047
18	0·43	1,106	0·130
30	0·56	1,834	0·210

The relationship between y_m and h found from the data in Table 3, in inch units, is $10y_m \simeq (y_m+h)^{\frac{1}{2}}$, $h \geqslant 2$.

8.23. Damping loss. The energy lost by W up to the time of maximum depression $y_m = 0·42$, is

$$(W/g)\frac{v_0^2}{2} + W \times 0·42 = \frac{2450}{6·43} + 60 \times 0·42 = 407 \text{ in. lb.} \qquad (1)$$

The loss due to damping is

$$r \int_0^{0·42} v \, dy = 2\kappa m \int_0^{0·42} v \, dy = 1185/6·44 \qquad (2)$$

$$= 184 \text{ in. lb.} \qquad (3)$$

Hence the proportional loss due to damping is $184/407 = 0·45$. This causes a reduction in the maximum depression of $(0·51-0·42) = 0·09$ inch, or about 18 per cent., so that damping assists in protecting the workers' feet to this extent.

8.30. Stability of operation of synchronous electrical motors. A machine of this type comprises essentially a cylindrical rotor within a coaxial stator, the two being separated by a narrow air gap. The stator consists of laminated rings of ferromagnetic material in which slots are cut parallel to the common axis. Conductors are embedded in the slots, and connected to form a number of circuits, each of which is associated with one of the phases of a polyphase electric supply source. The system of stator windings, i.e. the arrangement of conductors in the slots, is such that at any instant during operation, alternate north and south poles (in the usual terminology) occur at equal intervals round the inner periphery. By virtue of the different phase relations in the polyphase current supply, and the manner of connecting the stator windings, the magnetic field caused by the current rotates in the gap at the inner periphery. The rotor consists of disk laminations slotted at the edges, conductors being embedded in the slots. To start the motor, the stator circuits are connected to the polyphase supply source, and the rotor circuits are closed through variable resistances. The rotating magnetic field at the inner periphery of the stator induces a current in the rotor windings in such a sense that a repulsive force occurs between the two sets of windings, this being tangential to both stator and rotor. Thus the torque on the latter causes it to rotate in the same direction as the magnetic field. As the speed of the rotor increases, the resistances in series with its windings are gradually decreased until finally they are zero, i.e. the rotor is short-circuited on itself. The rotor speed is now slightly less than that of the magnetic field, the difference being called the 'slip'. It is such that the driving torque due to the current induced in the rotor is sufficient to equal the no-load torque corresponding to friction and windage. To synchronize the rotor speed with that of the rotating magnetic field, the rotor circuits are opened and connected almost simultaneously to a source of unidirectional current, known as the exciter. Just after this happens, there is alternating current in the rotor circuits, by virtue of slip, on which is superimposed a unidirectional current rising rapidly to an ultimate value. The effect of the latter current is to pull the rotor into step (synchronism) quickly with the rotating field. At a specific instant during the process, Fig. 72 A gives some idea of the relative configuration of rotor and stator. After synchronism is attained, the corresponding north and south poles, in rotor and stator, are not exactly opposite to each other, being displaced by θ_0 *electrical* degrees.† For in order to maintain the torque on the rotor, there must be a tangential pull. Consequently the lines of force must pass obliquely from rotor to stator to provide a component of force tangential to the rotor. Since the torque depends upon θ, an increase in load is accompanied by one in θ. If the load is increased *gradually*, the relationship between it and θ takes the form shown in Fig. 73. When the rotor and stator are displaced by 90 electrical degrees, the position being that of Fig. 72 B, the load has its maximum value for synchronous running. If it is suddenly

† 360 'electrical' degrees is the equivalent angular distance between two consecutive north or south poles.

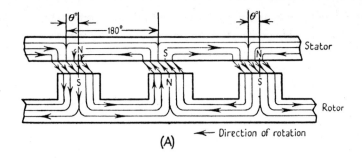

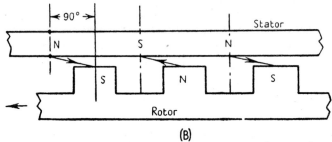

FIG. 72. A. Showing relative angular positions of rotor and stator of synchronous electric motor on 'light' load. B. As at A, but 'heavy' load.

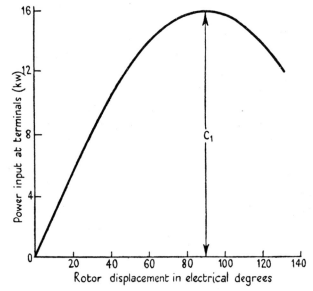

FIG. 73. Experimental data for non-salient pole synchronous motor, the load being applied gradually.

increased beyond this value, the machine falls out of step, slows down, and stops. If, however, the load is *gradually* decreased, the curve bends over as in Fig. 73, the angle θ increasing meanwhile, until finally it is 180°, the north poles being opposite to each other and the load zero. The motion is now unstable.

In practical operation the load is usually applied suddenly. Under this condition instability occurs when θ exceeds a certain value, so our problem is to calculate the magnitude of the suddenly applied load which will just cause the motor to fall out of step (synchronism), i.e. cause instability.

8.31. The differential equation.

In reference [93] it is shown that a simplified version of the equation pertaining to the stability of synchronous motors is

$$a_1 \frac{d^2\theta}{dt^2} + b_1 \frac{d\theta}{dt} + c_1 \sin\theta = P_0 + P_1 = P, \tag{1}$$

where

a_1 = power per unit angular acceleration (electrical degrees sec.$^{-2}$) at synchronous speed,

b_1 = power per unit change of angular velocity (electrical degrees sec.$^{-1}$) for small values of slip near synchronous speed,

c_1 = steady state pull-out synchronous power (see Fig. 73),

P_0 = initial load, P_1 = suddenly applied load.

It may be remarked that (1) is a differential equation for *power*. By making the necessary alteration in the various parameters, (1) may be expressed in the form

$$\mathbf{I}\ddot{\theta} + r\dot{\theta} + a\sin\theta = T, \tag{2}$$

where $\mathbf{I}$ is the moment of inertia, r a resistive damping torque coefficient, $a\sin\theta$ is the control torque, and T the load torque. As in § 3.160, the above equations are non-linear by virtue of $\sin\theta$.

8.32. Numerical example.

In reference [93] the following equation is given for a non-salient pole synchronous motor having a steady pull out power of 16 kilowatts (nominal power 5 kW, see Fig. 73):

$$0 \cdot 0041 \frac{d^2\theta}{dt^2} + 0 \cdot 0128 \frac{d\theta}{dt} + 16\sin\theta = 1 \cdot 3 + P_1 H(t), \tag{1}$$

where $H(t)$ is Heaviside's unit or step function which signifies that the machine is running at synchronous speed with load 1·3 kW, and at $t = 0$ an additional load P_1 is applied suddenly. In this case $P_0 = 1·3$ kW represents the initial or no-load power absorbed in windage, friction, and iron loss of the synchronous motor, also in the machine supplying the 'load', and in an additional machine used to measure the angular displacement θ. The three machines were coupled together mechanically. We have now to find the smallest

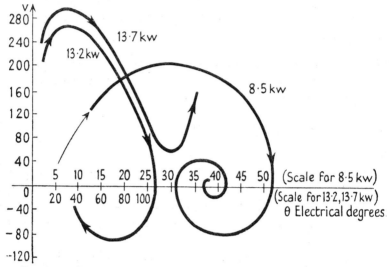

FIG. 74. v–θ curves for (3), (4), § 8.32, obtained by isocline construction.

value of the suddenly applied load P_1, which will throw the motor out of synchronism. To accomplish this, it is expedient to solve (1) for several values of P_1. From experiment it is known that

$$(P_1 + 1·3) < 16 \text{ kW, so } P_1 < 14·7 \text{ kW.}$$

Before P_1 is applied, the machine is running at synchronous speed, so $\ddot{\theta} = \dot{\theta} = 0$. Thus from (1) we have

$$\sin\theta = 1·3/16, \text{ giving } \theta = 4·66 \text{ electrical degrees,} \qquad (2)$$

as the condition at $t = 0$. Now (1) may be written

$$\frac{d^2\theta}{dt^2} + 3·12\frac{d\theta}{dt} + 3900\sin\theta = 317 + 244P_1, \qquad (3)$$

so with $v = d\theta/dt$, $v' = dv/d\theta$, we get

$$v = (317 + 244P_1 - 3900\sin\theta)/(v' + 3·12). \qquad (4)$$

Using the technique described in § 8.10, the curve in Fig. 74 marked

8·5 kW is obtained for this value of P_1. It spirals in towards the point $v = \dot{\theta} = 0$, $\theta = \sin^{-1}(1\cdot3+8\cdot5)/16 \simeq 37\cdot8°$, which is the value from (1) when synchronous speed is attained after application of the load. The corresponding values of t are found by the integration process described in § 8.10, and the θ–t relationship is depicted by the curve in Fig. 75 marked 8·5 kW. It represents a damped oscillation of

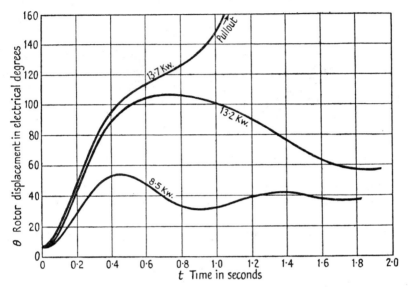

FIG. 75. Curves for synchronous motor showing relation between angle in electrical degrees (see Fig. 72), and time after the application of sudden loads of 8·5, 13·2, and 13·7 kW.

the rotor which settles down to the new value of θ, namely, 37·8°. The increase in angular displacement between rotor and stator, viz. $(37\cdot8-4\cdot66) = 33\cdot14°$, is needed to provide the extra torque to give an additional power of 8·5 kW.

Next we take $P_1 = 13\cdot2$ kW and repeat the above procedure. The resulting curve in Fig. 74 is marked 13·2 kW, and spirals towards the point $v = \dot{\theta} = 0$, $\sin^{-1}(14\cdot5/16) \simeq 65°$. The θ–t relationship in Fig. 75 is again a damped oscillation which settles down to $\theta \simeq 65°$. An oscillogram pertaining to this case is reproduced in Fig. 76, where the variation in θ is clearly shown, also the three-phase power input. The latter rises to a maximum exceeding 16 kW; it .then falls and fluctuates slowly, the ultimate input being 14·5 kW.

Finally the results for a suddenly applied load of 13·7 kW are depicted in Figs. 74, 75 by the curves so marked. The v–θ curve veers away from the θ-axis, which implies instability. In the θ–t curve, θ ultimately increases with increase in t, while the angle-volts steadily increase to a maximum (90°). Then θ increases suddenly to 180°, following to 270°, and so on, the machine having fallen out of synchronism, the rotor now slowing down. The solution curves in reference [93] were obtained by a differential analyser, and agree

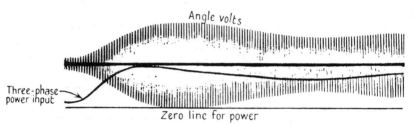

FIG. 76. Oscillogram showing relation between electrical input power to synchronous motor and angle-volts, when load is applied suddenly.

closely with the experimental results. Additional data useful for design purposes are given in [93].

8.33. Solution by method of finite differences. We take the equation in the form

$$\ddot{\theta}+2\kappa\dot{\theta}+a\sin\theta = FH(t), \tag{1}$$

where 2κ is the damping coefficient, $a\sin\theta$ the non-linear 'spring' control, and F a constant force applied at $t = 0$, by virtue of $H(t)$ the unit or step function. Writing $v = d\theta/dt$, $v' = dv/d\theta$, (1) becomes

$$vv'+2\kappa v+a\sin\theta = F, \text{ or } v' = [(F-a\sin\theta)/v]-2\kappa, \tag{2}$$

the presence of $H(t)$ being implied. Referring to Fig. 77 we see that the approximate slope at P is

$$(y_{r+1}-y_{r-1})/2h = y_r'. \tag{3}$$

Applying (3) to (2), and writing θ for x, v for y, we get

$$v_r' = (v_{r+1}-v_{r-1})/2h = [(F-a\sin\theta_r)/v_r]-2\kappa, \tag{4}$$

so $$v_{r+1} = [2h(F-a\sin\theta_r)/v_r]+v_{r-1}-4\kappa h. \tag{5}$$

To commence the computation we must know v_p and v_{p+1} corresponding to θ_p, θ_{p+1}, where $(\theta_{p+1}-\theta_p) = h$, so we now introduce numerical values. Let $\kappa = 0\cdot1$, $a = 1$, $F = 0\cdot505$, then (1) becomes

$$\ddot{\theta}+0\cdot2\dot{\theta}+\sin\theta = 0\cdot505H(t). \tag{6}$$

The initial conditions are $\theta = \dot\theta = 0$, and $\ddot\theta = 0{\cdot}505$ at $t = +0$.
By Maclaurin's theorem

$$\theta(t) = \theta(0) + t\dot\theta(0) + \frac{t^2}{2!}\ddot\theta(0) + \frac{t^3}{3!}\dddot\theta(0) + \dots . \tag{7}$$

Using the above initial conditions, (7) becomes

$$\theta(t) = \frac{t^2}{2!}\ddot\theta(0) + \frac{t^3}{3!}\dddot\theta(0) + \dots . \tag{8}$$

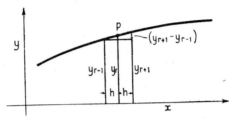

FIG. 77. Diagram used for method of finite
differences in § 8.33.

Differentiating (6) with respect to t gives

$$\dddot\theta + 0{\cdot}2\ddot\theta + \dot\theta\cos\theta = 0, \tag{9}$$

and since $\dot\theta = 0$, we get

$$\dddot\theta(0) = -0{\cdot}2\ddot\theta(0) = -0{\cdot}2 \times 0{\cdot}505 = -0{\cdot}101. \tag{10}$$

Also

$$\ddddot\theta + 0{\cdot}2\dddot\theta + \ddot\theta\cos\theta - \dot\theta^2\sin\theta = 0, \tag{11}$$

so

$$\ddddot\theta(0) = -[0{\cdot}2\dddot\theta(0) + \ddot\theta\cos(0)],$$
$$= -(-0{\cdot}2 \times 0{\cdot}101 + 0{\cdot}505) = -0{\cdot}4848. \tag{12}$$

Proceeding thus we find that

$$\theta^{(5)}(0) = 0{\cdot}198, \qquad \theta^{(6)}(0) = 0{\cdot}4452. \tag{13}$$

Additional terms are obtainable by aid of the recurrence formula

$$\theta^{(r+1)}(0) = -[0{\cdot}2\theta^{(r)}(0) + \theta^{(r-1)}(0)], \tag{14}$$

but usually the accuracy will decrease with increase in r. Substituting
from (10), (12), (13) into (8) leads to the approximate solution

$$\theta \simeq 0{\cdot}2525t^2 - 0{\cdot}0168t^3 - 0{\cdot}0202t^4 + 0{\cdot}00165t^5 + 0{\cdot}000618t^6. \tag{15}$$

This may be used to calculate θ in $0 \leqslant t \leqslant 2$. The accuracy decreases
with increase in t in the interval, being about 1 per cent. at $t = 2$.
If (15) is differentiated with respect to t, $\dot\theta$ may be calculated from

$$\dot\theta \simeq 0{\cdot}505t - 0{\cdot}0504t^2 - 0{\cdot}0808t^3 + 0{\cdot}00825t^4 + 0{\cdot}003708t^5. \tag{16}$$

8.34. Application of (5), § 8.33. Using (15), (16), § 8.33, we calculate θ, $\dot\theta$ for $t = 0\cdot3$, $0\cdot4,...$, and by interpolation find that when $\theta_2 = 0\cdot1$, $\theta_3 = 0\cdot15$, we get $\dot\theta_2 = v_2 = 0\cdot285$, $\dot\theta_3 = v_3 = 0\cdot345$. Then $h = 0\cdot05$ and (5), § 8.33, becomes

$$v_{r+1} = [0\cdot1(0\cdot505 - \sin\theta_r)/v_r] + v_{r-1} - 0\cdot02. \tag{1}$$

Substituting from above

$$v_4 = [0\cdot1(0\cdot515 - \sin 0\cdot15^c)/0\cdot345] + 0\cdot285 - 0\cdot02$$
$$\simeq 0\cdot369. \tag{2}$$

Also
$$v_5 = [0\cdot1(0\cdot515 - \sin 0\cdot2^c)/0\cdot369] + 0\cdot345 - 0\cdot02$$
$$\simeq 0\cdot408. \tag{3}$$

As the computation proceeds, the points (θ_r, v_r) should be plotted. The occurrence of irregularities which might be corrected would then be revealed. To obtain greater accuracy, a smaller common interval, say, $h = 0\cdot025$, would have to be used, especially for those parts of the θ–v curve where the curvature is large. However, the above illustrates the method of procedure, and having obtained the two initial values, it is easy to apply. If the computation is continued, sufficient data will be accumulated to plot a decreasing θ–v spiral of the form shown in Fig. 74, marked 8·5 kW. When $v = 0$, θ attains its maximum value. Thereafter the curve spirals round, and gradually approaches

$$\theta = \sin^{-1}0\cdot505, \quad v = 0.$$

The motion of a synchronous motor obeying the differential equation would be stable. It is now necessary to integrate as in § 8.10 to calculate t.

8.35. Numerical solution of (6), § 8.33. First we calculate θ, $\dot\theta$, $\ddot\theta$ when $t = 0, 0\cdot1, 0\cdot2$, using (15), (16), § 8.33, and the first derivative of the latter. This gives the first three rows of Table 4, and it is important that *they should be fairly accurate*, because errors once introduced are liable to be cumulative in any numerical process of the type given below. To compute additional rows in Table 4 we use the following formulae: If h is not too large

$$\dot\theta_{r+1} - \dot\theta_{r-1} \simeq 2h\ddot\theta_r, \tag{1}$$

so
$$\dot\theta_{r+1} \simeq 2h\ddot\theta_r + \dot\theta_{r-1}. \tag{2}$$

Also by Simpson's rule

$$\theta_{r+1} - \theta_{r-1} = \tfrac{1}{3}h(\dot\theta_{r+1} + 4\dot\theta_r + \dot\theta_{r-1}), \tag{3}$$

TABLE 4

Common interval $h = 0{\cdot}1$ in t

r	t	$\dot{\theta}$	θ	$\ddot{\theta}$	$\Delta\theta$	$\Delta^2\theta$	$\Delta^2\theta_r/h^2$
0	0·0	0·0000	0·0000	0·5050	—	—	—
1	0·1	0·0500	0·0025	0·4925	25	—	0·4950
2	0·2	0·0985	0·0099₅	0·4754	74·₅	49·₅	0·4750
3	0·3	$\left\{ {(0\cdot1449) \atop 0\cdot1451} \right.$	0·0221₅	0·4539	122	47·₅	0·4550
4	0·4	$\left\{ {(0\cdot1891) \atop 0\cdot1893} \right.$	0·0389	0·4283	167·₅	45·₅	0·4250
5	0·5	$\left\{ {(0\cdot2306) \atop 0\cdot2307} \right.$	0·0599	0·3990	210	42·₅	0·4000
6	0·6	$\left\{ {(0\cdot2690) \atop 0\cdot2691} \right.$	0·0849	0·3661	250	40·0	—
7	0·8	0·3357	0·1457	0·2929	608	—	0·2900
8	1·0	0·3863	0·2181	0·2112	724	116	—

which gives
$$\theta_{r+1} = \tfrac{1}{3}h(\dot{\theta}_{r+1}+4\dot{\theta}_r+\dot{\theta}_{r-1})+\theta_{r-1}. \tag{4}$$

Further
$$\ddot{\theta}_{r-1} \simeq \Delta^2\theta_r/h^2, \tag{5}$$

where $\Delta^2\theta_r$ is the second difference in θ_r. This formula may be used to make a rough check.

To obtain row 4 in Table 4, put $h = 0{\cdot}1$, $r = 2$ in (2), and use $\ddot{\theta}_2$, $\dot{\theta}_1$ from the table. Then
$$\dot{\theta}_3 \simeq 0{\cdot}2\times0{\cdot}4754+0{\cdot}05 = 0{\cdot}1451. \tag{6}$$

From (4) and the tabular values already given
$$\theta_3 = \tfrac{1}{30}(0{\cdot}1451+4\times0{\cdot}0985+0{\cdot}05)+0{\cdot}0025$$
$$= 0{\cdot}0221_5. \tag{7}$$

By (6), (7), and (6) § 8.33
$$\ddot{\theta}_3 = 0{\cdot}505-0{\cdot}2\times0{\cdot}1451-\sin 0{\cdot}0221_5^{r} = 0{\cdot}4539. \tag{8}$$

Rows 5–7 are computed in like manner.

The last column of Table 4 calculated from (5) provides a rough check on $\ddot{\theta}$. The values of θ may be (and should be!) checked as the computation proceeds, by aid of the Simpson's rule formula (see (4))
$$\dot{\theta}_{r+1} = \tfrac{1}{3}h(\ddot{\theta}_{r+1}+4\ddot{\theta}_r+\ddot{\theta}_{r-1})+\dot{\theta}_{r-1}. \tag{9}$$

Data so obtained are given in Table 4 in ( ). Also in place of (2), the formula
$$\dot{\theta}_{r+1} = \frac{4h}{3}(2\ddot{\theta}_r-\ddot{\theta}_{r-1}+2\ddot{\theta}_{r-2})+\dot{\theta}_{r-3}, \tag{10}$$

may be used.

The common interval in Table 4 may now be doubled to reduce labour, and the above process continued. The reader should extend the tabular values beyond $t = 1.0$, and try the effect of using $h = 0.4$ beyond $t = 1.6$. The method gives adequate accuracy for practical purposes, as may be verified by computing θ, $\dot{\theta}$, $\ddot{\theta}$ from (15), (16), § 8.33, up to $t = 2.0$. Small oscillations sometimes occur in θ, $\dot{\theta}$, $\ddot{\theta}$ which are detectable in differences. This may signify that the curvature of one or more of θ, $\dot{\theta}$, $\ddot{\theta}$ changes too rapidly for the interval h which is being used. A smaller interval may be chosen, or the Runge-Kutta method applied over the range where oscillation occurs [190].

The procedure used above is a slight modification of that in reference [15], where $\Delta^2\theta_r$ is calculated from (5). $\Delta\theta_r$ is then obtained by adding $\Delta^2\theta_r$ to $\Delta\theta_{r-1}$, and thence θ is found. A correction technique follows, and the results are improved at each 'cycle'. The original memoir should be consulted for further details. Other methods of numerical solution are set out in [190].

8.40. Analytical considerations; solution for undamped rotor.

We write (1), § 8.31, in the form

$$\frac{d^2\theta}{dt^2} + 2\kappa\frac{d\theta}{dt} + a\sin\theta = F_0 + F_1 H(t) = F \quad (t > 0), \tag{1}$$

where F_0 corresponds to the initial load, and F_1 to that applied suddenly at $t = 0$, when the motor is running at constant speed. With $\kappa = 0$ and $v = d\theta/dt$, (1) becomes

$$v\frac{dv}{d\theta} + a\sin\theta = F \quad (t > 0) \tag{2}$$

and, by integrating, we get

$$v^2 = 2(F\theta + a\cos\theta) + A, \text{ a constant.} \tag{3}$$

At $t = -0$, $v = \dot{\theta} = 0$, and the relative angular displacement of rotor and stator due to F_0 is θ_0, $0 < \theta_0 < \frac{1}{2}\pi$; also $\ddot{\theta} = 0$, so

$$F_0 = a\sin\theta_0.$$

In (3) when $v = 0$, $\theta = \theta_0$, so

$$A = -2(F\theta_0 + a\cos\theta_0), \tag{4}$$

and, therefore, in $t > 0$,

$$v = \pm\{2F(\theta - \theta_0) + 2a(\cos\theta - \cos\theta_0)\}^{\frac{1}{2}}. \tag{5}$$

When $v = 0$, excluding $\theta = \theta_0$, we have

$$F/a = (\cos\theta_0 - \cos\theta)/(\theta - \theta_0). \tag{6}$$

The critical condition corresponds to the maximum value of F which satisfies (6). Accordingly we must have

$$\frac{d}{d\theta}\left\{\frac{\cos\theta_0 - \cos\theta}{\theta - \theta_0}\right\} = \frac{\sin\theta}{(\theta - \theta_0)} - \frac{(\cos\theta_0 - \cos\theta)}{(\theta - \theta_0)^2} = 0, \tag{7}$$

which entails

$$(\theta - \theta_0)\sin\theta - (\cos\theta_0 - \cos\theta) = 0. \tag{8}$$

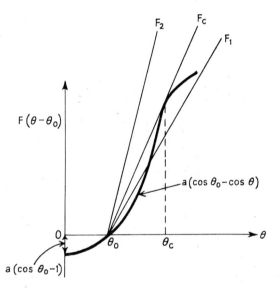

FIG. 78. Diagram for undamped synchronous motor.

The value of θ in $\frac{1}{2}\pi < \theta < \pi$ which satisfies (8) is the critical angle θ_c. Inserting this into (6) yields the critical F, namely,

$$F_c = a(\cos\theta_0 - \cos\theta_c)/(\theta_c - \theta_0), \tag{9}$$

and then

$$F_1 = F_c - F_0. \tag{10}$$

If $F_0 = \theta_0 = 0$, $\theta_c = 133°\ 34'$ and $F_c = 0\cdot725a$.

Fig. 78 shows (i) the curve $a(\cos\theta_0 - \cos\theta)$ for the range $\theta = (0, 2\pi)$, θ_0 being arbitrary, (ii) three straight lines $F(\theta - \theta_0)$ for

$$F = F_1, F_c, F_2, \qquad F_1 < F_c < F_2.$$

By (5), v is real if $F(\theta-\theta_0) > a(\cos\theta_0-\cos\theta)$. This is true if $F_2(\theta-\theta_0)$ lies wholly to the left of the curve, but in that case v is never zero, except at $\theta = \theta_0$. If $0 \leqslant \theta_0 < \frac{1}{2}\pi$, the line $F_1(\theta-\theta_0)$ intersects the curve, while $F_c(\theta-\theta_0)$ is tangential to it. The abscissa of the point of contact is the critical angle θ_c (see Fig. 78).

The v–θ curve may be plotted using (5). If $F < F_c$, it is closed, motion of the rotor being periodic and stable. If $F > F_c$, it is open, which entails instability; while if $F = F_c$, the v–θ curve is a separatrix (see Fig. 94). It is the frontier line between stability and instability.

8.41. Energy considerations. Suppose that (1), § 8.40, with $\kappa = 0$, relates to a mechanical system having a spring control (or its equivalent) $a\sin\theta$, e.g. a rigid type of pendulum, a vertical line through

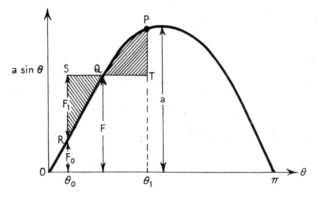

FIG. 79. Torque-control diagram for undamped synchronous motor.

the point of support corresponding to $\theta = 0$ (see § 3.160). Referring to Fig. 79, the angular displacement θ_0 is caused by a constant torque which corresponds to F_0. When $F_1 H(t)$ is applied, the system rotates until θ attains a value θ_1 where $v = 0$ momentarily. Thereafter, a periodic oscillation occurs, and the spring control varies with variation in θ along PR. At θ_1, the work done by $F = F_0+F_1 H(t)$ is equivalent to the area of the rectangle $\theta_0 ST\theta_1$. This is equal to the increase in the potential energy of the spring, equivalent to the area $\theta_0 RP\theta_1$, which entails equality of RSQ and QPT. Equating the work done to the potential energy, apart from a multiplier common to both sides, we obtain

$$F(\theta_1-\theta_0) = a\int_{\theta_0}^{\theta_1} \sin\theta\, d\theta = a(\cos\theta_0-\cos\theta), \qquad (1)$$

so

$$F/a = (\cos\theta_0-\cos\theta_1)/(\theta_1-\theta_0), \qquad (2)$$

which is identical with (6), § 8.40, if θ_1 replaces θ.

The critical case is illustrated in Fig. 80, where $F = F_c = a\sin\theta_c$. When $F < F_c$, T in Fig. 79 is an internal point of the area $OP\pi$, and a value of θ_1 can be found to satisfy (2), because the shaded areas are equal. But when $F > F_c$, in Fig. 80, the area $RSQ > QMT$, so the work done by F, i.e. $\theta_0 SQT\theta_c$, exceeds the potential energy of the spring, namely, $\theta_0 RQMT\theta_c$. Accordingly, the motion is unstable.

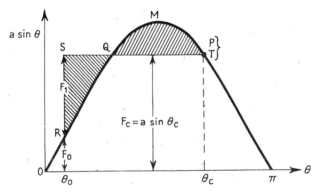

Fɪɢ. 80. Diagram illustrating 'critical' case of undamped synchronous motor, where P, T of Fig. 79 are coincident, and the areas RSQ, QMT are equal. If $F > F_c$, $RSQ > QMT$ and instability ensues.

An increase in θ_0 is accompanied by one in F, the limit being $\theta_0 = \frac{1}{2}\pi$ when $F = F_0 = a$, and then $F_1 = 0$, which corresponds to C_1 in Fig. 73. The larger θ_0 in $0 \leqslant \theta_0 < \frac{1}{2}\pi$, the smaller is F_1. The value of θ for steady running must lie in $0 < \theta < \frac{1}{2}\pi$.

8.42. Singular point of (2), § 8.40. The equation may be written

$$\frac{dv}{d\theta} = \frac{-a\sin\theta+F}{v}. \qquad (1)$$

Now, after application of F_1, oscillation occurs (so to say) about Q in Fig. 79, and we have $F = a\sin\theta_2$. It follows that $\theta = \theta_2$, $v = 0$ is a singular point. To determine its type, we move the origin to this point by writing $\theta = \theta_2 + \chi$. Then (1) gives

$$\frac{dv}{d\chi} = \frac{-a\sin(\theta_2+\chi)+a\sin\theta_2}{v}. \tag{2}$$

The numerator on the right-hand side of (2) is

$$-a(\sin\theta_2\cos\chi+\cos\theta_2\sin\chi)+a\sin\theta_2$$

$$= -a\left\{\left(1-\frac{\chi^2}{2!}+\ldots\right)\sin\theta_2+\left(\chi-\frac{\chi^3}{3!}+\ldots\right)\cos\theta_2\right\}+a\sin\theta_2. \tag{3}$$

Rejecting terms in χ of degree > 1, there remains $-(a\cos\theta_2)\chi$, so that (2) reduces to

$$\frac{dv}{d\chi} = \frac{-a(\cos\theta_2)\chi}{v}, \tag{4}$$

and the point $\chi = v = 0$, i.e. $\theta = \theta_2$, $v = 0$ is singular. By § 9.20, $\alpha = -a\cos\theta_2$, $\beta = \gamma = 0$, $\delta = 1$, so

$$\alpha\delta-\beta\gamma = -a\cos\theta_2,$$

$$\beta+\gamma = 0, \tag{5}$$

and $$D = (\beta-\gamma)^2+4\alpha\delta = -4\cos\theta_2.$$

If $0 < \theta_2 < \frac{1}{2}\pi$, then $D < 0$, and by § 9.22 the singularity is either a centre or a spiral point. From § 8.40 the v–θ curve is closed, so that $\theta = \theta_2$, $v = 0$ is a centre. If $\frac{1}{2}\pi < \theta_2 < \pi$, $\alpha\delta-\beta\gamma > 0$, $D > 0$, and by (ii), 1°, §§ 9.20, 9.22, the singular point is a col. Now θ_c lies in this θ_2 range, so it corresponds to a col, and if $\theta > \theta_c$, the rotor motion is unstable.

8.43. Solution for damped rotor. Writing (1), § 8.40, in the form

$$v\frac{dv}{d\theta}+2\kappa v+a\sin\theta = F \qquad (t > 0) \tag{1}$$

and integrating, we get

$$v^2 = 2(F\theta+a\cos\theta)-4\kappa\int_{\theta_0}^{\theta} v\,d\theta+A. \tag{2}$$

When $t = +0$, $\theta = \theta_0$, $v = \dot{\theta} = 0$, so $A = -2(F\theta_0 + a \cos \theta_0)$, and (2) becomes

$$v^2 = 2\{F(\theta - \theta_0) + a(\cos \theta - \cos \theta_0)\} - 4\kappa \int_{\theta_0}^{\theta} v \, d\theta. \tag{3}$$

The critical condition entails $v = 0$, so that F and θ must be determined to satisfy

$$F(\theta - \theta_0) = a(\cos \theta_0 - \cos \theta) + 2\kappa \int_{\theta_0}^{\theta} v \, d\theta, \tag{4}$$

compatible with F having its largest value.

To get a first approximation to $2\kappa \int_{\theta_0}^{\theta} v \, d\theta$, calculate v for a suitable θ-range using the F_c for $\kappa = 0$ in the { } part of (5), § 8.40. Then evaluate the integral numerically, re-calculate v from (3), and compute

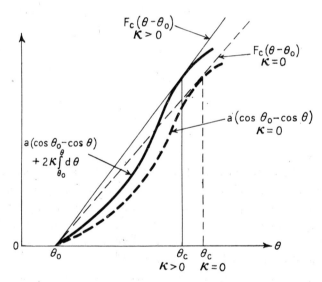

FIG. 81. Illustrating the finding of F_c and θ_c for a damped synchronous motor.

the integral again. Plot the right-hand side of (4) against θ (as in Fig. 81), using a large sheet of paper and suitable scales. Draw the straight line $F(\theta - \theta_0)$ tangential to the curve on the sheet. Approximations to F_c and θ_c will be obtained. Using the new F_c, the above procedure may be repeated. Differentiating F/a in (4) with respect to θ, and equating to zero, F_c is such that θ_c satisfies

$$(\theta-\theta_0)\sin\theta-(\cos\theta_0-\cos\theta)-2(\kappa/a)\int_{\theta_0}^{\theta}\theta\,dv = 0. \qquad (5)$$

Now κ, a, θ_0 are known constants, while v–θ values have been calculated. Then (5) may be solved approximately for $\theta = \theta_c$ by numerical procedure, and F_c can be calculated from (4).

Singular point of (1). The equation may be written

$$\frac{dv}{d\theta} = \frac{-a\sin\theta+F-2\kappa v}{v}. \qquad (6)$$

If $F = a\sin\theta_2$ in $0 < \theta_2 < \frac{1}{2}\pi$, the singular point has the same coordinates as that in § 8.42. By §§ 9.20, 9.22, the singularity is a stable spiral point about which the rotor oscillation subsides ultimately (see Fig. 74).

8.50. The heavy elastica.

The problem of the elastica mentioned in Chapter I and solved in §§ 3.180–3.183 was originally an academic one. It has, however, emerged from the academical archives, and the basic idea is now of service in industry. Herein we shall consider an application to determine the 'handle' of cloth in the clothing trade, and the 'feel' of leather in the leather trade. In years gone by, the essential qualities of these materials have been assessed entirely by persons with considerable aptitude, and experience in their purchase and use in manufacture. Instruments now exist for measuring and comparing cloths or leathers to a high degree of accuracy. The mathematical problem is to calculate particulars pertaining to the shape of a strip of material, uniform in breadth and thickness, when supported in certain ways and deformed by its own weight. Two arrangements are illustrated in Figs. 82, 83, namely, the cantilever

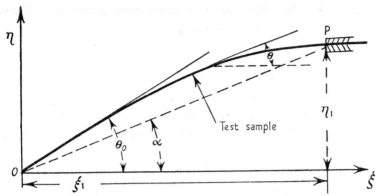

FIG. 82. Illustrating form taken when material clamped in a 'flexometer' bends
due to its own weight.

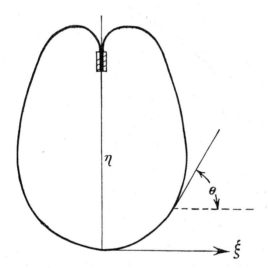

FIG. 83. Illustrating 'heart' loop used in testing flimsy fabrics.

and the heart loop. Herein we shall consider the former only. The
latter is used for flimsy materials like thin silk.

8.51. The differential equation [16]. Let

$B = EI =$ flexural rigidity of strip,

$w =$ weight per unit length,

$c = B^{\frac{1}{3}}w^{-1}$, defined as the 'bending length',

$s =$ arc length measured from a convenient origin,

θ = angle between tangent to bent strip and the horizontal,

x, y = rectangular coordinates $\left.\begin{array}{l}\\\\\\\\\\\end{array}\right\}$

S = shearing force

T = tension $\qquad$ at any point in the strip width.

M = bending moment

We also take the non-dimensional quantities $\sigma = s/c, \xi = x/c, \eta = y/c,$ $\tau = T/cw, \mu = M/c^2w$. The subscript 0 denotes the value of a quantity

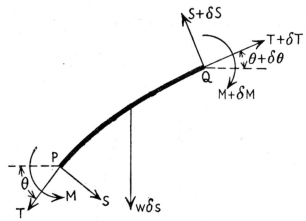

FIG. 84. Forces and moments diagram for element of heavy elastica.

at the origin of coordinates. It has been found by experiment that the curvature of the strip is directly proportional to the bending moment. Thus we have

$$d\theta/ds = M/B. \tag{1}$$

The forces acting on an elemental length of strip δs are depicted in Fig. 84. One condition for equilibrium is that the algebraic sum of the horizontal and vertical forces must vanish independently. For the former

$$\delta(T\cos\theta)-\delta(S\sin\theta) = 0, \tag{2}$$

so $\qquad T\cos\theta - S\sin\theta = T_0,$ a constant, $\tag{3}$

namely, the tension at the origin. For the vertical forces

$$\delta(T\sin\theta)+\delta(S\cos\theta) = w\,\delta s, \tag{4}$$

so $\qquad T\sin\theta + S\cos\theta = ws + S_0, \tag{5}$

where S_0 is the shearing force at the origin. The other condition for equilibrium is that the algebraic sum of the moments about any

point in a cross-section must vanish. Taking moments about P in Fig. 84,
$$M+\delta M = M-S\,\delta s, \qquad (6)$$
so
$$-S = dM/ds. \qquad (7)$$

Multiplying (5) by $\cos\theta$, (3) by $\sin\theta$, and subtracting the second from the first yields
$$-S = T_0\sin\theta-(S_0+ws)\cos\theta. \qquad (8)$$

Equating the right-hand sides of (7), (8) leads to
$$dM/ds = T_0\sin\theta-(S_0+ws)\cos\theta. \qquad (9)$$

Then from (1), (9) we obtain the general differential equation for the bent strip, namely,
$$B\,d^2\theta/ds^2-T_0\sin\theta+(S_0+ws)\cos\theta = 0. \qquad (10)$$

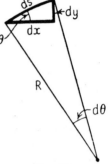

In the cases considered hereafter, $S_0 = 0$, so in terms of the non-dimensional symbols given above, the non-linear equation to be solved is
$$\frac{d^2\theta}{d\sigma^2}-\tau_0\sin\theta+\sigma\cos\theta = 0. \qquad (11)$$

Having found θ as a function of σ, numerically or otherwise, the values of ξ and η may be calculated as follows: from Fig. 85 we have
$$dx/ds = \cos\theta, \qquad (12)$$

Fig. 85.

and since $\sigma = s/c$,
$$\xi = x/c = \int\cos\theta\,d\sigma. \qquad (13)$$

Also
$$dy/ds = \sin\theta, \qquad (14)$$

so
$$\eta = y/c = \int\sin\theta\,d\sigma. \qquad (15)$$

8.52. Solution for cantilever. The specimen is clamped as shown diagrammatically in Fig. 82, the centre line of the clamp being horizontal. The specimen is allowed to sag freely, and the angle α between the chord and the horizontal is measured. Taking the origin as shown, $T_0 = S_0 = 0$, so (11), § 8.51, reduces to
$$d^2\theta/d\sigma^2+\sigma\cos\theta = 0. \qquad (1)$$

Also $M_0 = 0$, so $(d\theta/ds)_{s=0} = 0$, and, therefore, $(d\theta/d\sigma)_{\sigma=0} = 0$. This is one boundary condition at the free end of the strip, the other being $\theta = \theta_0$, $\sigma = 0$. By Maclaurin's theorem
$$\theta(\sigma) = \theta(0)+\sigma\theta'(0)+\frac{\sigma^2}{2!}\theta''(0)+\frac{\sigma^3}{3!}\theta'''(0)+\dots. \qquad (2)$$

Inserting the second boundary condition into (1), gives

$$\theta''(0) = 0. \tag{3}$$

Differentiating (1), we have

$$\theta''' = -\cos\theta + \sigma\theta'\sin\theta. \tag{4}$$

Inserting both boundary conditions into (4), we get

$$\theta'''(0) = -\cos\theta_0. \tag{5}$$

Continuing in this way, we find that $\theta^{(4)}(0) = \theta^{(5)}(0) = 0$, and

$$\theta^{(6)}(0) = -2\sin 2\theta_0. \tag{6}$$

Substituting from above into (2) yields the approximate solution

$$\theta \simeq \theta_0 - \frac{\sigma^3}{3!}\cos\theta_0 - \frac{2\sigma^6}{6!}\sin 2\theta_0. \tag{7}$$

Taking $\theta_0 = 10° \simeq 0{\cdot}1745^r$, we find that $\cos\theta_0 \simeq 0{\cdot}9848$, and $\sin 2\theta_0 \simeq 0{\cdot}3424$. Inserting these in (7), with $\theta = 0$ at the clamp, we obtain

$$\sigma_1^3 \simeq 1{\cdot}059, \quad \text{so} \quad \sigma_1 \simeq 1{\cdot}019. \tag{8}$$

The next step is to make a table of values of σ and θ using (7). From this table, the integrals (13), (15), § 8.51, for ξ_1 and η_1 may be computed by aid of Simpson's rule. Then in Fig. 82 the clamping point can be located, giving $\alpha = \tan^{-1}(\eta_1/\xi_1)$. In the above case $\alpha \simeq 7{\cdot}5°$, a value which should be checked by the reader as an exercise.

The angle at O in Fig. 82 is θ_0, and at P it is zero. The shape of the curve delineating the strip is unknown, but its length l is always measured before the bending test is made, and since $\sigma = s/c$, we have

$$l = c\int_0^{\sigma_1} d\sigma = c\sigma_1. \tag{9}$$

Hence the bending length is given by

$$c = l/\sigma_1. \tag{10}$$

8.53. Solution for larger values of θ_0. An additional term involving σ^9 in the series for θ at (7), § 8.52, may be found as shown in that section. This will enable σ_1 to be calculated up to $\theta_0 = 70°$ with an accuracy of 1 per cent. thereat, the accuracy increasing with decrease in θ_0. For greater accuracy a method of numerical integration may be used, e.g. that demonstrated in § 8.35 (see also references 15, 190, 211). The data in Table 5 are taken from reference [16], the computation being to an accuracy greater than that needed in practice, where 1 per cent. is probably adequate.

TABLE 5

Showing σ_1, α for various values of θ_0.

θ_0^0	σ_1^3	σ_1	α
10	1·0582	1·0190$_5$	7° 30·4′
20	2·1850	1·2976$_4$	15° 2·9′
30	3·4632	1·5129$_6$	22° 39·9′
40	5·0113	1·7112$_6$	30° 24·5′
50	7·0257	1·9152$_7$	38° 21·0′
60	9·8896	2·1464$_8$	46° 35·2′
70	14·5246	2·4398$_8$	55° 20·6′

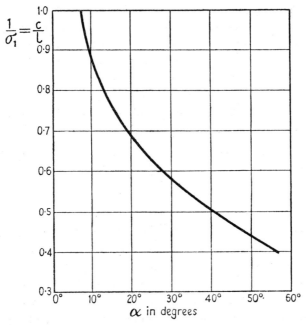

FIG. 86. Graph for obtaining the 'bending length' of a piece
of fabric or leather.

Having obtained a series of values of σ_1 and θ_0, a graph of $\sigma_1^{-1} = cl^{-1}$ and α is plotted as illustrated in Fig. 86. Then for a given l_1, if the angle measured on the testing machine is α_1, the corresponding value of σ_1 may be read off the graph. The 'bending length'

$$c_1 = l_1 \sigma_1^{-1}, \tag{1}$$

is an index of the quality of the material.

CHAPTER IX

SINGULAR POINTS OF DIFFERENTIAL EQUATIONS OF THE FIRST ORDER: STABILITY CRITERIA: FOUR THEOREMS

9.10. Introduction. Whenever possible, it is expedient to ascertain the type of solution of a non-linear differential equation before trying to solve it. The purpose of the present chapter is to assist in this direction. Stability criteria are provided by aid of which the behaviour of certain physical systems representable by second-order differential equations (including those for loss-free and for damped oscillations) may be determined. The equation is reduced to one of the first order, and application of the criteria frequently provides the desired information. Theorems 1, 2 in § 9.50 may be useful in some cases, while for certain driven systems, Theorems 3, 4 will be of value in determining whether or not the solution is periodic.

Definition. The type of equation to be considered may be written in the form [116, 192]

$$dv/dy = P(y, v)/Q(y, v), \tag{1}$$

P and Q being functions of (y, v). If $P(y_1, v_1) = Q(y_1, v_1) = 0$, the slope of the v–y curve is indeterminate, and the point (y_1, v_1) is defined to be a singular point of (1). If $Q(y, v) \to 0$ as (y_1, v_1) is approached, but $P(y_1, v_1) \neq 0$, the point (y_1, v_1) is not regarded as a singular one, although $dv/dy \to \infty$. Any non-singular point is called an *ordinary* or a *regular* point of the equation. If we write $v = dy/dt$, (1) becomes an equation of the second order in y, t. If it represents a physical system, the singularities of (1) are associated with equilibrium positions of the system, either stable or unstable, as the case may be.

9.11. Types of singularity [116, 192]

1°. *Nodes.* A node is a singular point of an equation of the type (1) § 9.10, which the v–y curves (sometimes called trajectories) either (i) start from or (ii) terminate at. In the first case the node is said to be unstable, but stable in the second. Several simple equations will now be considered.

We commence with the equation

$$dv/dy = v/y. \tag{1}$$

Here $P = v$, $Q = y$, and at the origin $P = Q = 0$. Then the right-hand side of (1) takes the indeterminate form $0/0$, so the origin is a singular point.

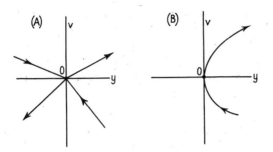

FIG. 87. A. Unstable node at origin if (y_0, v_0) is in quadrants 1 or 3. Stable node at O if (y_0, v_0) is in quadrants 2 or 4. B. When $0 < \mu < 1$, unstable (stable) node at O if (y_0, v_0) is in quadrants 1 or 4. The arrows indicate the 'direction' of the v–y curve for t increasing.

Integrating (1) we obtain $v = my$. With $v = dy/dt$, the y–t solution is $y = Ae^{mt}$, where A and m are arbitrary constants, taken to be real. Thus $v = Ame^{mt} = my$. If $A > 0$ when $t = 0$, and $m > 0$, the initial conditions point $(y(0) = y_0, v(0) = v_0)$ lies within† the first quadrant, so y and v increase with increase in t, which entails an unstable node at O. If $A < 0$ when $t = 0$, and $m > 0$, the point (y_0, v_0) lies within the third quadrant, so y and v increase negatively (decrease) with increase in t, which entails an unstable node at O. In both cases the v–y curves are straight lines having positive slopes m, and they are directed away from O in the first and third quadrants, as shown in Fig. 87 A.

If $A > 0$ when $t = 0$, and $m < 0$, (y_0, v_0) lies within the fourth quadrant, so y decreases but v increases (decreases negatively) with increase in t. If $A < 0$ when $t = 0$, and $m < 0$, (y_0, v_0) lies within the second quadrant, so y increases (decreases negatively) but v decreases with increase in t. In both cases the v–y curves are straight lines having negative slopes, and they are directed towards O, as shown in Fig. 87 A. The origin is a stable node. Hence for equation (1), the type of node depends upon the location of the initial conditions point (y_0, v_0).

Modification of equation (1). Multiplying the right-hand side by $\mu > 0$, but $\neq 1$, we obtain

$$dv/dy = \mu v/y. \tag{2}$$

† 'within' signifies that points on the coordinate axes are excluded.

When $y = v = 0$, $dv/dy = 0/0$, so the origin is a singular point. Integrating (2) yields

$$v = Ay^\mu, \tag{3}$$

A being a real constant. Taking $v = dy/dt$ and integrating (3) leads to

$$y^{1-\mu} = (1-\mu)(At+B), \tag{4}$$

which is a convenient form for $0 < \mu < 1$. When $\mu > 1$,

$$y^{\mu-1} = -1/(\mu-1)(At+B) \tag{5}$$

is a convenient form.

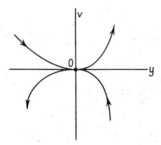

FIG. 88. μ an integer $\geqslant 2$, node at O: stability as for Fig. 87 A.

In the range $0 < \mu < 1$, μ is non-integral, and since A is to be real, we must have $y > 0$ for the reality of v. Thus $y_0 > 0$, so (y_0, v_0) must lie within quadrants one or four. From (3), $A = v_0/y_0^\mu$, which has the sign of v_0, while by (4), $B = y_0^{1-\mu}/(1-\mu) > 0$. Inserting these values into (4) leads to

$$y^{1-\mu} = y_0^{1-\mu} + (1-\mu)v_0 t/y_0^\mu. \tag{6}$$

If (y_0, v_0) lies within the first quadrant, $y_0, v_0 > 0$, and by (3), (6), both v and $y \to +\infty$ with t. The v–y curves have the form depicted in Fig. 87 B. They are tangential to the v-axis and directed away from O, which is an unstable node. If (y_0, v_0) lies within the fourth quadrant, $y_0 > 0$, $v_0 < 0$, and by (3), (6), both v and $y \to 0$ as $t \to y_0/(\mu-1)v_0$. The v–y curves (Fig. 87 B) are directed towards O, which is a stable node. They are tangential to the v-axis.

When $\mu > 1$, it may be either integral or non-integral. Using the initial conditions, (5) becomes

$$y^{\mu-1} = y_0^\mu/\{y_0 - (\mu-1)v_0 t\}. \tag{7}$$

For μ integral $\geqslant 2$, we deduce from (3) and (7) that if (y_0, v_0) lies within either the first or the third quadrant, both v and $y \to \infty$ as $t \to y_0/(\mu-1)v_0$. Thus O is an unstable node. If (y_0, v_0) lies within either the second or the fourth quadrant, both v and $y \to 0$ as $t \to \infty$, so the origin is a stable node. The v–y curves are depicted in Fig. 88, being tangential to the y-axis.

When $\mu > 1$ is non-integral, there are no v–y curves in quadrants 2 and 3, since $y > 0$ for the reality of A. The curves in the other quadrants have the form illustrated in Fig. 88.

Finally, we consider the equation

$$dv/dy = (y+v)/y, \qquad (8)$$

which has a singular point at $y = v = 0$. It may be written

$$\frac{d}{dy}(v/y) = \frac{1}{y}. \qquad (9)$$

Integrating and using the initial conditions leads to

$$v = y\{c_0 + \log(y/y_0)\}, \qquad (10)$$

where $c_0 = v_0/y_0$, and $y/y_0 > 0$ for the reality of v. Taking $v = dy/dt$ and integrating (10) yields

$$y = (e^{-c_0}/y_0)\exp\{c_0 e^t\}. \qquad (11)$$

It may be deduced from (10) and (11) that the origin is a node. If (y_0, v_0) lies within either the second or the fourth quadrant, the node is stable, but it is unstable if (y_0, v_0) lies within either of the other quadrants.

Physical considerations. Equation (1) may be written

$$v\frac{dv}{dy} - \frac{v^2}{y} = 0, \quad \text{so} \quad \frac{d^2y}{dt^2} - \left(\frac{v}{y}\right)\frac{dy}{dt} = 0. \qquad (12)$$

Lack of a control term $f(y)$ entails absence of oscillation in a physical system. If (y_0, v_0) lies within either the first or the third quadrant, the damping *coefficient* $v/y > 0$, which entails a negative resistance effect, and y increases monotonically with increase in t. Moreover, the origin is an unstable node. If (y_0/v_0) lies within either the second or the fourth quadrant, $v/y < 0$, the damping *coefficient* is positive, and y decreases monotonically with increase in t. The origin is now a stable node.

In the absence of a control term, stability at a node usually depends upon the location of (y_0, v_0). When the differential equation has both damping and control terms, the type of stability *at a node* is independent of (y_0, v_0). For instance (3), 3°, § 9.11 has a stable node at the origin if $\kappa^2 > a > 0$, and then the v–y curves enter O as $t \to \infty$, whatever the location of (y_0, v_0). Reference may be made also to Figs. 28 c and 107.

General remarks relating to nodes

Quadrant 1. If a v–y curve passes out of O, $dv/dy \geqslant 0$ initially. But y and $v = dy/dt > 0$, so that y increases with increase in t, and the y–t solution is unstable. Hence O is an unstable node. A curve cannot enter O if $dv/dy > 0$, since this would entail both y and v decreasing with increase in t, which is impossible with $v > 0$. Hence a v–y curve *cannot enter* O within the first quadrant.

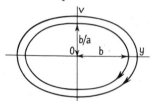

Fɪɢ. 89. The origin is a focal point or centre, which is enclosed by the v–y curves. The y–t curve is periodic. *In all diagrams,* the positive direction (for t-increasing) is clockwise: also $v' = (dv/dt)/(dy/dt) = \ddot{y}/\dot{y}$, and $v' = 0$, $v \neq 0$ entails the acceleration y being zero.

Quadrant 2. If a v–y curve enters O, $dv/dy \leqslant 0$ finally. But $y < 0$ and $v > 0$, so that y decreases negatively with increase in t. Hence O is a stable node. A curve cannot leave O if $dv/dy < 0$, since this would entail y decreasing and v increasing with increase in t, which is impossible with $v > 0$. Hence a v–y curve *cannot leave* O within the second quadrant.

Quadrant 3. Same conclusion as for quadrant 1.

Quadrant 4. Same conclusion as for quadrant 2.

It follows that a *stable* node must be approached within either the second or the fourth quadrant, while recession from an *unstable* node must occur within either the first or the third quadrant.

The preceding statements are applicable wherever the node is located in the v–y plane. If it is not at the origin, the quadrants relate to axes through the node which are parallel to the v and y-axes.

2°. *Centres.* In the case of the non-linear equation

$$dv/dy = -y/a^2v, \tag{1}$$

$y = v = 0$ is a singular point. Integrating (1) yields •

$$y^2 + a^2v^2 = b^2, \text{ a constant,} \tag{2}$$

or
$$y^2/b^2 + v^2/(b/a)^2 = 1, \tag{3}$$

so the v–y curves are ellipses with the origin as centre, having semi-axes b, b/a, as shown in Fig. 89. When $b > 0$, no integral curve passes into, or out of, O. The degenerate curve corresponding to $y^2+a^2v^2 = 0$ is at O, which in the present instance is called a *focal* point or *centre*. The motion of a physical system pertaining to (1) is periodic and stable, in virtue of the v–y curves being closed about the *centre*.

Writing $v = dy/dt$, $1/a^2 = \omega^2$ in (1) gives

$$d^2y/dt^2+\omega^2y = 0, \tag{4}$$

of which the complete solution is

$$y = A\cos\omega t+B\sin\omega t \tag{5}$$

$$= C\cos(\omega t-\varphi), \tag{6}$$

with $C = (A^2+B^2)^{\frac{1}{2}}$ and $\varphi = \tan^{-1}(B/A)$. This solution is the displacement–time relationship for a simple undamped mass-spring

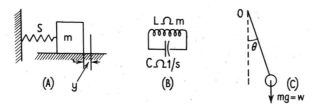

FIG. 90. Illustrating three undamped oscillatory systems, each having one degree of freedom. A. Mass-spring. B. Inductor-capacitor. C. Simple pendulum.

system (Fig. 90 A), or the quantity–time relationship for a loss-free L, C circuit (Fig. 90 B), or the angular displacement–time relationship for a simple pendulum with small amplitude (Fig. 90 C). The *centre* corresponds to the central position of rest, which is a position of stable equilibrium, since after displacement either way, the system tends to return to this position.

3°. *Spiral points.* The non-linear equation

$$dv/dy = (-y+v)/(y+v) \tag{1}$$

has a singular point at $y = v = 0$. Using the procedure in 2°, § 2.11,† in terms of r, θ coordinates, the integral curves are logarithmic spirals defined by

$$\log r = \theta+A, \quad \text{or} \quad r = ae^\theta. \tag{2}$$

Through each point in the y–v plane, except the origin, there passes *only one* curve of the family (obtained by assigning real positive

† With v for y, y for x, and $-\theta$ for θ as in Fig. 106. The altered sign of θ is due to the direction of rotation in the v–y diagrams being clockwise: because y decreasing corresponds to $dy/dt = v$ being negative.

values to a). The curves *spiral away* from O with increase in θ (Fig. 91). Accordingly the origin is called a *spiral* point. The criteria in § 9.20

FIG. 91. The origin is an unstable spiral point; $\kappa < 0$. The y–t curve is oscillatory and its amplitude increases with increase in time.

may be used to show that it is an *unstable* spiral point. Consider the linear equation

$$\ddot{y} + 2\kappa\dot{y} + ay = 0 \qquad (a, \kappa > 0). \tag{3}$$

With $v = dy/dt$, we get

$$d^2y/dt^2 = dv/dt = (dv/dy)(dy/dt) = v\, dv/dy.$$

Thus

$$v\, dv/dy = -(ay + 2\kappa v), \tag{4}$$

and, therefore,

$$dv/dy = -(ay + 2\kappa v)/v, \tag{5}$$

so the origin $y = v = 0$ is a singular point. The formal solution of (3) for $a > \kappa^2$ and $\alpha = \sqrt{(a - \kappa^2)}$ is

$$y = Ce^{-\kappa t}\cos(\alpha t - \varphi) \to 0 \tag{6}$$

as $t \to +\infty$. If $a < \kappa^2$ and $\beta = \sqrt{(\kappa^2 - a)}$, the formal solution is

$$y = e^{-\kappa t}(A\cosh\beta t + B\sinh\beta t) \to 0 \tag{7}$$

as $t \to +\infty$, since $\kappa > \beta$. In both cases y and v decrease with increase in t, and the v–y curve spirals *towards* the origin in the first case, but enters it as $t \to +\infty$ in the second (Fig. 92 A, B). This feature indicates stability in a physical system.

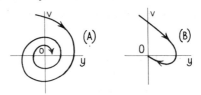

FIG. 92. A. The origin is a stable spiral point, $0 < \kappa^2 < a$, $\kappa > 0$. The y–t curve is oscillatory and its amplitude decreases with increase in time. B. The origin is a stable node which the v–y curve enters as $t \to +\infty$, $0 < a < \kappa^2$. The y–t curve is non-oscillatory. *In general*, when a v–y curve intersects the y-axis, $v = 0$, and a physical system would be at rest momentarily. If v' is infinite, y is then either a maximum or a minimum according as $y > $ or < 0.

If $\kappa < 0$, e.g. a negative resistance effect in an electrical system, the integral curve for $a > \kappa^2$ will spiral *outwards* with increase in t, thereby indicating that the system represented by the differential equation is unstable. (See Fig. 91.)

4°. *Cols.* Next we deal with the equation

$$dv/dy = -\mu v/y,\qquad(1)$$

where $\mu > 0$, and may be integral or non-integral.

The origin is a singular point. Integrating (1), we·have

$$\int dv/v + \mu \int dy/y = \text{a constant},\qquad(2)$$

so
$$\log(vy^\mu) = \text{a constant},\qquad(3)$$

and, therefore, $vy^\mu = A$, taken to be real.   (4)

For any *ordinary* point (y_0, v_0) such that y_0^μ is real, $A = v_0 y_0^\mu$.

Taking $v = dy/dt$ and integrating (4), we obtain

$$y^{\mu+1} = (\mu+1)(At+B)\qquad(5)$$

$$= y_0^\mu\{y_0 + (\mu+1)v_0 t\},\qquad(6)$$

after using the initial conditions. When μ is an *integer* $\geqslant 1$, y_0^μ is real, and the v–y curves exist in all four quadrants. They have the form

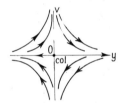

FIG. 93. The origin is a col. μ must be an integer for curves to exist in quadrants 2, 3.

depicted in Fig. 93, being asymptotic to both axes. In virtue of their resemblance to the contour lines for a mountain pass or 'col'—which on occasion may be similar in shape to a saddle, being concave along the horse's back but convex across it—the singularity is called a *saddle point* or *col*.

From (4) and (6) we deduce that if (y_0, v_0) lies within either the first or the third quadrant, $|y| \to \infty$ and $v \to 0$ as $t \to \infty$. If (y_0, v_0) lies within either of the other quadrants, $y \to 0$ and $|v| \to \infty$ as $t \to y_0/-(\mu+1)v_0$.

When $\mu > 0$ is *non-integral*, for the reality of A in (4), y_0 must be greater than 0. Consequently there are then no v–y curves in quadrants 2 and 3.

Physical considerations. Equation (1) may be written

$$v\frac{dv}{dy}+\mu\frac{v^2}{y} = 0, \quad \text{so} \quad \frac{d^2y}{dt^2}+\left(\frac{\mu v}{y}\right)\frac{dy}{dt} = 0, \tag{7}$$

which lacks a control term $f(y)$. The behaviour of a physical system, to which (7) pertains, may be considered in the same way as (12), $1°, \S\,9.11$.

Definition of separatrix. A curve which enters or leaves a col, and constitutes a dividing line or mathematical frontier between stable and unstable regions, is called a *separatrix.* It may be closed as in Fig. 95,

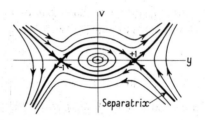

Fig. 94. v–y curves for $\ddot{y}+y-y^3 = 0$. Centre at origin, cols at $y = \pm 1$, $v = 0$. Separatrix enters cols with slope $v' = -2^{\frac{1}{2}}$ and leaves with slope $v' = 2^{\frac{1}{2}}$. The region within the closed part of the separatrix is stable. The regions outside it are unstable. For y–t solution (periodic) see $1°, \S\,3.20$ and Fig. 8 c.

partly open and partly closed as in Fig. 94, or open as in Fig. 101. v–y curves in an unstable region may be closed, e.g. those in Figs. 95, 97 B, which pertain to systems devoid of damping. In Fig. 95, all curves, except the separatrix, correspond to the periodic motion of a physical system, because they are closed. If (y_0, v_0) were located *on* the separatrix, but not at the origin, the system would come to rest at the col as $t \to \infty$. Referring to the f–y curve in Fig. 102 A, over the range $-1 < y < 1$, the control force acts *away* from the col at O, so that the motion *with respect thereto* is unstable. Outside the range $y = (-1, 1)$, the control force acts towards O, so that in

$$-(1+h) \leqslant y \leqslant (1+h) \qquad (h > 0)$$

the motion is periodic. In virtue of the range $-1 < y < 1$, being an unstable one, *by convention* we shall consider the region outside the separatrix (Fig. 102 B) to be unstable also.

Additional examples of cols. The v–y curves in Fig. 94, for the equation

$$dv/dy = -(y-y^3)/v, \tag{8}$$

are more appropriate in regard to the terminology below (6) than those in Fig. 93. There are three points for which the right-hand side of (8) takes the form $0/0$, namely, $y = 0$, ± 1, $v = 0$. The origin is a *centre*, while the points $y = \pm 1$, $v = 0$ are *cols*.

The equation
$$dv/dy = (y-y^3)/v \qquad (9)$$

has singularities at the same points as (8), but in virtue of the positive sign on the right-hand side of (9), the v–y curves take a form different

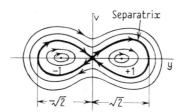

FIG. 95. v–y curves for $\ddot{y}-y+y^3 = 0$. Centres at $y = \pm 1$, $v = 0$, col at origin. The separatrix enters the origin with slope $v' = -1$ and leaves with slope $v' = 1$. The regions within the separatrix are stable, and the y–t solution periodic. The region outside the separatrix is unstable (with regard to the col), but the y–t solution is periodic. For this solution see $3°$, § 3.20 and Fig. 8 E.

from those in Fig. 94. They are portrayed in Fig. 95. Here the origin is a *col*, while the other singular points are *centres*. The curves exterior to the heavy ones in Figs. 94, 95 do not pass through the cols. This is concomitant with instability of the system in the neighbourhoods of the cols, since the potential energy has a maximum value (see § 9.31).

A physical system to which Fig. 94 pertains, has equilibrium positions at $y = 0$, ± 1. Suppose the system starts to move from the col at $y = 1$ with a velocity v_0 (at P_1). The v–y curve through P_1 is such that y increases with increase in t, so the system moves away from the col continually. If the initial velocity is $-v_0$ (at P_2), y will decrease with increase in t, and the system moves away from the col continually. Hence the motion is unstable in both cases.

9.20. Criteria for discriminating between different types of singularities.

Excepting (8), (9) in 4°, § 9.11, the equations dealt with hitherto are mainly particular cases of the type

$$dv/dy = (\alpha y + \beta v)/(\gamma y + \delta v) = (\beta/\delta)\{(\alpha/\beta)y + v\}/\{(\gamma/\delta)y + v\}, \qquad (1)$$

where $\alpha, \beta, \gamma, \delta$ are real constants, and $\alpha, \delta, \alpha\delta-\beta\gamma \neq 0$.† If $\alpha\delta-\beta\gamma = 0$, then $\alpha/\beta = \gamma/\delta$ and (1) becomes $dv/dy = \beta/\delta = c$, giving $y = A + Be^{ct}$, which need not concern us here.

$$\lambda^2 - (\beta+\gamma)\lambda - (\alpha\delta-\beta\gamma) = 0 \qquad (2)$$

is called the *characteristic* equation for (1). It is derived in § 9.41. By hypothesis $\alpha\delta-\beta\gamma \neq 0$, so (2) has no zero root. Solving (2) yields

$$\lambda_1, \lambda_2 = \tfrac{1}{2}\{(\beta+\gamma) \pm [(\beta+\gamma)^2 + 4(\alpha\delta-\beta\gamma)]^{\frac{1}{2}}\} \qquad (3)$$

$$= \tfrac{1}{2}\{(\beta+\gamma) \pm [(\beta-\gamma)^2 + 4\alpha\delta]^{\frac{1}{2}}\} \qquad (4)$$

$$= e \pm h. \qquad (5)$$

As in the case of an ordinary quadratic equation,

$$4h^2 = D = (\beta-\gamma)^2 + 4\alpha\delta$$

is called the *discriminant*. Various cases which arise are as follows:

1°. $D > 0$: (i) If $\alpha\delta-\beta\gamma < 0$, the singularity is a *node*. If $\beta+\gamma < 0$, both λ_1, λ_2 are negative, and the node corresponds to a point of stable equilibrium. The v–y curve moves *towards* the node as t increases. The y–t curve is non-oscillatory. If $\beta+\gamma > 0$, both λ_1, λ_2 are positive and the node corresponds to a point of unstable equilibrium. The v–y curve moves *away* from the node as t increases.

(ii) If $\alpha\delta-\beta\gamma > 0$, λ_1 is positive, λ_2 is negative, and the singularity is a *col* irrespective of the sign or value of $\beta+\gamma$. Under certain conditions this entails instability. See last paragraph of 4°, § 9.11.

2°. $D = 0$: Then $\lambda_1, \lambda_2 = \tfrac{1}{2}(\beta+\gamma)$, and the singularity is a *node*. $\beta+\gamma < 0$ corresponds to stability and $\beta+\gamma > 0$ to instability. The y–t curve is non-oscillatory.

3°. $D < 0$: Then $D^{\frac{1}{2}}$ is imaginary.

(i) If $\beta+\gamma = 0$, λ_1, λ_2 are both imaginary, and the singularity is a *focal point* or *centre*, which implies periodic motion and stability. The v–y curves enclose the singularity. They are closed. The y–t curve is oscillatory and periodic.

(ii) If $\beta+\gamma < 0$, λ_1, λ_2 are complex conjugate, both having negative real parts, and the singularity is a *stable spiral* point. The v–y curves spiral inwards, with increase in t, to the singularity. y, $v \to 0$ as $t \to +\infty$. The y–t curve is a damped oscillation.

---

† In (1) and (2), 1°, § 9.11, $\alpha = \delta = 0$ and $\beta\gamma > 0$. The consequence of α, δ being zero is stated in the last paragraph of § 9.20. In (1), 4°, § 9.11, $\alpha = \delta = 0$ but $\beta\gamma < 0$, and the type of singularity differs from that when $\beta\gamma > 0$.

(iii) If $\beta+\gamma > 0$, λ_1, λ_2 are complex conjugate, both having positive real parts, and the singularity is an *unstable spiral* point. The v–y curves spiral outwards, with increase in t, away from the singularity. y, $v \to \infty$ as $t \to +\infty$. The y–t curve is oscillatory, and the amplitude increases with increase in t.

It will be seen that for stability $\beta+\gamma < 0$, and for instability $\beta+\gamma > 0$, except in (ii), 1°. The sign of $\beta+\gamma$ as a stability criterion *for nodes*, is based upon the hypothesis that α and δ are non-zero. If α and/or $\delta = 0$, while $\beta\gamma > 0$, stability depends upon the location of the initial conditions point (y_0, v_0). This is considered in 1°, § 9.11. The numerator and denominator of the expression $(\alpha y+\beta v)/(\gamma y+\delta v)$ in (1) must not be multiplied by -1, because this would alter the sign of $\beta+\gamma$, thereby entailing a change in the stability. From (1) we deduce that if $\gamma = 0$, the v–y curves cross the y-axis ($v = 0$) orthogonally, and the v-axis ($y = 0$) with slope β/δ, which vanishes when $\beta = 0$.

9.21. Examples

1°. The linear equation

$$\ddot{y}+2\kappa\dot{y}+ay = 0 \quad (a > 0) \tag{1}$$

pertains to either a simple L, C, R electrical circuit or a mass-spring system with viscous damping.† If $\kappa > 0$, the damping is positive, whereas if $\kappa < 0$ it is negative. In the first case the system is stable, but in the second it is unstable.

Then from (5), 3°, § 9.11,

$$dv/dy = -(ay+2\kappa v)/v, \tag{2}$$

and the origin $y = v = 0$ is the only singular point of the equation. (2) has the form (1), § 9.20, with $\alpha = -a$, $\beta = -2\kappa$, $\gamma = 0$, $\delta = 1$. Thus

$$\left.\begin{aligned} \alpha\delta-\beta\gamma &= -a < 0 \\ D &= (\beta-\gamma)^2+4\alpha\delta = 4(\kappa^2-a) \\ \beta+\gamma &= -2\kappa \end{aligned}\right\} \tag{3}$$

(i) If $\kappa^2 > a$, $D > 0$, and by 1°, § 9.20, the origin is a node, stable if $\kappa > 0$, unstable if $\kappa < 0$.

(ii) If $\kappa^2 = a$, $D = 0$, and by 2°, § 9.20, the origin is a node, stable if $\kappa > 0$, unstable if $\kappa < 0$.

(iii) If $\kappa^2 < a$, $D < 0$, and by 3°, § 9.20, the origin is a *spiral* point, stable if $\kappa > 0$, unstable if $\kappa < 0$. See Figs. 92 A, 91, respectively.

† See Fig. 2.

2°. The linear equation [187]

$$\ddot{\theta}+2\kappa\dot{\theta}-a\theta = 0 \quad (\kappa, a > 0), \tag{1}$$

with θ small, pertains to the directional stability of a ship set on a definite course with its rudder amidships. 2κ is the positive damping coefficient, and $-a\theta$ represents the control torque, which is negative for θ positive. Thus the ship deviates from its course and the equilibrium is unstable. The torque may be represented more accurately by $-a\theta+b\theta^3$, so that when $\theta > \sqrt{(a/b)}$ it is positive.

With $v = d\theta/dt$, (1) gives

$$v\,dv/d\theta = a\theta - 2\kappa v, \tag{2}$$

so
$$dv/d\theta = (a\theta - 2\kappa v)/v, \tag{3}$$

and $\theta = v = 0$ is a singular point. Here $\alpha = a$, $\beta = -2$, $\gamma = 0$, $\delta = 1$. Then

$$\left.\begin{aligned}
\alpha\delta - \beta\gamma &= a > 0 \\
D = (\beta-\gamma)^2 + 4\alpha\delta &= 4(\kappa^2+a) > 0 \\
\beta+\gamma &= -2
\end{aligned}\right\}, \tag{4}$$

and

so by (ii) in 1°, § 9.20, the singularity is a *col*.

9.22. Extension of (1), § 9.20 [116, 192].

Hitherto we have been concerned with singularities which arise in this type of equation, where y, v occur to the first power only. Poincaré investigated the *criteria* when the equation takes the form

$$dv/dy = [\alpha y + \beta v + P_1(y, v)]/[\gamma y + \delta v + Q_1(y, v)], \tag{1}$$

and has a singular point at $y = v = 0$. If α, δ, $\alpha\delta - \beta\gamma \neq 0$, and P_1, Q_1 are polynomials whose terms take the form $y^2, y^3,..., v^2, v^3,..., yv, y^2v,...,$ there being no constant terms,† the criteria set out in § 9.20 are valid,‡ *with one exception*. In (i), 3°, § 9.20, the condition $\beta+\gamma = 0$ is not sufficient to discriminate between a *centre* and a *spiral point*, and an auxiliary test is needed [258 a]. For instance, if it can be shown that the v–y curves are closed and contain the singularity, it is a *centre*. Additional information is given in § 9.23.

---

† This restriction applies at the origin $y = v = 0$. If the origin is moved to the singular point and no constant terms occur, the criteria may be applied then. (See § 9.24.)

‡ As the origin is approached, higher order terms become negligible in comparison with those of the first order.

9.23. Examples

1°. Consider (1), § 3.10, namely,

$$d^2y/dt^2+ay+by^3 = 0 \quad (a, b > 0). \tag{1}$$

Then
$$v \, dv/dy = -(ay+by^3), \tag{2}$$

$$dv/dy = -(ay+by^3)/v, \tag{3}$$

and $P_1(y, v) = -by^3$, $Q_1(y, v) = 0$. The origin $y = v = 0$ is a singular point, since the right-hand side of (3) takes the indeterminate form 0/0.

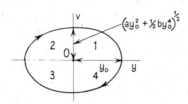

Fig. 96. Typical v–y curve for $\ddot{y}+ay+by^3 = 0$, with initial conditions point $(y_0, v_0 = 0)$. The resulting motion of a physical system is unaffected by the position of (y_0, v_0) on the curve. The origin is a centre. For y–t solution (always periodic for $a, b > 0$) see § 3.14, 2°, § 3.20, and Fig. 8 D.

In accordance with § 9.20 we have $\alpha = -a, \beta = \gamma = 0, \delta = 1$. Thus

$$\left.\begin{aligned}\alpha\delta-\beta\gamma &= -a < 0 \\ D = (\beta-\gamma)^2+4\alpha\delta &= -4a < 0 \\ \beta+\gamma &= 0\end{aligned}\right\}. \tag{4}$$

while

This exemplifies the exceptional case cited in § 9.22, and the singularity is either a centre or a spiral point. In (1) the control term is $f(y) = ay+by^3$, so that $df/dy = a > 0$ at the origin, which by § 9.30 is a centre. Alternatively, the v–y relationship may be used. Integrating (2), we obtain

$$\tfrac{1}{2}v^2 = A_1-\tfrac{1}{2}ay^2-\tfrac{1}{4}by^4, \tag{5}$$

where A_1 is the constant of integration. Let the initial conditions (at $t = 0$) be $y = y_0 \neq 0, v = 0$. Then

$$A_1 = \tfrac{1}{2}ay_0^2+\tfrac{1}{4}by_0^4, \text{ the initial potential energy,} \tag{6}$$

and (5) becomes
$$v^2 = a(y_0^2-y^2)+\tfrac{1}{2}b(y_0^4-y^4), \tag{7}$$

so
$$v = \pm[a(y_0^2-y^2)+\tfrac{1}{2}b(y_0^4-y^4)]^{\frac{1}{2}}. \tag{8}$$

In virtue of the duality of sign, the v–y curves are symmetrical about the y-axis. Since v is real, $|y| \leqslant y_0$, and when $y = \pm y_0, v = 0$, so the v–y curves cross the y-axis at only these two points, which are extrema. Also when $y = 0$, $v = \pm(ay_0^2 + \frac{1}{2}by_0^4)^{\frac{1}{2}}$, so the v–y curves cross the v-axis at only these extrema. Hence the singularity cannot be a spiral point, so it must be a centre.

We may proceed also in the following way:

Consider the first quadrant in Fig. 96, where y, v are positive. By (3), dv/dy is negative, while by changing the sign of y, dv/dy is positive, i.e. in the second quadrant. Also for any v, dv/dy is equal but opposite in the two quadrants. Similarly, by changing the sign of v for any y, dv/dy is equal but opposite in quadrants 1, 4, and also in 2, 3. Thus the v–y curves are symmetrical about both axes. Also, when $v \to 0$ for any $y \neq 0$, (3) gives $dv/dy = \infty$, while if $y = 0$ for any $v \neq 0$, $dv/dy = 0$, so the v–y curves cross both axes orthogonally. In addition, v is a continuous function of y in $-y_0 \leqslant y \leqslant y_0$. It follows that the v–y curves are closed about the origin (Fig. 96) which is, therefore, a *centre*. Hence the motion of the system is periodic and stable.

2°. Consider (1), § 3.17, namely

$$d^2y/dt^2 + 2\kappa\, dy/dt + ay + by^3 = 0 \qquad (a, b > 0). \tag{1}$$

Then
$$v\, dv/dy = -(ay + 2\kappa v + by^3), \tag{2}$$

$$dv/dy = -(ay + 2\kappa v + by^3)/v, \tag{3}$$

and
$$P_1(y, v) = -by^3, \qquad Q_1(y, v) = 0.$$

The origin $y = v = 0$ is a singular point, since the right-hand side of (3) takes the indeterminate form $0/0$. Here we have $\alpha = -a$, $\beta = -2\kappa$, $\gamma = 0$, $\delta = 1$. Thus

$$\left.\begin{array}{l} \alpha\delta - \beta\gamma = -a < 0 \\[4pt] D = (\beta - \gamma)^2 + 4\alpha\delta = 4(\kappa^2 - a) \\[4pt] \beta + \gamma = -2\kappa \end{array}\right\}, \tag{4}$$

and

so the motion is stable or unstable according as $\kappa > 0$ or $\kappa < 0$.

(i) If $\kappa^2 > a$, $D > 0$, and the origin is either a stable or an unstable node.

(ii) If $\kappa^2 = a$, $D = 0$, and conclusion (i) applies.

(iii) If $\kappa^2 < a$, $D < 0$, and the origin is either a stable or an unstable spiral point.

3°. *The v–y curves for $\ddot{y} - \epsilon(1 - y^2)\dot{y} + y = 0$, $\epsilon > 0$.* This equation for a thermionic valve oscillator is derived in § 4.10. It may be written

$$y + \dot{v} = \epsilon(1 - y^2)v. \tag{1}$$

In Figs. 58, 60, 61 let $r^2 = y^2 + v^2$, and we get

$$r(dr/dt) = (y+\dot{v})v = \epsilon(1-y^2)v^2, \tag{2}$$

from (1), so

$$dr/dt = \epsilon(1-y^2)v^2/r. \tag{3}$$

Now if $v \neq 0$, $\epsilon v^2/r$ is positive, so the sign of dr/dt is that of $1-y^2$. When $|y| < 1$, $dr/dt > 0$ and r increases with increase in t. If ϵ is small and $|y| \ll 1$ initially, the v-y curve spirals outwards as in Fig. 58. But if $|y| \gg 1$ initially, $dr/dt < 0$ and the curve spirals inwards as in Fig. 58. Since the outgoing and incoming curves cannot intersect, each is asymptotic ultimately to a closed curve, namely, the *limit cycle*, which entails periodic motion.

Singular point. The equation may be written in the form

$$dv/dy = \{-y+\epsilon(1-y^2)v\}/v. \tag{4}$$

Case 1 with $|y| \ll 1$ gives the approximation

$$dv/dy \simeq -(y-\epsilon v)/v, \tag{5}$$

so $y = v = 0$ is a singular point. Here we have $\alpha = -1$, $\beta = \epsilon$, $\gamma = 0$, $\delta = 1$, so

$$\left. \begin{aligned} \alpha\delta - \beta\gamma &= -1 < 0 \\ D = (\beta-\gamma)^2 + 4\alpha\delta &= \epsilon^2 - 4 \\ \beta+\gamma &= \epsilon > 0 \end{aligned} \right\}. \tag{6}$$

and

When $|y| \ll 1$ and $0 < \epsilon < 2$, $D < 0$ and by (ii), 3°, § 9.20, the origin *may be regarded* as an unstable spiral point (see Figs. 58, 60). If $\epsilon > 2$, $D > 0$, and by (i), 1°, § 9.20, the origin *may be regarded* as an unstable node (see Fig. 61).

Case 2 with $|y| \gg 1$ gives the approximation

$$dv/dy \simeq -(y+\epsilon y^2 v)/v, \tag{7}$$

so $y = v = 0$ is a singular point. Then $\alpha = -1$, $\beta = \gamma = 0$, $\delta = 1$, so

$$\left. \begin{aligned} \alpha\delta - \beta\gamma &= -1 < 0 \\ D &= -4 < 0 \\ \beta+\gamma &= 0 \end{aligned} \right\}. \tag{8}$$

and

By § 9.22, the origin is either a centre or a spiral point. To ascertain which, we put the equation in the approximate form

$$\ddot{y} + \epsilon y^2 \dot{y} + y = 0. \tag{9}$$

Then the damping coefficient ϵy^2 is always positive, so it follows by 1°, § 9.50 that $|y|$ decreases with increase in t. Accordingly when $|y| \gg 1$, the origin *may be regarded* as a stable spiral point.

9.24. Change of origin

1°. If (1), § 9.22, takes the form 0/0 for points other than $y = v = 0$, the types of singularity may be determined by moving the origin to each point in turn, and then applying the criteria. As an example consider the equation

$$\frac{d^2y}{dt^2} + 3y - 4y^3 + y^5 = 0. \tag{1}$$

Then $$\frac{dv}{dy} = \frac{-y(y^4 - 4y^2 + 3)}{v} = \frac{-y(y^2 - 1)(y^2 - 3)}{v}, \tag{2}$$

so there are five singular points at $y = 0$, $y = \pm 1$, $y = \pm 3^{\frac{1}{2}}$, $v = 0$, as illustrated in Fig. 97 A. That $y = v = 0$ is a centre may be demonstrated using the procedure in 1°, § 9.23, or by reference to § 9.30.

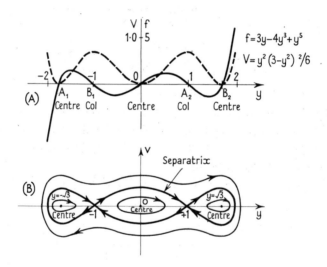

FIG. 97. A. f–y and V–y curves for $\ddot{y} + 3y - 4y^3 + y^5 = 0$. See § 9.31 for definition of V. B. v–y curves for above equation. Centres at $y = 0$, $\pm 3^{\frac{1}{2}}$, $v = 0$; cols at $y = \pm 1$, $v = 0$. Slopes at cols, $v' = \pm 2$.

We now consider the singular point $y = 1$, $v = 0$. For convenience (2) may be written

$$\frac{dv}{dy} = \frac{-y(y+1)(y-1)(y^2 - 3)}{v}. \tag{3}$$

Let $y = \chi + 1$ or $\chi = y - 1$, thereby moving the origin to the singular point. Then

$$\frac{dv}{dy} = \frac{dv}{d\chi} = \frac{-(\chi+1)(\chi+2)\chi(\chi^2+2\chi-2)}{v}$$

$$= \frac{4\chi+8\chi^2-5\chi^4-\chi^5}{v}. \tag{4}$$

Here $\alpha = 4, \beta = \gamma = 0, \delta = 1$, which gives

$$\left.\begin{array}{c} \alpha\delta-\beta\gamma = 4 \neq 0 \\ D = (\beta-\gamma)^2+4\alpha\delta = 16 > 0 \\ \beta+\gamma = 0 \end{array}\right\}, \tag{5}$$

and

so by 1°, § 9.20, the singular point is a *col*. The other singular points may be treated in the same way.

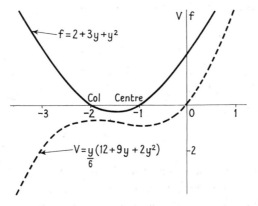

FIG. 98. f–y and V–y curves for $\dot{y}+2+3y+y^2 = 0$. See § 9.31 for definition of V.

Slope of v–y curve on entering and leaving col. Since the right-hand side of (4) is indeterminate when $\chi = v = 0$, we apply l'Hospital's rule, and obtain

$$v'_\chi(0) = \left[\frac{4+16\chi-20\chi^3-5\chi^4}{v'}\right]_{\chi=0} = \frac{4}{v'_\chi(0)}, \tag{6}$$

so

$$v'_y(1) = v'_\chi(0) = \pm 2. \tag{7}$$

The slope of the curve on leaving the col at $y = 1, v = 0$ ($\chi = 0$, $v = 0$) is 2, and -2 on entering it.

2°. When either $P_1(y, v)$, $Q_1(y, v)$ in (1), § 9.22, or both of them, have constant terms, Poincaré's criteria are inapplicable. For, if we put $y = v = 0$, dv/dy does not have the form $0/0$. If there are one or more singular points, their types may be determined by moving the origin to each point in turn, and then applying the criteria.

For the equation
$$\frac{d^2y}{dt^2} + 2 + 3y + y^2 = 0, \tag{1}$$

we have
$$\frac{dv}{dy} = \frac{-(y+1)(y+2)}{v}, \tag{2}$$

so there are singular points at $y = -1$, $y = -2$, $v = 0$, as illustrated in Fig. 98. To determine the type of singularity at $y = -2$, $v = 0$, let $y = \chi - 2$ or $\chi = y + 2$, thereby moving the origin to it. Then by (2),
$$\frac{dv}{dy} = \frac{dv}{d\chi} = \frac{\chi - \chi^2}{v}, \tag{3}$$

so $\alpha = 1$, $\beta = \gamma = 0$, $\delta = 1$. Accordingly
$$\left.\begin{array}{r}\alpha\delta - \beta\gamma = 1 \neq 0 \\ D = (\beta - \gamma)^2 + 4\alpha\delta = 4 > 0 \\ \beta + \gamma = 0 \end{array}\right\}, \tag{4}$$
and

so by 1°, § 9.20, the singular point is a *col*. Moving the origin to the singular point $y = -1$, $v = 0$, we get
$$\frac{dv}{dy} = \frac{dv}{d\chi} = \frac{-(\chi + \chi^2)}{v}, \tag{5}$$

which exemplifies the exceptional case cited in § 9.22, when the criteria fail. Using the procedure in 1°, § 9.23, or by reference to 1°, § 9.30, the singular point is found to be a *centre*.

9.25. Vibration problem introducing change of origin.
Hitherto we have considered free oscillations of systems in which the position of statical equilibrium was $y = 0$, e.g. using an equation of the type
$$m\ddot{y} + s_1 y + s_3 y^3 = 0 \qquad (s_1, s_3 > 0). \tag{1}$$
If, however, the spring control (or its equivalent) is strained initially, a constant term occurs on the right-hand side of (1), and the statical equilibrium position is moved from O to P, as illustrated in Fig. 99. The free oscillation will now occur over a range of the f–y curve where its slope—and, therefore, the spring stiffness—differs from that of the initially unstrained spring, and the control is asymmetrical.

Suppose that the spring is anchored at one end, and hangs with its axis vertical. A weight $w = mg$ is put on the free end, being supported so that the spring is unstrained (neglecting its own weight). If w is

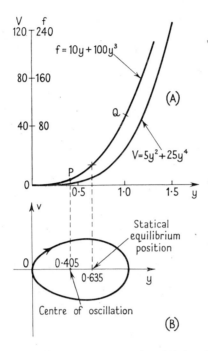

FIG. 99. $f–y$, $V–y$, and $v–y$ curves for $\ddot{y}+10y+100y^3 = 32$. The position of statical equilibrium $y = \theta = 0.635$, $v = 0$ is a centre. See § 9.31 for definition of V.

released at $t = 0$, determine its subsequent motion. Neglecting the inertia of the spring, the differential equation is

$$m\ddot{y}+s_1 y+s_3 y^3 = mg, \qquad (2)$$

so

$$\ddot{y}+ay+by^3 = g, \qquad (3)$$

where $a = s_1/m$, $b = s_3/m$, and y is the displacement *below* the initial position.

Let $y = x+\theta$, $\theta > 0$, and we get

$$\ddot{x}+a(x+\theta)+b(x^3+3x^2\theta+3x\theta^2+\theta^3) = g, \qquad (4)$$

or

$$\ddot{x}+a_1 x+b_1 x^2+c_1 x^3 = 0, \qquad (5)$$

where $a_1 = a+3b\theta^2$, $b_1 = 3b\theta$, $c_1 = b$, $b\theta^3+a\theta-g = 0$. Since $a, b, g > 0$, the latter equation in θ has only one real root, which is the (positive) value of y when $\ddot{y} = 0$, i.e. the new statical equilibrium position. Since x represents the vertical displacement relative thereto, the control characteristic $f(x) = a_1 x + b_1 x^2 + c_1 x^3$ differs from that when $f(y) = ay + by^3$.

Writing $\dot{x} = v_x$, (5) becomes

$$v_x \frac{dv_x}{dx} + a_1 x + b_1 x^2 + c_1 x^3 = 0, \tag{6}$$

so

$$\frac{dv_x}{dx} = \frac{-x(a_1 + b_1 x + c_1 x^2)}{v_x}. \tag{7}$$

By §§ 9.20, 9.22, $x = v_x = 0$ is a singular point of (7), and it is the only one, since $c_1 x^2 + b_1 x + a_1 = 0$ has no real roots. Applying the criteria in §§ 9.20, 9.22, we have $\alpha = -a_1, \beta = \gamma = 0, \delta = 1$, so

$$\left.\begin{array}{c} \alpha\delta - \beta\gamma = -a_1 < 0 \\ \beta + \gamma = 0 \\ D = (\beta - \gamma)^2 + 4\alpha\delta = -4a_1 < 0 \end{array}\right\}. \tag{8}$$

and

Hence by § 9.22 the singularity is either a centre or a spiral point. Writing $\dot{y} = v$, $\ddot{y} = v\, dv/dy$ and integrating (3), we obtain

$$\tfrac{1}{2}v^2 + \tfrac{1}{2}ay^2 + \tfrac{1}{4}by^4 = gy + A, \text{ a constant.} \tag{9}$$

Now when $t = 0, y = 0$, and $v = 0$, so $A = 0$ and the equation of the v–y curve is

$$v = \pm\{y(2g - ay - \tfrac{1}{2}by^3)\}^{\frac{1}{2}}. \tag{10}$$

This indicates two extrema on the positive y-axis in the v–y plane. One is at $y = 0$, the other at $y = h$, the only real root (positive) of $2g - ay - \tfrac{1}{2}by^3 = 0$. The duality of sign in (10) indicates symmetry about the y-axis. Since the v–y curve intersects the y-axis twice only, it follows that the singularity at $y = 0$, $v = 0$ cannot be a spiral point, so it must be a centre. Hence the motion of w is periodic and stable.

We shall now show that h is the largest displacement of w below its initial position $y = 0$, i.e. $x = -\theta$. When $y = h$, V, the potential energy stored in the spring, is equal to that lost by w, i.e. mgh. Also

$$V = \int_0^h (s_1 y + s_3 y^3)\, dy = \tfrac{1}{2}s_1 h^2 + \tfrac{1}{4}s_3 h^4. \tag{11}$$

Equating the two energies gives

$$\tfrac{1}{2}s_1 h^2 + \tfrac{1}{4}s_3 h^4 = mgh, \quad \text{or} \quad \frac{s_1 h}{m} + \frac{s_3 h^3}{2m} = 2g, \tag{12}$$

i.e.

$$2g - ah - \tfrac{1}{2}bh^3 = 0, \tag{13}$$

which is identical with the equation three lines below (10) if h replaces y. The control, v–y, and V–y curves with $a = 10$, $b = 100$— as in § 3.12—are depicted in Fig. 99.

9.26. Solution of (5), § 9.25. Using the method of iteration (see § 4.130), the solution of (5), § 9.25, in the second approximation, is

$$x = -\frac{3b\theta^3}{2\omega^2} - \theta\left(1 - \frac{33b\theta^2}{32\omega^2}\right)\cos\omega t + \frac{b\theta^3}{2\omega^2}\cos 2\omega t - \frac{b\theta^3}{32\omega^2}\cos 3\omega t, \quad (1)$$

where $\omega^2 \simeq a + 15b\theta^2/4$, and $y = x + \theta$.

(1) shows that the 'centre of oscillation' is at a point $3b\theta^3/2\omega^2$ *above* the position of statical equilibrium $x = 0$, i.e. $y = \theta$. This must be so in order that the sum of the kinetic energy of m and the potential energy of the spring at any y shall be equal to mgy, the potential energy lost by w in falling through a vertical distance y. That is to say, (9), § 9.25, in the form

$$\tfrac{1}{2}mv^2 + \tfrac{1}{2}s_1 y^2 + \tfrac{1}{4}s_3 y^4 = mgy, \quad (2)$$

must be satisfied. For a linear spring $s_3 = 0$, so $b = 0$, and the two positions are coincident.

Numerical data. As in § 3.12, take $a = 10$, $b = 100$. Then with $g = 32$ ft. sec.$^{-2}$, we get approximately $\theta = 0\cdot635$, $\omega^2 = 161\cdot5$, $-3b\theta^3/2\omega^2 = -0\cdot23$, $h = 1\cdot024$. Also the respective amplitude ratios of the second and third harmonics to that of the fundamental are $0\cdot16$ and $0\cdot01$.

In the present case, oscillation occurs over an asymmetrical control characteristic (see Fig. 99), whereas in § 3.14 the characteristic is anti-symmetrical about O in Fig. 12 B. The solution in the present case resembles that at (16), § 4.131. It has a prominent second harmonic but a weak third harmonic. There is no second harmonic pertaining to the anti-symmetrical control of Fig. 12 B, and the third harmonic is small compared with the second harmonic pertaining to the asymmetrical control of Fig. 99. As in § 4.130, the 'centre of oscillation' is not at the statical equilibrium point, so a 'rectification' effect occurs. Also, the origin having been moved to $y = \theta > 0$ entails operation over a portion of the characteristic which has a greater average slope (Fig. 99) than that when $\theta = 0$ (Fig. 12 B). Accordingly, although the amplitude of vibration is now only about half the value in § 3.14, ω is greater in the present case. For equal amplitude, the frequency in § 3.14 would be approximately $0\cdot4$ that herein.

9.30. Control characteristic as stability criterion

1°. The differential equation

$$\frac{d^2y}{dt^2}+f(y)=0 \tag{1}$$

may be written

$$\frac{dv}{dy}=\frac{-f(y)}{v}, \tag{2}$$

so the singular points are given by $v = 0$, and those values of y for which $f(y) = 0$. They are located where the control characteristic† intersects (or may be tangential to) the y-axis. At an intersection,

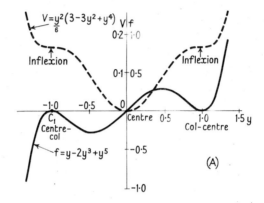

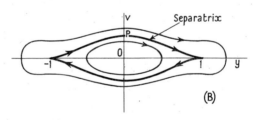

Fig. 100. A. f–y and V–y curves for $\ddot{y}+y-2y^3+y^5 = 0$. See § 9.31 for definition of V. B. v–y curves for above equation. Centre at origin; centre-col at $y = 0$, $v = -1$; col-centre at $y = 0$, $v = 1$.

df/dy is either $> $ or < 0. Since (1) has no term in dy/dt (absence of damping), its singular points must be either centres or cols. The control force tends to move a physical system towards or away from an equilibrium position, according as $df/dy > $ or < 0; so the respective types of singular point are centre and col. These remarks are illustrated in Fig. 97 A, where the two types of singularity are interlaced.

† When the differential equation has the form at (1), $f(y)$—the control characteristic—refers to unit mass in a dynamical system, as is explained in the second footnote on p. 48.

If $f(y)$ has a double zero, the control curve is tangential to the y-axis as in Fig. 100 A. Referring to Fig. 97 A, we may imagine the points A_1 and B_1 to approach each other, and finally to coalesce as in Fig. 100 A at C_1. This mixed type of singular point may be regarded as a centre-col, or a col-centre according as $f(y)$ is a maximum or a minimum. Poincaré's criteria are inapplicable here.

The v–y curves corresponding to $f(y)$ in Fig. 97 A are depicted in Fig. 97 B, all of them being closed. The curve passing round the centres and through the cols is the separatrix. It enters a col as $t \to +\infty$, and a physical system to which (1) pertained would come to rest, the force acting on it then being zero. For this to happen, the initial conditions point (y_0, v_0) must be *on* the separatrix. Apart from the separatrix, the motion corresponding to any v–y curve is periodic. The closer the curves are to the separatrix, the longer is the periodic time.

Equation of separatrix for (1), 1°, § 9.24. Integrating (2), 1°, § 9.24, we obtain

$$\int v \, dv = A_1 - \int (3y - 4y^3 + y^5) \, dy, \tag{3}$$

so
$$v^2 = A - 3y^2 + 2y^4 - \tfrac{1}{3}y^6. \tag{4}$$

At the col, $y = 1$, $v = 0$, which gives $A = \tfrac{4}{3}$, and, therefore,

$$v^2 = \tfrac{1}{3}(4 - 9y^2 + 6y^4 - y^6), \tag{5}$$

which is the required equation. Application of l'Hospital's rule for $y = 1$ to (3), 1°, § 9.24, gives $v'^2 = 4$, so $v'(1) = \pm 2$ as at (6), 1°, § 9.24.

v–y curves for Fig. 100 A. These are shown in Fig. 100 B, and as before, all of them are closed. The two outer lobes of the separatrix in Fig. 97 B are evanescent, and the separatrix terminates at the cols, where it has cusps. Applying the procedure in the preceding paragraph to the differential equation $\ddot{y} + y - 2y^3 + y^5 = 0$, the equation of the separatrix is found to be

$$v^2 = \tfrac{1}{3}(1 - y^2)^3, \tag{6}$$

while the slope at each cusp is given by

$$v'^2 = [-1 + 6y^2 - 5y^4]_{y=1} = 0. \tag{7}$$

Time of entry of separatrix to col-centre. From (6), taking the positive root,
$$3^{\frac{1}{2}} v = (1 - y^2)^{\frac{3}{2}}, \tag{8}$$

so with $v = \dfrac{dy}{dt}$, $3^{\frac{1}{2}} \displaystyle\int \frac{dy}{(1 - y^2)^{\frac{3}{2}}} = t + B$, a constant,   (9)

and, therefore, $3^{\frac{1}{2}} y / (1 - y^2)^{\frac{1}{2}} = t + B.$ (10)

5077

At P in Fig. 100 B, $y = 0$, so if $t = 0$, we get $B = 0$ and, therefore,

$$3y^2 = t^2(1-y^2), \tag{11}$$

or
$$y = t/(3+t^2)^{\frac{1}{2}} \to 1, \tag{12}$$

as $t \to +\infty$, using the positive root of (11). Hence the separatrix and, therefore, the physical system represented by the differential equation $\ddot{y}+y-2y^3+y^5 = 0$, tends to the col-centre as $t \to +\infty$.

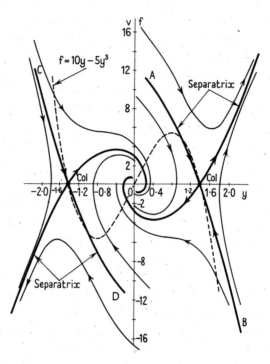

FIG. 101. f–y, and v–y curves for $\ddot{y}+\dot{y}+10y-5y^3 = 0$. Stable spiral point at origin; cols at $v = 0$, $y = \pm 2^{\frac{1}{2}}$. Stable region lies between the branches AB, CD of the separatrix.

2°. The differential equation

$$\frac{d^2y}{dt^2} + 2\kappa\frac{dy}{dt} + f(y) = 0 \tag{1}$$

may be expressed in the form

$$\frac{dv}{dy} = \frac{-f(y)-2\kappa v}{v}. \tag{2}$$

Obviously the coordinates of the singular points $f(y) = 0$, $v = 0$ are unaffected by presence of the term $-2\kappa v$. Hence they may be determined by the methods described above. Except in the case of a *col*—which in accordance with (ii), 1°, § 9.20, is not affected by the term $2\kappa v$—the *type* of singularity depends upon κ. If $\kappa > 0$, it may be either a stable spiral point or a stable node, according as $\kappa >$ or $<$ some positive quantity κ_1, which latter depends upon $f(y)$. If $\kappa < 0$, the foregoing is true, but the points are now unstable. The type of singularity may be determined by aid of Poincaré's criteria.

By way of illustration, let $f(y) = ay - by^3$, with a, b, $\kappa > 0$, and (2) becomes

$$\frac{dv}{dy} = \frac{-y(a - by^2) - 2\kappa v}{v}, \tag{3}$$

so there are three singular points at $y = 0$, $y = \pm(a/b)^{\frac{1}{2}}$, $v = 0$. Then, for the point $y = v = 0$,

$$\alpha = -a, \quad \beta = -2\kappa, \quad \gamma = 0, \quad \delta = 1$$

so

$$\alpha\delta - \beta\gamma = -a < 0, \qquad \beta + \gamma = -2\kappa \tag{4}$$

and

$$D = (\beta - \gamma)^2 + 4\alpha\delta = 4(\kappa^2 - a) \geqslant 0 \text{ or } < 0$$

according as $\kappa \geqslant$ or $< a^{\frac{1}{2}}$. If $\kappa \geqslant a^{\frac{1}{2}} > 0$, by 1°, § 9.20 and § 9.22, the origin is a stable node, whereas if $0 < \kappa < a^{\frac{1}{2}}$, it is a stable spiral point. The singular point is an unstable one if $\kappa < 0$. By moving the origin to each of the points $y = \pm(a/b)^{\frac{1}{2}}$, $v = 0$ in turn—as in § 9.24—it is found that they are cols. This may be checked by the reader as an exercise. v-y curves for $\kappa = 0\cdot5$, $a = 10$, $b = 5$ are shown in Fig. 101. Instability occurs unless the curve spirals towards O. Compare with Fig. 94.

9.31. Potential energy as stability criterion.

The potential energy associated with the control in (1), 1°, § 9.30, is

$$V = \int_0^y f(y)\, dy,$$

and by 1°, § 9.30, the singular points where $f(y) = 0$, $v = 0$ correspond to $dV/dy = 0$, $v = 0$, i.e. the maxima and minima of the V-y curve. If $df/dy = d^2V/dy^2 > 0$, by 1°, § 9.30, the singular point is a centre, while if $df/dy = d^2V/dy^2 < 0$, it is a col. Thus a minimum of V corresponds to a centre, and a maximum to a col. In Fig. 100 A, the point C_1, at which the f-y curve is tangential to the y-axis, corresponds to a minimum-maximum of V (a point of inflexion), and the singularity is a centre-col.

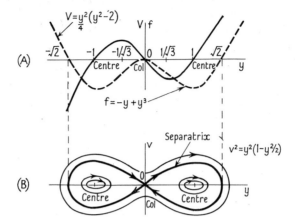

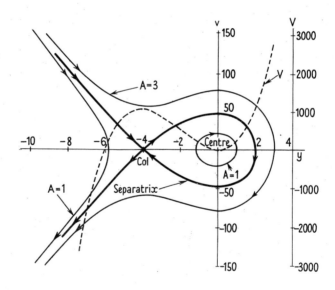

FIG. 102. A. f–y, and V–y curves for $\ddot{y}-y+y^3 = 0$. B. v–y curves for above equation. Col at origin; centres at $y = \pm 1$, $v = 0$.

FIG. 103. f–y, V–y, and v–y curves for $\ddot{y}+400y+100y^2 = 0$.

$$V = 200y^2(1+y/6), \quad v = \pm 20\{(A^2-y^2)+\tfrac{1}{8}(A^3-y^3)\}^{\frac{1}{2}}, \quad A = 1, 2, 3.$$

All v–y curves intersect the $+y$ and v-axes orthogonally. If $A < 2$ the v–y curves intersect the $-y$ axis orthogonally. Separatrix enters and leaves col with slopes $v' = \mp 20$. See §§ 4.130, 4.131 for y–t solution.

The V–y curves relating to

$$\ddot{y}+3y-4y^3+y^5 = 0 \quad \text{and} \quad \ddot{y}+y-2y^3+y^5 = 0$$

are displayed in Figs. 97 A, 100 A, while the f–y, v–y, and V–y curves for $\ddot{y}-y+y^3 = 0$ and $\ddot{y}+400y+100y^2 = 0$ are shown in Figs. 102, 103. The approximate solution of $\ddot{y}-y+y^3 = 0$ for stable periodic oscillation about either $y = \pm1$ (which correspond to the respective v–y curves within the separatrix), may be obtained after moving the origin to the point (centre) in question. (See §§ 9.25, 9.26.)

Although the *coordinates* of the singular points of (1), 2°, § 9.30, may be determined on a potential-energy basis, Poincaré's criteria must be used (as in 2°, § 9.30) to determine the *type* of singularity.

Equation for .v–y curves in Fig. 102 B.

$$\ddot{y}-y+y^3 = 0, \tag{1}$$

so
$$v\,dv/dy-y+y^3 = 0. \tag{2}$$

Integrating, we obtain

$$v^2-y^2+\tfrac{1}{2}y^4 = A, \text{ a constant.} \tag{3}$$

If the initial conditions point is $y = y_0$, $v = v_0$, then

$$A = v_0^2-y_0^2+\tfrac{1}{2}y_0^4, \tag{4}$$

so from (3), (4) we get the equation for the v–y curves, namely,

$$v^2 = v_0^2-(y_0^2-y^2)+\tfrac{1}{2}(y_0^4-y^4). \tag{5}$$

The extrema on the y-axis are obtained from (5) with $v = 0$. Thus

$$y^4-2y^2-2A = 0, \quad \text{so } y^2 = 1\pm(1+2A)^{\frac{1}{2}}, \tag{6}$$

and, therefore,
$$y = \pm[1\pm(1+2A)^{\frac{1}{2}}]^{\frac{1}{2}}, \tag{7}$$

the minus sign outside the radical being discarded when $A > 0$.

9.40. Linear transformation.

To derive (2) in § 9.20 and the stability criteria which follow, it is expedient to apply a linear transformation to (1) in § 9.20. For real variables this is equivalent (in effect) to referring points in the v–y plane to oblique instead of rectangular axes. The scheme is depicted in Fig. 104, where the rectangular coordinates of P are y and v.

Then

$$OM = y_1 = R\cos(\theta-\psi) = R(\cos\theta\cos\psi + \sin\theta\sin\psi) \tag{1}$$
$$= y\cos\psi + v\sin\psi; \tag{2}$$
$$ON = v_1 = R\cos(\phi-\theta) = R(\cos\theta\cos\phi + \sin\theta\sin\phi) \tag{3}$$
$$= y\cos\phi + v\sin\phi. \tag{4}$$

To avoid OY_1 and OV_1 being collinear, $\psi \neq \phi$. (2) and (4) may be written in the form

$$y_1 = py+qv \left.\right\}$$
and $$v_1 = ry+sv \left.\right.$$ (5)

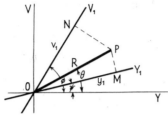

Fig. 104. Diagram illustrating oblique coordinate axes. $OP = R, y = R \cos \theta$,
$v = R \sin \theta$.

Since $\psi \neq \phi$, it follows that $p/q \neq r/s$. (5) constitutes a linear transformation since all variables occur to the first power. In (5), $|p|$, etc., $\leqslant 1$; nevertheless the transformation is still linear if these quantities are unrestricted but finite.

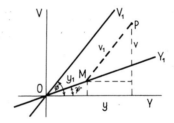

Fig. 105. Diagram illustrating oblique coordinate axes which differ from those of Fig. 104.

In Fig. 104 the coordinates y_1, v_1 are obtained by dropping perpendiculars from P on the axes OY_1, OV_1. However, in the conventional oblique coordinates, they are taken parallel to the axes. Thus in Fig. 105, $y_1 = OM$, and $v_1 = MP$, so

$$y = y_1 \cos \psi + v_1 \cos \phi,$$ (6)
and $$v = y_1 \sin \psi + v_1 \sin \phi.$$ (7)

Solving (6), (7) for y_1 and v_1, we obtain

$$y_1 = \frac{y \sin \phi}{\sin(\phi-\psi)} - \frac{v \cos \phi}{\sin(\phi-\psi)}$$ (8)

and $$v_1 = -\frac{y \sin \psi}{\sin(\phi-\psi)} + \frac{v \cos \psi}{\sin(\phi-\psi)}.$$ (9)

(8), (9) have the same form as (2), (4), and constitute a linear transformation.

9.41. Derivation of (2), § 9.20. In the following discussion, y
and v are real variables, $\dot{y} = dy/dt = v$, while p, q, r, s, are unrestricted
finite numbers. Differentiating both sides of the relationships in (5)
§ 9.40 with respect to t, gives

$$\left.\begin{array}{l} p\ddot{y}+q\dot{v} = \dot{y}_1 \\ r\ddot{y}+s\dot{v} = \dot{v}_1 \end{array}\right\}, \tag{1}$$

and

y_1 and v_1 being unrestricted. Suppose that $y_1 = Ae^{\lambda_1 t}$, $v_1 = Be^{\lambda_2 t}$,
where A, B are real constants, while λ_1 and λ_2 are either real or complex
constants to be determined later. Then by aid of (5) § 9.40, we have

$$\left.\begin{array}{l} \dot{y}_1 = \lambda_1 y_1 = \lambda_1(py+qv), \quad \text{and} \quad \dot{v}_1 = \lambda_2 v_1 = \lambda_2(ry+sv) \\ \dfrac{\dot{v}_1}{\dot{y}_1} = \dfrac{dv_1}{dy_1} = \dfrac{\lambda_2 v_1}{\lambda_1 y_1} \end{array}\right\}. \tag{2}$$

so

From (1) and the upper line of (2), we get

$$p\ddot{y}+q\dot{v} = \lambda_1(py+qv) \tag{3}$$

and

$$r\ddot{y}+s\dot{v} = \lambda_2(ry+sv). \tag{4}$$

Now take

$$\dot{v} = \alpha y+\beta v, \quad \text{and} \quad \dot{y} = \gamma y+\delta v, \tag{5}$$

so that

$$\frac{\dot{v}}{\dot{y}} = \frac{dv}{dy} = \frac{\alpha y+\beta v}{\gamma y+\delta v}, \tag{6}$$

as in (1) § 9.20. Substituting for $\ddot{y}$ and $\dot{v}$ from (5) into (3), (4), we obtain

$$p(\gamma y+\delta v)+q(\alpha y+\beta v) = \lambda_1(py+qv), \tag{7}$$

and

$$r(\gamma y+\delta v)+s(\alpha y+\beta v) = \lambda_2(ry+sv). \tag{8}$$

Equating coefficients of y, v on both sides of (7), with α, δ, p, q non-zero,
yields

$$p(\lambda_1-\gamma)-q\alpha = 0 \quad \text{and} \quad p\delta-q(\lambda_1-\beta) = 0, \tag{9}$$

so

$$(\lambda_1-\gamma)/\alpha = q/p = \delta/(\lambda_1-\beta), \tag{10}$$

which leads to the quadratic equation

$$\lambda_1^2-(\beta+\gamma)\lambda_1-(\alpha\delta-\beta\gamma) = 0. \tag{11}$$

In like manner, from (8), with α, δ, r, s non-zero, we obtain (11) with
λ_2 for λ_1. Hence for (2), (3) to hold, λ_1 and λ_2 must be roots of the
characteristic equation

$$\lambda^2-(\beta+\gamma)\lambda-(\alpha\delta-\beta\gamma) = 0. \tag{12}$$

From § 9.20,

$$D = (\beta-\gamma)^2+4\alpha\delta, \tag{13}$$

with

$$\alpha, \delta, \text{ and } \alpha\delta-\beta\gamma \neq 0. \tag{14}$$

9.42. Application of § 9.41 with $\alpha, \delta \neq 0$

1°. If $D > 0$, $\beta + \gamma \neq 0$, $\alpha\delta - \beta\gamma < 0$, then λ_1 and λ_2 are real, unequal, but have the same sign. Thus the second line of (2), § 9.41, has the same form as (2), 1°, § 9.11, with $\mu = \lambda_2/\lambda_1$, so the origin in the v_1-y_1 plane is a node. To investigate stability, we use the relationships

$$y_1 = A e^{\lambda_1 t} \quad \text{and} \quad v_1 = B e^{\lambda_2 t}, \tag{1}$$

from § 9.41. When $\beta + \gamma < 0$, $\lambda_2 < \lambda_1 < 0$, so that y_1 and $v_1 \to 0$ as $t \to \infty$. Hence $y_1 = v_1 = 0$ is a stable node. In virtue of (5), § 9.40 being a linear transformation, $y = v = 0$ in (6), § 9.41 is also a stable node. When $\beta + \gamma > 0$, $\lambda_1 > \lambda_2 > 0$, so $|y_1|$ and $|v_1| \to \infty$ with t. Hence $y_1 = v_1 = 0$ is an unstable node, as also is $y = v = 0$. These two cases pertain to 1°, (i), § 9.20.

2°. If $D > 0$, $\alpha\delta - \beta\gamma > 0$, then $\lambda_1 > 0$ and $\lambda_2 < 0$ independent of the sign of $\beta + \gamma$. In this case (2), § 9.41, has the same form as (1), 4°, § 9.11, so the singularity at $y_1 = v_1 = 0$, and, therefore, that of (6), § 9.41 at $y = v = 0$ is a col.

3°. If $D = 0$, $\lambda_1 = \lambda_2 = \frac{1}{2}(\beta + \gamma)$, so from 1° above it follows that the singularity of (6), § 9.41 at $y = v = 0$ is a node, stable if $\beta + \gamma < 0$, but unstable if $\beta + \gamma > 0$.

9.43. Complex roots of (2), § 9.20. When $D < 0$,

$$D^{\frac{1}{2}} = i\{-[(\beta - \gamma)^2 + 4\alpha\delta]\}^{\frac{1}{2}}$$

is imaginary. Taking $\{\ \}^{\frac{1}{2}} = f > 0$, we have $\lambda_1 = e + if$ and $\lambda_2 = e - if$, which are complex conjugate. For $\beta + \gamma = 0$, $e = 0$, so λ_1, λ_2 are then imaginary conjugate. From (5), § 9.40, we obtain

$$y = C(sy_1 - qv_1), \tag{1}$$

and

$$v = C(pv_1 - ry_1), \tag{2}$$

where $C = 1/(ps - qr)$. Thus

$$\frac{\dot{v}}{\dot{y}} = \frac{dv}{dy} = \frac{p\dot{v}_1 - r\dot{y}_1}{s\dot{y}_1 - q\dot{v}_1}. \tag{3}$$

Since p, q, r, s are unrestricted, we shall write $p = i, r = -i, q = s = 1$. Inserting these, and also the values of $\dot{y}_1, \dot{v}_1$ from (2), § 9.41 into (3), yields

$$\frac{dv}{dy} = \frac{i(\lambda_1 y_1 + \lambda_2 v_1)}{(\lambda_1 y_1 - \lambda_2 v_1)}. \tag{4}$$

Substituting for y_1, v_1 from (5), § 9.40, and using the above values of $p, \ldots, s$, gives

$$\frac{dv}{dy} = \frac{(\lambda_2 - \lambda_1)y + i(\lambda_2 + \lambda_1)v}{i(\lambda_2 + \lambda_1)y - (\lambda_2 - \lambda_1)v}. \tag{5}$$

From above, $\lambda_2 + \lambda_1 = 2e$, $\lambda_2 - \lambda_1 = -2if$, so (5) becomes

$$\frac{dv}{dy} = \frac{-fy + ev}{ey + fv} = \frac{-y + kv}{ky + v}, \tag{6}$$

where $k = e/f$. Then (6) has the same form as (1), § 9.20 and (6), § 9.41.

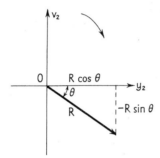

Fig. 106. Illustrating polar coordinates R, θ. The rotation of R is clockwise, which corresponds to t increasing, as in the case of v–y curves.

To determine the type of singularity in (6), when $y = v = 0$, we ascertain the type of curve the D.E. represents. Writing $y = R \cos \theta$, $v = -R \sin \theta$, as in Fig. 106, leads to

$$dR/d\theta = kR, \tag{7}$$

so

$$\log R = k\theta + A_1 \quad \text{or} \quad R = Ae^{k\theta}, \tag{8}$$

which is the formula for a logarithmic spiral. The curve spirals towards or away from the origin, according as $k < 0$ or > 0. Since $k = e/f$, and $f > 0$, it follows that for stability $e < 0$, while for instability $e > 0$. Referring to (4), § 9.20, we see that the former entails $\beta + \gamma < 0$, and the latter $\beta + \gamma > 0$, which correspond, respectively, to (ii), (iii), in 3°, § 9.20.

It is not permissible to write (6) in the form

$$\frac{dy}{dv} = \frac{y - kv}{-(ky + v)}, \tag{9}$$

because this alters the sign of k, thereby entailing a change from stability to instability or vice versa.

Finally when $e = 0$, we get $k = 0$, and $\lambda_1 = if$, $\lambda_2 = -if$, so (6) reduces to

$$\frac{dv}{dy} = -\frac{y}{v}.$$

(10)

Integrating (10) leads to

$$v^2 + y^2 = a^2,$$

(11)

the equation of a circle having centre O. Hence by $2°$, § 9.11, the origin is a 'centre', so the y–t solution is stable and periodic.

9.50. Four theorems

$1°$. *Theorem* 1. In the differential equation

$$\frac{d^2y}{dt^2} + g(y)\frac{dy}{dt} + f(y) = 0,$$

(1)

if (i) $g(0) \geqslant 0$, $g(y) > 0$ when $|y| > 0$, (ii) $f(y)$ is odd, continuous, bounded, and > 0 in $0 < y \leqslant l$, while $\int_0^l f(y)\, dy$ exists and tends to infinity with l, then for any initial conditions

$$y(0) = y_0, \qquad \dot{y}(0) = v(0) = v_0,$$

both y and $\dot{y}$ tend to zero as $t \to +\infty$.

Proof. With $v = dy/dt$, (1) may be written

$$v\, dv/dy + g(y)v + f(y) = 0,$$

(2)

so

$$\int v\, dv + \int f(y)\, dy = A - \int g(y)v\, dy,$$

(3)

where A is the constant of integration. Since $dy = v\, dt$, (3) may be expressed in the form

$$\tfrac{1}{2}v^2 + \int^y f(y)\, dy = A - \int_0^t g(y)v^2\, dt = W, \text{ say.}$$

(4)

In virtue of (i), the t-integral is positive; also by (ii), the left-hand side of (4) is positive; while for the initial conditions specified, we have

$$A = \tfrac{1}{2}v_0^2 + \int^{v_0} f(y)\, dy,$$

(5)

so $0 \leqslant W \leqslant A$. When $t \to +\infty$,

(a) if v were oscillatory, the t-integral in (4) would increase without limit, which is impossible, since $0 \leqslant W \leqslant A$;

(b) if v tended to a limit other than zero, y would tend to $-\infty$, which is impossible, since $0 \leqslant W \leqslant A$;

(c) if y tends to a limit, both $\dot{y}$ and $\ddot{y} \to 0$, so by (1) $f(y)$ must do likewise, and in virtue of oddness, $y = 0$. Hence both y and $\dot{y} \to 0$ as $t \to +\infty$. This theorem is applicable to (1), §§ 4.132, 5.13, and (3), § 5.172.

$2°$. *Theorem 2*. In the differential equation

$$\frac{d^2y}{dt^2} + 2\kappa \frac{dy}{dt} + f(y) = 0, \tag{1}$$

if (i) $\kappa > 0$, (ii) $f(y) = ay + by^3 + cy^5 + ...$, $a > 0$, b, c,... $\geqslant 0$, then for any initial conditions $y(0) = y_0$, $\dot{y}(0) = v(0) = v_0$, y is ultimately non-oscillatory provided that $\kappa^2 \geqslant f'(0)$.†

Proof. From (1)

$$\frac{dv}{dy} = v' = \frac{-\{f(y) + 2\kappa v\}}{v}, \tag{2}$$

and in virtue of (ii) the origin $y = v = 0$ is the only singular point. By theorem 1, y and $\dot{y} \to 0$ as $t \to +\infty$. Since y is to be non-oscillatory when $t > t_1$, say, the parameters must be such that the origin is a stable node. Using l'Hospital's rule, (2) gives

$$v'(0) = -f'(0)/v'(0) - 2\kappa, \tag{3}$$

so

$$v'^2(0) + 2\kappa v'(0) + f'(0) = 0, \tag{4}$$

and, therefore,

$$v'(0) = -\kappa \pm \{\kappa^2 - f'(0)\}^{\frac{1}{2}}. \tag{5}$$

Since $v'(0)$ must be real for the v–y curve to enter the origin, it follows that $\kappa^2 \geqslant f'(0)$. Owing to duality of sign in (5), the slope of the v–y curve is ambiguous. This point is considered later.

If $|y_0|$ and/or $|v_0|$ is large enough, the v–y curve will pass round the origin a finite number of times before ultimate entry as $t \to +\infty$. When $\kappa^2 < f'(0)$, the roots of (4) are complex conjugate with negative real parts, the origin is a stable spiral point, and the y–t curve is oscillatory but damped.

By (ii) $f(y)$ has only one real zero, i.e. $y = 0$, but if the signs of a, b, c,... are mixed, $f(y)$ may have an *odd* number of real zeros $\alpha_1, \alpha_2, ..., \alpha_{2n+1}$. Each zero corresponds to a singular point of the equation. If α_1 and α_{2n+1} are either stable spiral points or stable nodes,‡

---

† In a mechanical system, $f'(0)$ is the control stiffness in the central position.

‡ The even zeros $\alpha_2, \alpha_4, ...$ are then cols (see §§ 9.20, 9.22).

then $f'(\alpha_1) > 0$ and $f'(\alpha_{2n+1}) > 0$, and the theorem is valid. The particular spiral point or node in $\alpha_1,..., \alpha_{2n+1}$ towards which the motion tends ultimately, is dependent upon the initial conditions.

If α_1 and α_{2n+1} are cols,† the motion is stable for certain ranges of initial conditions, but otherwise it is unstable.

An exceptional v–y curve. (5) suggests that *when the singular point is a stable node*, the v–y curves which enter it as $t \to +\infty$ may have one of two different slopes. It may be shown that all the v–y curves, except one, enter the node with the same slope. The point at issue may be illustrated in a simple way if we consider the linear differential equation

$$\ddot{y}+2\kappa\dot{y}+ay = 0, \tag{6}$$

under the condition that $\kappa^2 > a > 0$, which entails a non-oscillatory y–t solution. Then

$$\frac{dv}{dy} = v' = \frac{-ay-2\kappa v}{v}, \tag{7}$$

and $y = v = 0$ is the only singular point. Application of l'Hospital's rule yields

$$v'^2(0) = -a-2\kappa v'(0),$$

and, therefore, $\qquad v'(0) = -\kappa \pm \sqrt{(\kappa^2-a)}. \tag{8}$

The y–t solution may be written

$$y = e^{-\kappa t}(Ae^{\beta t}+Be^{-\beta t}), \tag{9}$$

where $\beta = (\kappa^2-a)^{\frac{1}{2}}$, and with non-zero initial conditions $y(0) = y_0$, $\dot{y}(0) = v_0$, (9) yields

$$A+B = y_0, \qquad A(\beta-\kappa)-B(\beta+\kappa) = v_0,$$

so $\quad A = \{v_0+y_0(\beta+\kappa)\}/2\beta \quad$ and $\quad B = \{y_0(\beta-\kappa)-v_0\}/2\beta. \tag{10}$

Now $(dv/dt)/(dy/dt) = \ddot{y}/\dot{y} = dv/dy$, so by aid of (9), (10), we obtain

$$v' = \frac{dv}{dy} = \frac{A(\beta-\kappa)^2+B(\beta+\kappa)^2e^{-2\beta t}}{A(\beta-\kappa)-B(\beta+\kappa)e^{-2\beta t}}. \tag{11}$$

If $A \neq 0$, then as $t \to +\infty$, $v' \to \beta-\kappa = -\kappa+(\kappa^2-a)^{\frac{1}{2}}$, irrespective of the value of B, which may be zero. But if $A = 0$ and $B \neq 0$, then as $t \to +\infty$,

$$v' \to -(\beta+\kappa) = -\kappa-(\kappa^2-a)^{\frac{1}{2}}. \tag{12}$$

---

† The even zeros are then either stable spiral points or stable nodes, according to the value of κ (see §§ 9.20, 9.22).

Moreover, **from (10)**, we get

$$v_0/y_0 = -(\beta+\kappa) = -\kappa-(\kappa^2-a)^{\frac{1}{2}} \quad \text{and} \quad B = y_0. \qquad (13)$$

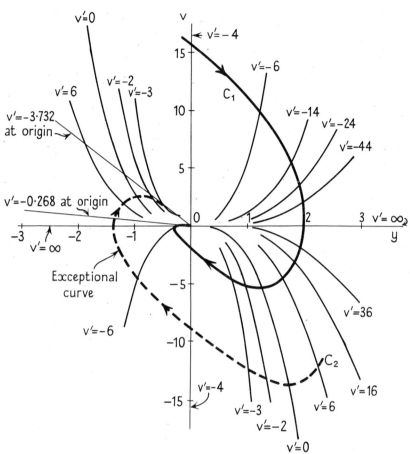

Fig. 107. v–y curves for $\ddot{y}+4\dot{y}+y+10y^3 = 0$ obtained by method of iso-clines described in Chapter VIII. $v = -y(1+10y^2)/(4+v')$. All curves like C_1 enter the origin with slope $v' = -0.268$ as $t \to +\infty$. If the initial con-ditions point (y_0, v_0) lies on C_2, the v–y curve is exceptional and enters the origin with slope $v' = -3.732$ as $t \to +\infty$.

Hence if the initial conditions are such that the point (y_0, v_0) lies on the straight line

$$v = -\{\kappa+(\kappa^2-a)^{\frac{1}{2}}\}y, \qquad (14)$$

this line is the v–y curve, and as $t \to +\infty$ it enters the node with slope $-\{\kappa+(\kappa^2-a)^{\frac{1}{2}}\}$, which differs from that of all other curves, i.e. it is exceptional. If $\kappa < 0$, the exceptional curve *leaves* the node.

Example. We consider the equation

$$\ddot{y}+4\dot{y}+y+10y^3 = 0. \tag{15}$$

Then
$$v' = \frac{-y(1+10y^2)}{v}-4,$$

and by §§ 9.20, 9.22, the origin is a stable node. Applying l'Hospital's rule when $y = v = 0$, we get

$$v'(0) = -\{1/v'(0)\}-4,$$

i.e.
$$v'^2(0)+4v'(0)+1 = 0, \tag{16}$$

which yields

$$v'(0) = -2\pm 3^{\frac{1}{2}} \simeq -0{\cdot}268 \text{ or } -3{\cdot}732. \tag{17}$$

Let (y_0, v_0) be any point near O such that $10y_0^3 \ll y_0$. Then to a close approximation (15) may be written $\ddot{y}+4\dot{y}+y = 0$, which has the form at (6). Thus the analysis between (6) and (15) may be used to show that all the v–y curves, except one, enter O with a slope $-0{\cdot}268$.

Some v–y curves obtained by the method of isoclines, described in Chapter VIII, are depicted in Fig. 107. The exceptional curve (shown broken) may be drawn by starting from the origin with a slope $-3{\cdot}732$, and working backwards.

3°. *Theorem* 3. In the differential equation

$$\frac{d^2y}{dt^2}+g(y,\dot{y})\frac{dy}{dt}+f(y) = E(t), \tag{1}$$

if (i) $E(t)$ is a continuous periodic function of t having period τ, (ii) $f(y)$ and $g(y,\dot{y})$ have first derivatives, (iii) m, n, p, all positive numbers, exist such that

(a) $g(y,\dot{y}) > n > 0$ when $|y|$ and $|\dot{y}| > m$, otherwise $g(y,\dot{y}) > -p$,
(b) $yf(y) > 0$ when $|y| > m$,

(c) $\lim\limits_{|y|\to\infty} |f(y)| = \infty$, so that if $F(y) = \int\limits_0^y f(y)\,dy$, $\lim\limits_{y\to+\infty} \dfrac{f(y)}{F(y)} = 0$,

then (1) has a solution of period τ. The proof is given in [83]. This theorem is applicable to (1) in § 4.140, the equations in §§ 4.16, 4.194, and problems 37, 38 at the end of the book.

4°. *Theorem* 4. In the differential equation

$$\frac{d^2y}{dt^2} + g(y)\frac{dy}{dt} + y = E(t), \tag{1}$$

if (i) $E(t)$ is a continuous periodic function having period τ, (ii) $g(y) > 0$ is continuous except possibly at a finite number of points where $g(y\pm 0)$ exist, (iii) $\int^{\infty} g(y)\, dy = \infty$, or $\int_{-\infty} g(y)\, dy = \infty$, then (1) has a solution of period τ, and all other solutions tend to this one as $t \to +\infty$. The proof is given in [84]. This theorem is applicable to problem 36 at the end of the book.

9.60. Stability of forced oscillations. The differential equation now has a term representing the driving force, which is a function of time. Moreover, the method of investigation as used in § 9.20 et seq. needs modification before it can be applied here. To demonstrate the procedure, we commence with Mathieu's equation, which is linear, namely,

$$\frac{d^2y}{dz^2} + (a - 2q\cos 2z)y = 0, \tag{1}$$

where $z = \omega t$. With q small > 0, the parametric point (a, q) being situated between a_1 and b_1 in Fig. 38, in the first approximation we assume that

$$y = A(z)\cos z + B(z)\sin z. \tag{2}$$

A and B are slowly varying functions of $z = \omega t$, such that

$$A'' \ll A' \ll A \quad \text{and} \quad B'' \ll B' \ll B, \tag{3}$$

but neither A nor B need be oscillatory. From (1), (2), by discarding terms in A'' and B'', we get

$$\left.\begin{aligned}
y'' &= (2B' - A)\cos z - 2(A' + B)\sin z \\
ay &= a(A\cos z + B\sin z) \\
-(2q\cos 2z)y &= -q(A\cos z - B\sin z + A\cos 3z + B\sin 3z)
\end{aligned}\right\}. \tag{4}$$

Equating the coefficients of $\sin z$ and $\cos z$ to zero independently, we find that

$$\sin z: \ -(2A' + B) + (a+q)B = 0, \quad \text{so} \quad 2A' = B(a+q-1), \tag{5}$$

$$\cos z: \ (2B' - A) + (a-q)A = 0, \quad \text{so} \quad 2B' = -A(a-q-1). \tag{6}$$

Hence

$$\frac{dA}{dB} = \frac{B(a+q-1)}{-A(a-q-1)}. \tag{7}$$

We now apply Poincaré's criteria to (7)—which is the differential equation for the variable coefficients A, B in (2)—instead of the equation relating v and y, as in § 9.21. The only singular point is $A = B = 0$. Then we have

$$\alpha = a-1+q, \qquad \beta = \gamma = 0, \qquad \delta = -(a-1-q),$$

so

$$\alpha\delta - \beta\gamma = q^2 - (a-1)^2,$$

$$\beta + \gamma = 0, \tag{8}$$

and

$$D = (\beta - \gamma)^2 + 4\alpha\delta = 4[q^2 - (a-1)^2].$$

If $q > a-1$, i.e. $1+q > a$, or if $q > 1-a$, i.e. $a > 1-q$, then $D > 0$ and $\alpha\delta - \beta\gamma > 0$, so by 1°, (ii), § 9.20, the singular point in the A–B plane at $A = B = 0$ is a col. Hence the motion of a physical system—to which equation (1) pertains—once started from rest, would be unstable. In this case (a, q) lies in the unstable region between a_1 and b_1 in Fig. 38.

Values of $A(z)$ and $B(z)$. From (5) and (6) we find that

$$A = c_1 e^{\mu z} + c_2 e^{-\mu z}, \qquad B = c_3 e^{\mu z} + c_4 e^{-\mu z}, \tag{9}$$

where $\mu^2 = \tfrac{1}{4}\{q^2 - (a-1)^2\}$, the c_r being arbitrary constants. If $1+q > a$, or if $a > 1-q$, $\mu^2 > 0$ and, from (9) and (2), it is evident that y is oscillatory and $\to \pm\infty$ as $z \to +\infty$. If $a > 1+q$, or if $1-q > a$, $\mu = i\beta$ is imaginary and y is oscillatory but bounded. When β is a rational fraction, (2) is periodic, but if β is irrational, (2) is non-periodic. If $q = \pm(a-1)$, $\mu = 0$ and (2) has period 2π in z (see § 7.11).

The analysis given above, although confined to the first approximation, demonstrates that application of Poincaré's criteria to the coefficients A, B leads to the same results as those deducible from Fig. 38.

9.61. Application of § 9.60 to $y'' + 2\kappa y' + (a - 2q \cos 2z)y + by^3 = 0$, $a, b, q, \kappa > 0$. When the point (a, q) lies between a_1 and b_1 in Fig. 38, suppose that, in the first approximation with q *small* > 0, the solution has the form at (2), § 9.60. Then we get

$$\left.\begin{aligned}
y'' &= (2B' - A)\cos z - (B + 2A')\sin z \\
2\kappa y' &= 2\kappa\{(A' + B)\cos z + (B' - A)\sin z\} \\
ay &= a(A \cos z + B \sin z) \\
-(2q \cos 2z)y &= q(-A \cos z + B \sin z - A \cos 3z - B \sin 3z) \\
by^3 &= (3b/4)\{AY^2 \cos z + BY^2 \sin z + \\
&\qquad + A(A^2 - 3B^2)\cos 3z + B(3A^2 - B^2)\sin 3z\}
\end{aligned}\right\} \tag{1}$$

with $Y^2 = A^2 + B^2$. Equating the coefficients of $\sin z$ and $\cos z$ to zero yields

$$\sin z: \quad -(B+2A')+2\kappa(B'-A)+(a+q)B+\frac{3b}{4}BY^2 = 0, \quad (2)$$

$$\cos z: \quad (2B'-A)+2\kappa(B+A')+(a-q)A+\frac{3b}{4}AY^2 = 0. \quad (3)$$

If $A' \gg \kappa B'$ and $B' \gg \kappa A'$, (2), (3) may be written in the approximate forms

$$2A' = B\left(a+q-1+\frac{3b}{4}Y^2\right)-2\kappa A, \quad (4)$$

and

$$2B' = -\left\{2\kappa B+A\left(a-q-1+\frac{3b}{4}Y^2\right)\right\}. \quad (5)$$

Thus

$$\frac{dA}{dB} = \frac{B\{(a+q-1)+(3b/4)(A^2+B^2)\}-2\kappa A}{-[2\kappa B+A\{(a-q-1)+(3b/4)(A^2+B^2)\}]}, \quad (6)$$

and $A = B = 0$ is a singular point in the A–B plane. Then

$$\alpha = (a+q-1), \quad \beta = \gamma = -2\kappa, \quad \delta = -(a-q-1),$$

so

$$\alpha\delta-\beta\gamma = q^2-(a-1)^2-4\kappa^2 > 0,$$

provided that $q > \{(a-1)^2+4\kappa^2\}^{\frac{1}{2}}$, while

$$D = (\beta-\gamma)^2+4\alpha\delta = 4\{q^2-(a-1)^2\} > 0,$$

provided that $a > 1-q$ or $< 1+q$. By 1°, (ii), § 9.20 and § 9.22, the origin is a col, so the motion of a physical system, once started, is unstable (initially at least), because the point (a, q) lies in an unstable region between the curves a_1 and b_1 of Fig. 38.

If we suppose that the motion tends to a steady state as $t \to +\infty$, then A' and $B' \to 0$, while $A \to A_0$, and $B \to B_0$, neither being zero. (4) and (5) become, respectively,

$$B_0\left(a-1+q+\frac{3b}{4}Y_0^2\right)-2\kappa A_0 = 0, \quad (7)$$

and

$$A_0\left(a-1-q+\frac{3b}{4}Y_0^2\right)+2\kappa B_0 = 0, \quad (8)$$

which are identical with (4), (3), § 7.232. Also from (7), § 7.232,

$$\frac{3b}{4}Y_0^2 = \{(1-a)+(q^2-4\kappa^2)^{\frac{1}{2}}\}, \quad (9)$$

with $q > \{(a-1)^2+4\kappa^2\}^{\frac{1}{2}}$, so

$$\frac{3b}{4}Y_0^2+(a-1\pm q) = \pm q+(q^2-4\kappa^2)^{\frac{1}{2}}. \tag{10}$$

From (7), (8), and (10), we get

$$\frac{B_0}{A_0} = \frac{2\kappa}{q+(q^2-4\kappa^2)^{\frac{1}{2}}}, \qquad \frac{A_0}{B_0} = \frac{2\kappa}{q-(q^2-4\kappa^2)^{\frac{1}{2}}}, \tag{11}$$

which yield $\qquad \dfrac{B_0}{A_0}-\dfrac{A_0}{B_0} = -(q^2-4\kappa^2)^{\frac{1}{2}}/\kappa. \qquad (12)$

The singularity at (A_0, B_0). This point is singular in virtue of the assumed ultimate steady state, and the right-hand side of (6) then takes the indeterminate form 0/0. To investigate the singularity, we move the origin there by writing $A = A_0+\zeta$, $B = B_0+\chi$ in (6), which gives

$$\frac{d\zeta}{d\chi} = \frac{\begin{matrix}(B_0+\chi)(a-1+q)-2\kappa(A_0+\zeta)+\\+(3b/4)(B_0+\chi)[(A_0+\zeta)^2+(B_0+\chi)^2]\end{matrix}}{-\{(A_0+\zeta)(a-1-q)+2\kappa(B_0+\chi)+\\+(3b/4)(A_0+\zeta)[(A_0+\zeta)^2+(B_0+\chi)^2]\}}. \tag{13}$$

Using (7), (8), and discarding terms in χ^2, ζ^2, $\chi\zeta$, etc., (13) takes the simpler form

$$\frac{d\zeta}{d\chi} = \frac{\{2\kappa(A_0/B_0)+(3bB_0^2/2)\}\chi-\{2\kappa-(3bA_0B_0/2)\}\zeta}{-\{2\kappa+(3bA_0B_0/2)\}\chi+\{(2\kappa B_0/A_0)-(3bA_0^2/2)\}\zeta}. \tag{14}$$

Thus

$$\alpha = \{(2\kappa A_0/B_0)+(3bB_0^2/2)\}, \qquad \beta = -\{2\kappa-(3bA_0B_0/2)\},$$

$$\gamma = -\{2\kappa+(3bA_0B_0/2)\}, \qquad \delta = \{(2\kappa B_0/A_0)-(3bA_0^2/2)\},$$

so $\qquad\qquad \alpha\delta-\beta\gamma = 3\kappa bY_0^2\left(\dfrac{B_0}{A_0}-\dfrac{A_0}{B_0}\right)$

$$= -3bY_0^2(q^2-4\kappa^2)^{\frac{1}{2}} < 0; \tag{15}$$

by (12), $\qquad\qquad \beta+\gamma = -4\kappa, \tag{16}$

and using (9), (12),

$$D = (\beta-\gamma)^2+4\alpha\delta = 16\kappa^2\left\{5-\frac{q^2+(1-a)(q^2-4\kappa^2)^{\frac{1}{2}}}{\kappa^2}\right\}. \tag{17}$$

Now $D \geqslant 0$ if $5\kappa^2 \geqslant q^2 + (1-a)(q^2-4\kappa^2)^{\frac{1}{2}}$, so by §§ 9.20, 9.22, (A_0, B_0) is a stable node, and the amplitude of the oscillation $Y \to (A_0^2 + B_0^2)^{\frac{1}{2}}$ monotonically as $t \to +\infty$. Also $D < 0$ if $5\kappa^2 < q^2 + (1-a)(q^2-4\kappa^2)^{\frac{1}{2}}$, and (A_0, B_0) is then a stable spiral point, so Y oscillates ultimately with decreasing amplitude about the final value Y_0. Moreover, this behaviour corresponds to the approach to a limit cycle in the v–y plane (see § 8.12). For the reality of (15) and (17), we must have $q > 2\kappa$. Accordingly, the above analysis shows that, in the first approximation, the solution of (1), § 7.232 with $a, b, q, \kappa > 0$ is periodic ultimately, the period being twice that of $\cos 2z$.

Values of A_0, B_0. By definition

$$Y_0^2 = A_0^2\{1 + (B_0/A_0)^2\} = A_0^2\left\{1 + \frac{4\kappa^2}{[q+(q^2-4\kappa^2)^{\frac{1}{2}}]^2}\right\}, \quad \text{from (11)},$$

$$= A_0^2\left\{\frac{2q}{q+(q^2-4\kappa^2)^{\frac{1}{2}}}\right\}, \tag{18}$$

so, by (9),

$$A_0^2 = (2/3bq)\{q+(q^2-4\kappa^2)^{\frac{1}{2}}\}\{(1-a)+(q^2-4\kappa^2)^{\frac{1}{2}}\}. \tag{19}$$

From (11) and (19),

$$B_0^2 = (2/3bq)\{q-(q^2-4\kappa^2)^{\frac{1}{2}}\}\{(1-a)+(q^2-4\kappa^2)^{\frac{1}{2}}\}. \tag{20}$$

If $a = 1$ and $q \gg 2\kappa$, we get

$$|A_0| \simeq (4q/3b)^{\frac{1}{2}}, \quad |B_0| \simeq 2\kappa/(3bq)^{\frac{1}{2}}. \tag{21}$$

The values of A_0, B_0 in (18)–(20) are identical with those of A_1, B_1, respectively, in (2), § 7.232. If $\kappa = 0$, $B_0 = 0$, and the differential equation is that in § 7.230. A_0 in (19) above is then identical with A_1 in (7), § 7.230.

CHAPTER X

FLUID FLOW IN TWO DIMENSIONS

10.1. Potential flow. In this case the following assumptions are made:

   (i) Motion is irrotational, i.e. no vortices occur.

  (ii) Fluid is incompressible, so its density is uniform.

 (iii) Fluid is inviscid, there is absence of loss, and the fluid does not cross a stream line.

Definition. A *stream line* is a curve whose tangent indicates the direction of the resultant velocity of flow of fluid at the point in

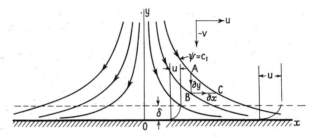

Fig. 108. Diagram illustrating streamlines in fluid flow in two dimensions.

question. Moreover, fluid does not cross a stream line, but follows along it. The stream function $\psi(x, y)$ represents, symbolically, the flux or volume of fluid crossing a curved surface whose base line is in the x–y plane, of unit height perpendicular to that plane, in unit time (Figs. 108, 110). The stream lines are given by ψ = a constant. In virtue of irrotational flow, there is a velocity potential ϕ whose gradients with respect to x and y give the velocities u, v in these directions. The resultant velocity along the stream line is $(u^2 + v^2)^{\frac{1}{2}}$.

Then
$$u = \partial\phi/\partial x \quad \text{and} \quad v = \partial\phi/\partial y. \tag{1}$$

Referring to Fig. 108, u is the velocity of flow perpendicular to $AB = \partial y$, the flux across ∂y is $\partial\psi = u\,\partial y$, so
$$u = \partial\psi/\partial y = \partial\phi/\partial x, \tag{2}$$

Also $-v$ is the velocity of flow perpendicular to $BC = \partial x$, so the flux across it is $\partial\psi = -v\,\partial x$, and, therefore,
$$v = -\partial\psi/\partial x = \partial\phi/\partial y. \tag{3}$$

From (2), (3)

$$\partial\phi/\partial x = \partial\psi/\partial y \quad \text{and} \quad \partial\phi/\partial y = -\partial\psi/\partial x. \tag{4}$$

These are the Cauchy–Riemann conditions for the existence of a 'flow' function such that

$$f(z) = f(x+iy) = \phi(x,y)+i\psi(x,y). \tag{5}$$

In virtue of (4), ϕ and ψ are conjugate functions and satisfy Laplace's equation in two dimensions, i.e. $\nabla^2_{x,y}\phi = \nabla^2_{x,y}\psi = 0$. Also the stream lines $\psi = c_1$, and the equipotential lines $\phi = c_2$ intersect orthogonally.

10.20. Determination of potential and stream functions in plane flow.

Let the flow in the x_1-direction (Fig. 109) have a constant velocity a, then by (2), § 10.1,

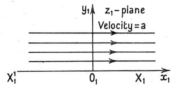

FIG. 109. Diagram illustrating streamlines in fluid flow parallel to X_1-axis, in region $-\infty < x_1 < \infty$, $y_1 \geqslant 0$.

$$\partial\psi_1/\partial y_1 = a, \quad \text{so} \quad \psi_1 = ay_1, \tag{1}$$

and

$$\partial\phi_1/\partial x_1 = a, \quad \text{so} \quad \phi_1 = ax_1, \tag{2}$$

the constants of integration being zero, since

$$\left.\begin{matrix}\psi_1\\\phi_1\end{matrix}\right\} = 0 \quad \text{when} \quad \left.\begin{matrix}y_1\\x_1\end{matrix}\right\} = 0.$$

Thus the flow function is

$$f(z_1) = \phi_1(x,y)+i\psi_1(x,y) = az_1. \tag{3}$$

To determine the flow in the region $y \geqslant 0$, $x \geqslant 0$ (Fig. 110), we use a conformal transformation such that the part of the x_1-axis $O_1 X_1'$ in Fig. 109, becomes the y-axis in Fig. 110. Accordingly we put $z = z_1^{\frac{1}{2}}$ or $z^2 = z_1$, which gives

$$az_1 = a(x^2-y^2)+2iaxy, \tag{4}$$

so the new potential and stream functions are, respectively,

$$\phi = a(x^2-y^2), \tag{5}$$

and

$$\psi = 2axy. \tag{6}$$

The stream lines $\psi = c$ are the rectangular hyperbolae

$$xy = c/2a, \text{ a constant,} \qquad (7)$$

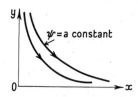

Fig. 110. Diagram illustrating streamlines in fluid flow in region $x \geqslant 0$, $y \geqslant 0$.

while the equipotential lines, orthogonal to the stream lines, are those parts of the rectangular hyperbolae

$$x^2 - y^2 = b^2, \text{ a constant, or } \frac{x^2}{b^2} - \frac{y^2}{b^2} = 1, \qquad (8)$$

in the first quadrant, whose common asymptote is the straight line $y = x$ (Fig. 111).

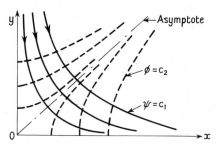

Fig. 111. Streamlines and equipotential lines (orthogonal trajectories) for case of Fig. 110.

10.21. Inclusion of small viscosity. In absence of viscosity, by (6), § 10.20 the stream function is

$$\psi(x, y) = 2axy. \qquad (1)$$

When small viscosity is included we write [257]

$$\psi(x, y) = xg(y), \qquad (2)$$

where $g(y)$ is a function of y to be determined. From (2) and (2), (3), § 10.1,

$$u = xg'(y) \quad \text{and} \quad -v = g(y). \qquad (3)$$

When y is positive and large enough, the influence of viscosity is assumed to be negligible, and then ψ is given by (1). Thus as $y \to +\infty$, (1) together with (2), (3), § 10.1 yields the boundary conditions

$$u = 2ax, \qquad v = -2ay. \tag{4}$$

Accordingly from (3), (4) for $x > 0$

$$g = 2ay, \qquad g' = 2a, \qquad y \to +\infty; \tag{5}$$

while at the surface of the plate where $y = 0$, we have $u = v = 0$, so

$$g(0) = g'(0) = 0. \tag{6}$$

In virtue of the transformation $z^2 = z_1$, for u, v, to have dimensions lt^{-1}, that of a must now be t^{-1}.

10.22. Differential equation for $g(y)$.

In absence of viscosity, the pressure is given by Bernoulli's equation

$$p = p_0 - \tfrac{1}{2}\rho \, \text{vel.}^2 = p_0 - 2\rho a^2(x^2 + y^2), \tag{1}$$

the velocity being $2a(x^2 + y^2)^{\frac{1}{2}}$. For viscous flow we take [257]

$$p = p_0 - 2a^2\rho[x^2 + G(y)], \tag{2}$$

where $G(y)$ is a function to be determined.

The Navier–Stokes equations for steady fluid flow are [257]

$$u\frac{\partial u}{\partial x} + v\frac{\partial u}{\partial y} = -\frac{1}{\rho}\frac{\partial p}{\partial x} + \nu\left(\frac{\partial^2 u}{\partial x^2} + \frac{\partial^2 u}{\partial y^2}\right), \tag{3}$$

and

$$u\frac{\partial v}{\partial x} + v\frac{\partial v}{\partial y} = -\frac{1}{\rho}\frac{\partial p}{\partial y} + \nu\left(\frac{\partial^2 v}{\partial x^2} + \frac{\partial^2 v}{\partial y^2}\right), \tag{4}$$

where $\nu = (\mu/\rho)$ is the kinematic viscosity of the fluid.† From (3), § 10.21, (2) and (3) above, we obtain

$$\nu\frac{d^3g}{dy^3} + g\frac{d^2g}{dy^2} - \left(\frac{dg}{dy}\right)^2 + 4a^2 = 0. \tag{5}$$

Writing $\xi = (2a/\nu)^{\frac{1}{2}}y$, $(2a\nu)^{\frac{1}{2}}w(\xi) = g(y)$, gives

$$\frac{dg}{dy} = \frac{dg}{d\xi}\frac{d\xi}{dy} = (2a\nu)^{\frac{1}{2}}w'(\xi)(2a/\nu)^{\frac{1}{2}} = 2aw', \tag{6}$$

so

$$\frac{d^2g}{dy^2} = 2a\frac{dw'}{d\xi}\frac{d\xi}{dy} = [(2a)^{\frac{3}{2}}/\nu^{\frac{1}{2}}]w'', \tag{7}$$

and

$$\frac{d^3g}{dy^3} = [(2a)^{\frac{3}{2}}/\nu^{\frac{1}{2}}](2a/\nu)^{\frac{1}{2}}w''' = 4a^2w'''/\nu. \tag{8}$$

† μ is the dynamic viscosity having dimensions $ml^{-1}t^{-1} = $ pressure $\times$ time $=$ force/ unit vel./unit length.

Substituting from (6)–(8) into (5) leads to the third order non-linear equation [257]

$$w''' + ww'' - w'^2 + 1 = 0. \tag{9}$$

This must be solved to satisfy the three boundary conditions

(i) $w(0) = 0$,

(ii) $w'(0) = 0$,

(iii) $w'(\infty) = 1$ (from (5), § 10.21 and (6)), for all $x \geqslant 0$. (10)

From above and (3), § 10.21, for a given x

$$u = 2axw'(\xi), \quad \text{so} \quad u \propto w'(\xi), \tag{11}$$

while

$$v = -(2a\nu)^{\frac{1}{2}}w(\xi), \text{ independent of } x. \tag{12}$$

The differential equation for $G(y)$ derived from (3), § 10.21, (2), and (4), is

$$G'(y) = (\nu g'' + gg')/2a^2, \tag{13}$$

differentiation being with respect to y. By solving (9) for $w(\xi)$ and using the substitutions below (5), $G'(y)$ may be found.

10.30. Solution of (9), § 10.22. To date, a closed form of solution has not been published, so we shall use the Maclaurin theorem procedure outlined in Chapter VIII. Then we have the expansion

$$w(\xi) = w_0 + \xi w_0^{(1)} + \frac{\xi^2}{2!}w_0^{(2)} + \ldots + \frac{\xi^n}{n!}w_0^{(n)} + \ldots = \sum_{n=0}^{\infty} \frac{\xi^n}{n!}w_0^{(n)}, \tag{1}$$

where $w_0^{(n)} = \dfrac{d^n w}{d\xi^n}\bigg|_{\xi=0}$. The boundary conditions at the origin are $w = 0$, $w' = 0$, and it follows from (9), § 10.22 that $w_0^{(3)} = -1$. $w_0^{(2)}$ is unknown, so we shall call it α. After the solution has been obtained in terms of α, its value must be determined to satisfy the boundary condition at infinity, i.e. $w' = 1$, $\xi = \infty$. By repeated differentiation of (9), § 10.22, the following table is obtained:

TABLE 6

Successive derivatives of $w''' + ww'' - w'^2 + 1 = 0$

Derivative	$w^{(n)}(0) = w_0^{(n)}$
$w^{(4)} + ww^{(3)} - w^{(1)}w^{(2)} = 0$	$w_0^{(4)} = 0$
$w^{(5)} + ww^{(4)} - [w^{(2)}]^2 = 0$	$w_0^{(5)} = \alpha^2$
$w^{(6)} + ww^{(5)} + w^{(1)}w^{(4)} - 2w^{(2)}w^{(3)} = 0$	$w_0^{(6)} = -2\alpha$
$w^{(7)} + ww^{(6)} + 2w^{(1)}w^{(5)} - w^{(2)}w^{(4)} - 2[w^{(3)}]^2 = 0$	$w_0^{(7)} = 2$
$w^{(8)} + ww^{(7)} + 3w^{(1)}w^{(6)} + w^{(2)}w^{(5)} - 5w^{(3)}w^{(4)} = 0$	$w_0^{(8)} = -\alpha^3$
$w^{(9)} + ww^{(8)} + 4w^{(1)}w^{(7)} + 4w^{(2)}w^{(6)} - 4w^{(3)}w^{(5)} - 5[w^{(4)}]^2 = 0$	$w_0^{(9)} = 4\alpha^2$

. . . .

See Abac for additional values of $w_0^{(n)}$.

Consideration of the sequence of coefficients in the expressions for the derivatives in Table 6 suggested the accompanying Abac for calculation of the coefficients by mere arithmetic. For instance, take the seventh row, which corresponds to $n = 9$. The eighth row is obtained by adding successive pairs of numbers in the seventh. Thus $(1+4) = 5$, $(4+4) = 8$, $(4-4) = 0$, $-4-5 \times 2 = -14$. The 2 in parenthesis signifies that the number has to be doubled. $w^{(4)}$ is squared in the seventh row, which entails the multiplier 2 when the next derivative is found. Having constructed the Abac, the columns may be checked by differencing each repeatedly. The final differences should be zero. For example, the fourth (fifth) difference for column five (six) is zero.

Inserting the values of $w_0^{(n)}$ from the Abac into (1), yields the series solution

$$w(\xi) = -\frac{1}{3!}\xi^3 + \frac{2}{7!}\xi^7 + \frac{16}{11!}\xi^{11} + \frac{2128}{15!}\xi^{15} + \frac{721664}{19!}\xi^{19} + \dots +$$

$$+\alpha\left\{\frac{1}{2!}\xi^2 - \frac{2}{6!}\xi^6 - \frac{16}{10!}\xi^{10} - \frac{2128}{14!}\xi^{14} - \frac{721664}{18!}\xi^{18} - \dots\right\} +$$

$$+\alpha^2\left\{\frac{1}{5!}\xi^5 + \frac{4}{9!}\xi^9 + \frac{840}{13!}\xi^{13} + \frac{299684}{17!}\xi^{17} + \frac{212311872}{21!}\xi^{21} + \dots\right\} -$$

$$-\alpha^3\left\{\frac{1}{8!}\xi^8 + \frac{181}{12!}\xi^{12} + \frac{70117}{16!}\xi^{16} + \frac{52214273}{20!}\xi^{20} + \dots\right\} +$$

$$+\alpha^4\left\{\frac{27}{11!}\xi^{11} + \frac{10725}{15!}\xi^{15} + \frac{8391913}{19!}\xi^{19} + \dots\right\} -$$

$$-\alpha^5\left\{\frac{951}{14!}\xi^{14} + \frac{916656}{18!}\xi^{18} + \dots\right\} +$$

$$+\alpha^6\left\{\frac{51465}{17!}\xi^{17} + \frac{92852282}{21!}\xi^{21} + \dots\right\} -$$

$$-\alpha^7\left\{\frac{3355837}{20!}\xi^{20} + \dots\right\} + \dots . \tag{2}$$

$$w'(\xi) = \text{term by term differentiation of (2).} \tag{3}$$

10.31. Asymptotic solution.

At the origin $w = w' = 0$, and from physical considerations, when $\xi \propto y > 0$, w, w', $w'' > 0$, so $w_0^{(2)} = \alpha > 0$. The boundary condition to be satisfied at infinity is

Abac for calculating coefficients in series solution of $w''' + ww'' - w'^2 + 1 = 0$

n	$w'^{(n)}$	$w'w^{n-2}$	w^2w^{n-3}	w^3w^{n-4}	w^4w^{n-5}	w^5w^{n-6}	w^6w^{n-7}	w^7w^{n-8}	w^8w^{n-9}	w^9w^{n-10}	$w^{10}w^{n-11}$	$w_0^{(n)}$
4	1	-1										0
5	1	0	$-1(2)$									α^2
6	1	1	-2									-2α
7	1	2	-1	$-2(2)$								2
8	1	3	1	-5								$-\alpha^3$
9	1	4	4	-4	$-5(2)$							$4\alpha^2$
10	1	5	8	0	-14							-16α
11	1	6	13	8	-14	$-(14)2$						$(16+27\alpha^4)$
12	1	7	19	21	-6	-42						$-181\alpha^3$
13	1	8	26	40	15	-48	$-42(2)$					$840\alpha^2$
14	1	9	34	66	55	-33	-132					$-(2128\alpha+981\alpha^5)$
15	1	10	43	100	121	22	-165	$-132(2)$				$2128+10725\alpha^4$
16	1	11	53	143	221	143	-143	-429				$-70117\alpha^3$
17	1	12	64	196	364	364	0	-572	$-429(2)$			$(299684\alpha^2+51465\alpha^6)$
18	1	13	76	260	560	728	364	-572	-1430			$-(721664\alpha+916656\alpha^5)$
19	1	14	89	336	820	1288	1092	-208	-2002	$-1430(2)$		$(721664+8391913\alpha^4)$
20	1	15	103	425	1156	2108	2380	884	-2210	-4862		$-(5221473\alpha^3+3355837\alpha^7)$
21	1	16	118	528	1581	3264	4488	3264	-1326	-7072	$-4862(2)$	$(212311872\alpha^2+92852282\alpha^6)$
22	1	17										
23	1	18										

$\lim\limits_{\xi \to \infty} w'(\xi) = 1$. Thus $w''(\infty) = w'''(\infty) = 0$, and for ξ large and positive, (9), § 10.22 reduces to the approximation

$$w' = 1, \tag{1}$$

the positive root being used in virtue of the foregoing boundary condition. Thus
$$w = \xi + k, \text{ a constant}, \tag{2}$$

is an asymptotic solution. The sign of k depends upon the shape of the

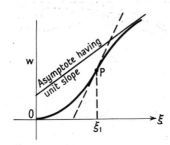

Fig. 112. P is an assumed point of inflexion in the w–ξ curve.

early part of the w–ξ curve. If the curve is below the asymptote as
in Fig. 112, in order to satisfy the above conditions at the origin,
there must be an inflexion at some point ξ_1, where $w'(\xi_1) > 1$, the
slope of the asymptote. Then $w''(\xi_1) = 0$, so by (9), § 10.22

$$w'^2(\xi_1) = 1 + w'''(\xi_1). \tag{3}$$

At the inflexion $w'(\xi_1)$ is a maximum, so $w'''(\xi_1) < 0$, which entails
$|w'|$ being < 1. Hence, an inflexion cannot occur, and the w–ξ
curve has the form depicted in Fig. 114, with $k = -b = -ON$; so the
asymptotic solution is $w = (\xi - b)$, with $b > 0$.

10.32. Determination of $w_0^{(2)} = \alpha$, and b.

Theoretically the
boundary condition $w'(\infty) = 1$ has to be satisfied, but in practical computation we aim to obtain an adequate approximation thereto. First
we take trial values of α, and calculate, using a machine, the corresponding values of $w'(\xi)$ over a range of $\xi \geqslant 1$. The results for $\alpha = 1\cdot2$,
$1\cdot22$, $1\cdot23$, $1\cdot24$ are illustrated in Fig. 113. When $\alpha = 1\cdot2$, $1\cdot22$, $1\cdot23$,
the curves have maximum values in the range $1 \leqslant \xi \leqslant 2\cdot6$. But for
larger ξ, their ordinates exceed unity, as exemplified in the case
$\alpha = 1\cdot24$. This effect may be avoided by using an adequate number
of additional terms in the series solution (2), § 10.30. If we accept the

approximation $w'(3) = 1$, the value of α is about 1·233. Using this in (2), and (3), § 10.30, the curves shown in Fig. 114 may be computed.

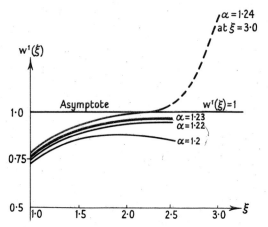

FIG. 113. Curves illustrating method of determining $w_0^{(2)} = \alpha$.

Taking the values of w at $\xi = 2\cdot5$, and 3, b may be calculated. Its value is approximately 0·648. To attain greater accuracy, the range

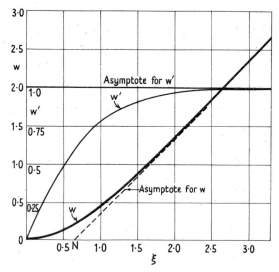

FIG. 114. Graphs of $w(\xi)$ and $w'(\xi)$ for the equation $w''' + ww'' - w'^2 + 1 = 0$, the boundary conditions being (i), (ii) $w = w' = 0$ when $\xi = 0$; (iii) $w' = 1$ when $\xi = \infty$. $ON = b$ in the asymptotic solution (broken line is asymptote)

$$w = \xi - b.$$

of ξ must be extended, and this entails more terms in the solution at (2), § 10.30 being used.

10.33. Thickness of boundary layer. This is the distance δ from the plate where the velocity u at any x tends to constancy. Then from Fig. 113, $\xi \simeq 3$, and since $\xi = (2a/\nu)^{\frac{1}{2}}y$, we get

$$\delta = y = 3(\nu/2a)^{\frac{1}{2}}, \tag{1}$$

so for a given velocity a, the thickness of the boundary layer varies as $\nu^{\frac{1}{2}}$. For air at 20° C., $p_0 = 760$ mm. Hg, $\nu = 14\cdot9 \times 10^{-6}$ m.² sec.$^{-1}$, and for water $\nu = 1\cdot01 \times 10^{-6}$ m.² sec.$^{-1}$ Thus the *kinematic* viscosity of air is nearly 15 times that of water. If $a = 20$ m. sec.$^{-1}$, $\delta = 1\cdot83$ mm. for air.

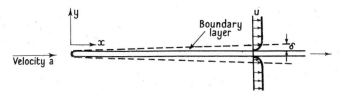

FIG. 115. Diagram illustrating the 'boundary layer' in fluid flow along a flat plate.

10.40. Steady fluid flow along a flat plate (Fig. 115) [257]. For low viscosity, the Navier–Stokes equations (3), (4), § 10.22 may be reduced to the approximation

$$u\frac{\partial u}{\partial x} + v\frac{\partial u}{\partial y} = \nu\frac{\partial^2 u}{\partial y^2}, \tag{1}$$

and the equation of continuity is

$$\frac{\partial u}{\partial x} + \frac{\partial v}{\partial y} = 0, \tag{2}$$

the boundary conditions being $u = v = 0$ when $y = 0$, and $u = a$ when y is infinite.

For potential flow, we have from (1), § 10.20, the stream function

$$\psi = ay, \tag{3}$$

which has dimensions $l^2 t^{-1} =$ velocity $\times$ length.

It is expedient to introduce a dimensionless coordinate η replacing y (in a sense), so we write $y = (\nu x/a)^{\frac{1}{2}}\eta$, or $\eta = (a/\nu x)^{\frac{1}{2}}y$, where $(a/\nu x)^{\frac{1}{2}}$ has dimension l^{-1}.

Then (3) becomes $\psi = (a\nu x)^{\frac{1}{2}}\eta.$ (4)

To take viscous flow into account in the boundary layer, as before (in (2), § 10.21) we put

$$\psi = (a\nu x)^{\frac{1}{2}}g(\eta), \tag{5}$$

where $g(\eta)$ is a function to be determined. Using $u = \partial\psi/\partial y$, $v = -\partial\psi/\partial x$, and (1), (2) above, we obtain, ultimately,

$$2\, d^3g/d\eta^3 + g\, d^2g/d\eta^2 = 0, \qquad (6)$$

which is the non-linear differential equation for the dimensionless function $g(\eta)$. Taking $g(\eta) = 2w(\eta)$, (6) becomes

$$w''' + ww'' = 0. \qquad (7)$$

The boundary conditions are

$$\text{(i), (ii)} \quad w(0) = 0, \qquad w'(0) = 0,$$

and $\qquad\qquad\qquad\text{(iii)} \quad w'(\infty) = \tfrac{1}{2}.$

The solution of (7) on the lines set out in § 10.30 et seq. is left as an exercise for the reader, being problem 52 at the end of the book.

APPENDIX I

Sound Waves of Finite Amplitude in a Loudspeaker Horn

1. Introduction. In Chapter I we mentioned that the classical theory of sound is based upon infinitesimal pressure variation and, therefore, infinitesimal amplitude of longitudinal vibration. But in modern loudspeaking apparatus, and in all musical instruments such as the pedal organ, which generate high sound pressure, the amplitude at the source is certainly not in the infinitesimal category! The pressures employed in fog-signalling apparatus, and in public address loudspeakers used in cinemas and at open-air events, are colossal from the viewpoint of the classical theory. For example the pressure at the throat of a horn-type loudspeaker radiating 500 watts of sound power might be 10^4 dynes

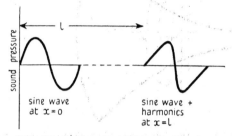

FIG. 116. Illustrating distortion of plane sinusoidal sound wave of finite amplitude, with increase in distance from source.

per cm.^{2} Since a pressure of 3 dynes cm.$^{-2}$ in the ear canal is perceived as a loud sound, the great strength of the modern acoustical source will be realized.

At any instant during the propagation of a plane sound wave of finite amplitude, the density of the air varies from a maximum at a crest to a minimum at a trough, so the crests gradually gain on the troughs, as the distance from some arbitrary origin increases. This is illustrated in Fig. 116, which indicates a change in wave form, it being accompanied by the creation of higher harmonic tones. The shape of the distorted wave is such that the second harmonic predominates over those of higher order. Since there is absence of lateral expansion in plane-wave propagation, the alteration in wave form is much more marked than that in waves emitted from a loudspeaker horn or a large conical diaphragm. Expansion is accompanied by a gradual reduction in pressure amplitude, which implies smaller variations in density and, therefore, less distortion than in a plane wave under comparable conditions. The smaller the throat of a horn loudspeaker, the greater the pressure amplitude thereat for a given acoustical power output, and the greater the distortion arising from the creation of alien tones. There is a limit to the degree of distortion which the ear can tolerate. For sports events and the like this is appreciably higher than that for the reproduction of speech and music indoors! In the analytical work which follows we shall obtain formulae whereby horn loudspeakers may be designed so that the power associated with alien tones does not exceed a prescribed level. To avoid undue complication, transmission loss in the air will be omitted. It is of importance chiefly at the higher audio frequencies. Apart from introducing the type of distortion mentioned above, a small horn throat causes appreciable frictional loss, since the air velocity at the entrance to the horn is then relatively high.

2. The differential equation. This is derived in [183, p. 199] to which reference may be made. The horn is assumed to have a long linear axis, to be rigid and frictionless, the size at the *mouth* being large enough to avoid appreciable reflection at the lowest frequency to be adequately reproduced. The law

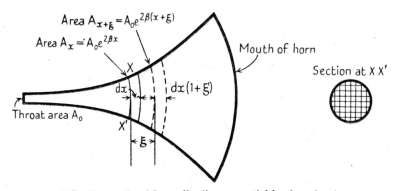

FIG. 117. Illustrating 'channelized' exponential loudspeaker horn.

of variation of the cross-section with distance is unrestricted, except that for obvious reasons there must be no abrupt changes, while from an analytical viewpoint the expansion must follow a law which makes the analysis tractable. In addition we suppose the horn to be subdivided into a large number of channels or conduits whose cross-sectional dimensions are small compared with the wave-length of the highest frequency to be reproduced. By so doing we avoid the untenable assumption that the wave front is plane, while transverse modes of vibration in the horn are rendered innocuous. In practice a non-channelized horn exhibits objectionable directional properties, which are mitigated by the above construction. At a distance x from the horn throat, the wave front will be a sectionized curved surface, the sound pressure being equal at all points thereon. The periphery of the outer cross-section is usually circular, rectangular, or square.

Referring to Fig. 117, the non-linear equation with which we have to deal is

$$\frac{\partial^2 \xi}{\partial x^2} + \frac{\chi'}{\chi}(1 + \partial\xi/\partial x) - (1 + \partial\xi/\partial x)^{\gamma+1}\frac{\chi^{\gamma-1}}{c^2}\frac{\partial^2 \xi}{\partial t^2} = 0, \tag{1}$$

where ξ is the particle displacement at a distance x from the throat measured along the curved axis of a channel, $\chi = \dfrac{\text{cross-sectional area at } (x+\xi)}{\text{cross-sectional area at } x}$, c is the velocity of sound waves of infinitesimal amplitude, and $\gamma = 1\cdot4$ for air.

3. Exponential horn† [41]. From the viewpoint of design, the problem is to calculate the smallest throat, so that the horn will transmit an assigned acoustical power over a given frequency band, the degree of distortion due to the medium, by virtue of its non-linear characteristic (adiabatic curve), being less than a stipulated value. In practice it is usually adequate to confine consideration to some fundamental frequency‡ and its second harmonic.

From Fig. 117 the area at any x is

$$A = A_0 e^{2\beta x}, \tag{1}$$

A_0 being the throat area, and 2β the flare index.§ Thus

$$\chi = A(x+\xi)/A(x) = e^{2\beta\xi}, \tag{2}$$

so

$$\chi' = 2\beta \frac{\partial\xi}{\partial x} \cdot e^{2\beta\xi}, \tag{3}$$

and, therefore,

$$\chi'/\chi = 2\beta\xi'. \tag{4}$$

Substituting (2), (4) into (1), § 2, we obtain the non-linear equation for the propagation of sound waves of finite amplitude in an exponential horn, namely,

$$\xi'' + 2\beta\xi'(1+\xi') = (\ddot{\xi}/c^2)(1+\xi')^{\gamma+1} e^{2(\gamma-1)\beta\xi}, \tag{5}$$

with $\xi' = \partial\xi/\partial x$, $\xi'' = \partial^2\xi/\partial x^2$, $\ddot{\xi} = \partial^2\xi/\partial t^2$. On the assumption that ξ, $\xi' \ll 1$, we expand the right-hand side of (5) and obtain

$$(\ddot{\xi}/c^2)\left[\left\{1+(\gamma+1)\xi'+\frac{(\gamma+1)\gamma\xi'^2}{2!}+\dots\right\}\left\{1+(\gamma-1)2\beta\xi+\frac{(\gamma-1)^2}{2!}4\beta^2\xi^2+\dots\right\}\right]$$
$$= (\ddot{\xi}/c^2)[1+(\gamma-1)2\beta\xi+(\gamma+1)\xi'+\text{terms of higher orders in } \xi, \xi']. \tag{6}$$

Neglecting the higher order terms, since ξ, $\xi' \ll 1$, and also taking

$$2(\gamma-1)\beta\xi \ll 1,$$

(6) yields the approximation

$$(\ddot{\xi}/c^2)[1+2(\gamma-1)\beta\xi+(\gamma+1)\xi']. \tag{7}$$

Replacing the right-hand side of (5) by (7), and rearranging, leads to

$$\xi'' + 2\beta\xi' - (\ddot{\xi}/c^2) = (\ddot{\xi}/c^2)[2(\gamma-1)\beta\xi+(\gamma+1)\xi'] - 2\beta\xi'^2. \tag{8}$$

All terms on the left-hand side of (8) are of order ξ, while those on the right-hand side are of order ξ^2, so the equation is non-linear.

4. First approximation to solution of (8), § 3. We neglect the right-hand side and then the equation to be solved is the linear type

$$\xi'' + 2\beta\xi' - (\ddot{\xi}/c^2) = 0. \tag{1}$$

At the horn throat where $x = 0$, we suppose there is a diaphragm of area A_0 vibrating axially so that $\xi = \xi_0 \cos \omega t$, i.e. the particle amplitude is ξ_0. This is the boundary condition at the throat. We shall deal with steady oscillations, so the need to specify initial conditions at $t = 0$ does not arise. We assume that

$$\xi = \text{Re}[\psi(x)e^{i\omega t}], \tag{2}$$

† Spherical sound waves of finite amplitude are dealt with in [100].
‡ Two different frequencies are considered in [101].
§ 2β has been chosen instead of the usual β to avoid the fraction $\frac{1}{2}$ in subsequent analysis.

ψ being a function of x. Substituting (2) into (1) gives

$$\psi'' + 2\beta\psi' + k^2\psi = 0, \tag{3}$$

with $k = \omega/c = 2\pi/\lambda$, λ being the wave-length, and in practice $k > \beta$. The formal solution of (3) is

$$\psi = e^{-\beta x}[Ae^{im_1 x} + Be^{-im_1 x}], \tag{4}$$

A, B being arbitrary constants, and $m_1^2 = k^2 - \beta^2$. Then by (2), (4)

$$\xi = e^{-\beta x}\mathrm{Re}[Ae^{i(\omega t + m_1 x)} + Be^{i(\omega t - m_1 x)}]. \tag{5}$$

By hypothesis there is no reflection at the horn mouth, so we require a solution for outward transmission of power. Thus

$$\xi_1 = e^{-\beta x}\mathrm{Re}[Be^{i(\omega t - m_1 x)}] = Be^{-\beta x}\cos\theta_1, \tag{6}$$

with $\theta_1 = (\omega t - m_1 x)$, and assuming B real. If $B = \xi_0$,

$$\xi_1 = \xi_0 e^{-\beta x}\cos\theta_1, \tag{7}$$

and the boundary condition $\xi = \xi_0\cos\omega t$ at $x = 0$ is satisfied. Then (7) is the first approximation to the solution of (8), § 3, being in fact the solution for the linear case of infinitesimal amplitude. The attenuation factor $e^{-\beta x}$ is due to expansion of the sound waves as they travel down the horn, there being no power loss over a cross-section.

5. Second approximation. To derive this we substitute (7), § 4, into the right-hand side of (8), § 3 and obtain the linear equation

$$\xi'' + 2\beta\xi' - (\ddot{\xi}/c^2) = -\tfrac{1}{2}\xi_0^2 e^{-2\beta x}[A_1 + B_1\cos 2\theta_1 + C_1\sin 2\theta_1], \tag{1}$$

where $A_1 = \beta k^2(\gamma - 1)$, $B_1 = \beta\{k^2(\gamma - 5) + 4\beta^2\}$, $C_1 = m_1\{k^2(\gamma + 1) - 4\beta^2\}$. The complementary function of (1)—right-hand side zero—for the second harmonic of frequency ω/π, may be found from (6), § 4, by writing 2ω for ω, m_2 for m_1, and B_2 for B. Thus

$$\xi_{2c} = e^{-\beta x}\mathrm{Re}[B_2 e^{i(2\omega t - m_2 x)}] = e^{-\beta x}\mathrm{Re}(B_2 e^{i\theta_2}), \tag{2}$$

with $m_2^2 = 4k^2 - \beta^2$, and $\theta_2 = (2\omega t - m_2 x)$. To derive the particular integral of (1), we use (2) in the formula

$$\xi_{2p} = \xi_{2c}\int^x \xi_{2c}^{-2} e^{-\int P_1 dx}\left[\int^x \xi_{2c} e^{\int P_1 dx} S\, dx\right] dx, \tag{3}$$

where P_1 is the coefficient of ξ' in (1), and S is the right-hand side of (1) [167].

We find that

$$\xi_{2p} = \xi_0^2 e^{-2\beta x}[(A_1/4\beta)x + \mathrm{Re}(F_1 e^{2i\theta_1})], \tag{4}$$

with $F_1 = (D_1 - iE_1)$, $D_1 = (1/8\beta)[k^2(\gamma + 1) - 2\beta^2\gamma]$, $E_1 = \tfrac{1}{4}m_1(2 - \gamma)$. Hence by (2), (4) the solution of (1) for the second harmonic is

$$\xi_2 = \xi_{2c} + \xi_{2p} = e^{-\beta x}\{\mathrm{Re}[B_2 e^{i\theta_2}] + \xi_0^2 e^{-\beta x}[(A_1/4\beta)x + \mathrm{Re}(F_1 e^{2i\theta_1})]\}. \tag{5}$$

At the throat $x = 0$ and $\xi_2 = 0$, so we must have

$$B_2 e^{2i\omega t} + \xi_0^2 F_1 e^{2i\omega t} = 0, \tag{6}$$

giving

$$B_2 = -\xi_0^2 F_1. \tag{7}$$

Substituting this into (5) yields

$$\xi_2 = \xi_0^2\{e^{-2\beta x}(A_1/4\beta)x + e^{-\beta x}\mathrm{Re}[(e^{2i\theta_1 - \beta x} - e^{2i\theta_2})F_1]\}. \tag{8}$$

Hence by (7), § 4, and (8) above, to the second approximation, the solution of (5), § 3, for outgoing waves is [41]

$$\xi = \xi_1 \text{ (fundamental)} + \xi_2 \text{ (second harmonic)} + \text{unidirectional displacement} \quad (9)$$

$$= \xi_0 e^{-\beta x} \cos(\omega t - m_1 x) + \xi_0^2 e^{-2\beta x}[D_1 \cos 2(\omega t - m_1 x) + E_1 \sin 2(\omega t - m_1 x)] -$$

$$- \xi_0^2 e^{-\beta x}[D_1 \cos(2\omega t - m_2 x) + E_1 \sin(2\omega t - m_2 x)] + \tfrac{1}{4}\xi_0^2 k^2(\gamma - 1)xe^{-2\beta x}. \quad (10)$$

In the solution of (1) there is also a complementary function $(1 - e^{-2\beta x})$ independent of t which vanishes at $x = 0$, this being a solution of $\xi'' + 2\beta\xi' = 0$. Any multiple of $(1 - e^{-2\beta x})$ may be added to (10), but in the present case it is not required. Thus the solution, without prescribed initial conditions (in which we have no interest here), is indeterminate in the above respect, but this is inconsequential.

The last term in (10) represents a unidirectional particle displacement. It is due to the adiabatic curve for air not being antisymmetrical (see §§ 4.130, 4.140) about the operating point thereon, so the pressure variations for $\pm v_0$ are different. In radio terminology it is in the nature of a 'rectification' effect. The unidirectional displacement increases with increase in x from $x = 0$, and attains a maximum value at $x = \tfrac{1}{2}\beta$. Thereafter it decreases monotonically with increase in x.

6. Sound pressure. In [41, 183] it is shown that the excess pressure at *variable* distance $(x + \xi)$ from the horn throat to the second order in ξ is given by

$$p = \rho_0 c^2[-2\beta\xi - \xi' + 2\beta\gamma\xi\xi' + 2\beta^2\gamma\xi^2 + \tfrac{1}{2}(\gamma + 1)\xi'^2], \quad (1)$$

provided $2\beta\gamma\xi \ll 1$, $\xi' \ll 1$, ρ_0 being the undisturbed air density. Substituting from (10), § 5, for ξ, ξ', ξ'' into (1), and rejecting terms of orders higher than ξ^2, we find the excess pressure at $(x + \xi)$ to be

$$p = -\rho c^2 k e^{-\beta x}[\xi_0 \sin(\theta_1 + \alpha_1) + \xi_0^2 k^{-1}(M_1^2 + M_2^2)^{\frac{1}{2}} \sin(2\omega t + \alpha_2)] + \tfrac{1}{2}\rho_0 c^2 \xi_0^2 k^2 e^{-2\beta x}, \quad (2)$$

where $\alpha_1 = \tan^{-1}(\beta/m_1); \quad \alpha_2 = \tan^{-1}(M_2/M_1);$

$$M_1 = e^{-\beta x}[G_1 \cos 2m_1 x + H_1 \sin 2m_1 x] - [J_1 \cos m_2 x - K_1 \sin m_2 x];$$

$$M_2 = e^{-\beta x}[-G_1 \sin 2m_1 x + H_1 \cos 2m_1 x] + [J_1 \sin m_2 x + K_1 \cos m_2 x];$$

$$(M_1^2 + M_2^2) = (J_1^2 + K_1^2) + e^{-2\beta x}(G_1^2 + H_1^2) -$$

$$- 2e^{-\beta x}[(J_1^2 + K_1^2)(G_1^2 + H_1^2)]^{\frac{1}{2}} \sin\{(2m_1 - m_2)x + \alpha_3\}$$

$$\simeq (J_1^2 + K_1^2) = 4k^2(D_1^2 + E_1^2) \text{ when } x \text{ is large enough so that } e^{-\beta x} \ll 1;$$

$$\alpha_3 = \tan^{-1}[(G_1 J_1 - H_1 K_1)/(G_1 K_1 + H_1 J_1)]; \quad G_1 = 2m_1 D_1 - \tfrac{1}{2}m_1\beta(\gamma - 1);$$

$$H_1 = \tfrac{1}{4}(\gamma + 1)(k^2 - 2\beta^2) - 2m_1 E_1; \quad J_1 = m_2 D_1 + \beta E_1; \quad K_1 = m_2 E_1 - \beta D_1.$$

The last term in (2) represents a unidirectional excess pressure which decays exponentially with increase in x. It may be explained as in the last paragraph of § 5.

7. Particle velocity. At variable distance $(x + \xi)$ from the horn throat, this is found by differentiating (10), § 5, with respect to t. Thus

$$\dot{\xi} = -\omega e^{-\beta x}\xi_0[\sin\theta_1 + 2\xi_0(N_1^2 + N_2^2)^{\frac{1}{2}} \sin(2\omega t + \psi_2)], \quad (1)$$

with $N_1 = e^{-\beta x}[D_1 \cos 2m_1 x - E_1 \sin 2m_1 x] - [D_1 \cos m_2 x - E_1 \sin m_2 x];$

$$N_2 = e^{-\beta x}[-D_1 \sin 2m_1 x - E_1 \cos 2m_1 x] + [D_1 \sin m_2 x + E_1 \cos m_2 x];$$

$$N_1^2 + N_2^2 = (D_1^2 + E_1^2)[1 + e^{-2\beta x} - 2e^{-\beta x}\cos(2m_1 - m_2)x] \simeq (D_1^2 + E_1^2),$$

when x is large enough so that $e^{-\beta x} \ll 1$; $\psi_2 = \tan^{-1}(N_2/N_1)$.

8. Acoustical power transmitted down horn.

We may imagine the air particles (so called) over the wave front at any x to be replaced by a massless vibrating curved lamina. The area varies with ξ; it is $A = A_0 e^{2\beta(x+\xi)}$, ξ being given by (10), § 5. The alternating sound pressure on the fictitious diaphragm is represented by (2), § 6, and the velocity by (1), § 7. The power associated with the diaphragm is the mean value of $p\dot{\xi}A_0 e^{2\beta(x+\xi)} = p\dot{\xi}A_0 e^{2\beta x}e^{2\beta\xi}$, over a period of the fundamental frequency. When x is large enough, $2\beta\xi \ll 1$, and $e^{2\beta\xi} \simeq 1$, so we have to calculate the mean value of $p\dot{\xi}A_0 e^{2\beta x}$ in $t = (0, 2\pi/\omega)$. Thus the power is given by

$$P = A_0 e^{2\beta x} \frac{\omega}{2\pi} \int_0^{2\pi/w} p\dot{\xi}\, dt. \qquad (1)$$

Substituting from (2), § 6, for p, and from (1), § 7, for $\dot{\xi}$ into (1) above, we find that

$$P = \tfrac{1}{2}\rho_0 cA_0 \omega^2\xi_0^2\cos\alpha_1\left[1+(2\xi_0^2/k)\{(M_1^2+M_2^2)(N_1^2+N_2^2)\}^{\frac{1}{2}}\frac{\cos(\alpha_2-\psi_2)}{\cos\alpha_1}\right] \qquad (2)$$

$$= P_1+P_2, \qquad (3)$$

where $\quad P_1 = $ power in fundamental $= \tfrac{1}{2}\rho_0 cA_0 \omega^2\xi_0^2\cos\alpha_1,$ $\qquad (4)$

and $\qquad P_2 = $ power in second harmonic

$$= P_1\left[(2\xi_0^2/k)\{(M_1^2+M_2^2)(N_1^2+N_2^2)\}^{\frac{1}{2}}\frac{\cos(\alpha_2-\psi_2)}{\cos\alpha_1}\right] \qquad (5)$$

$$= P_1\varphi_h. \qquad (6)$$

$\cos\alpha_1$ is the acoustical power factor for the fundamental, while $\cos(\alpha_2-\psi_2)$ is that for the harmonic. The pressure and particle velocity are out of phase by α_1 for the first, and by $(\alpha_2-\psi_2)$ for the second.

Now P_1 represents the power supplied at fundamental frequency by the diaphragm at the throat, while $P_1\varphi_h$ is the power in the harmonic. It appears, therefore, that the total power in the horn increases with increase in distance from the throat. This apparent paradox is due to the analysis being restricted to terms of order 2 in ξ. If carried further and terms in ξ^3, ξ^4,.... were introduced, terms involving θ_1, $2\theta_1$, $3\theta_1$,.... would appear. The net result would be that as x increased, the pressure and particle velocity of the fundamental would gradually fall below the values given at (2), § 6, (1), § 7, the amplitudes approaching limiting values asymptotically. As the waves travel down the horn, the power lost by the fundamental is transferred to the harmonics. At a certain distance from the throat the transfer of power to the harmonics is substantially complete. That is to say, further transfer is prevented owing to the increased rate of expansion of the cross-sectional area. The ratio φ_h has then attained its ultimate value and may be evaluated with $e^{-\beta x} \ll 1$. Under this condition terms involving $e^{-\beta x}$ in the expressions for M_1, M_2, N_1, N_2 are negligible and we obtain

$$\varphi_h = \tfrac{1}{4}\xi_0^2[(k^4/4\beta^2)(\gamma+1)^2 - k^2(5\gamma-4)+4\beta^2(\gamma-1)]\cos(\alpha_2-\psi_2)/\cos\alpha_1. \qquad (7)$$

Since $\alpha_1 = \tan^{-1}(\beta/m_1)$, $\cos\alpha_1 = m_1/k$; also when

$$e^{-\beta x} \ll 1, \qquad (\alpha_2-\psi_2) \simeq \tan^{-1}(\beta/m_2),$$

so $\cos(\alpha_2-\psi_2) \simeq m_2/k$. Substituting in (7) for $\cos\alpha_1$, $\cos(\alpha_2-\psi_2)$, we find that

$$\varphi_h \simeq (\xi_0^2 m_2/8m_1)[(k^4/4\beta^2)(\gamma+1)^2 - k^2(5\gamma-4)+4\beta^2(\gamma-1)]. \qquad (8)$$

It will be evident that calculation of the power in the second harmonic must be restricted by the condition $\varphi_h \ll 1$.

Since $\cos\alpha_1 = (m_1/k)$, (4) gives

$$\xi_0^2 = 2P_1/\rho_0\,c^3km_1\,A_0. \tag{9}$$

Substituting from (9) into (8) yields

$$\varphi_h = P_1m_2[(k^4/4\beta^2)(\gamma+1)^2 - k^2(5\gamma-4) + 4\beta^2(\gamma-1)]/4\rho_0\,c^3km_1^2\,A_0, \tag{10}$$

$$\simeq 1\cdot48\times10^{-4}(P_1/A_0)(\omega/\omega_c)^2, \tag{11}$$

provided $\omega \gg \omega_c$, $e^{-\beta x} \ll 1$. In (11) P_1 is in watts, A_0 in cm.², $\omega/2\pi$ the fundamental frequency in c.p.s., while $\omega_c/2\pi = \beta c/2\pi$ is the cut-off frequency of the horn below which (in the hypothetical case) power cannot be transmitted.†
For high-quality reproduction of speech and music, the level of the second harmonic should be not less than 30 decibels (db.) below that of the fundamental. In other words, the power in the harmonic must not exceed 10^{-3} that in the fundamental, so $\varphi_h \leqslant 10^{-3}$. Using this in (11), we obtain the simple but important design formula

$$A_0 \geqslant 0\cdot148P_1(\omega/\omega_c)^2. \tag{12}$$

It will be seen from (11) that if P_1 remains constant for a given horn, the power in the second harmonic increases as the square of the frequency.

9. Numerical example [41]. To illustrate application of the foregoing analysis, we shall calculate the throat area of an adequately long horn, having a cut-off frequency of 30 c.p.s., to transmit 30 watts at $\omega = 2\pi\times200$, the second harmonic of 400 c.p.s. being at least 30 db. below the level of the fundamental. Inserting these data in (12), § 8, we get

$$A_0 \geqslant 0\cdot148\times30\times(200/30)^2, \tag{1}$$

so

$$A_0 \geqslant 197 \text{ cm.}^2 \tag{2}$$

Thus the throat radius

$$r_0 \geqslant (197/\pi)^{\frac{1}{2}} = 7\cdot92 \text{ cm.}, \tag{3}$$

or about 6·25 inches in diameter.

Suppose the throat radius were 0·85 cm., the area A_0 then being about 1/80 its value at (2). The level of the second harmonic would be much higher than -30 db. Using (11), § 8, we have

$$\varphi_h = 1\cdot48\times10^{-4}(30/2\cdot265)(200/30)^2, \tag{4}$$

$$= 0\cdot087. \tag{5}$$

The ultimate level of the second harmonic relative to that of the fundamental is

$$10\log_{10}\varphi_h = -10\cdot6 \text{ db.} \tag{6}$$

instead of -30 db. with the proper size of throat. The growth of the harmonic in the small throat horn is depicted in Fig. 118 A.

10. Influence of flare in reducing second harmonic. In § 1 we remarked on this property of a loudspeaker horn, so we now illustrate the point numerically. By taking the limiting values of (2), § 6, and (1), § 7, when $\beta \to 0$, and proceeding on the lines of § 8, we obtain

$$\varphi_t \simeq 1\cdot3\times10^{-13}P_1\,x^2\omega^2/A_0, \tag{1}$$

† The 'phase' velocity is then infinite, but the 'group' velocity is zero, so power is not transmitted down the horn. In practice, horns are of limited length, and the general conditions such that the 'cut-off' is not absolute.

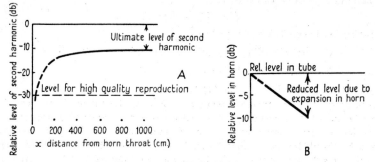

FIG. 118. A. Showing increase in level of second harmonic with distance from throat of exponential loudspeaker horn, for finite pressure amplitude. B. As at A, but for uniform frictionless tube.

provided $x \gg \frac{1}{2}k$. This formula gives the ratio of the power in the harmonic to that in the fundamental in a long uniform tube of cross-section A_0. To compare the level of the harmonic in the exponential horn having a throat area

$$A_0 = 2 \cdot 265 \text{ cm.}^2 \quad (r_0 = 0 \cdot 85 \text{ cm.})$$

with that in a tube of like area, we take $10 \log_{10}(\varphi_h/\varphi_t)$. This gives the level of the harmonic in the horn below that in the tube, as illustrated in Fig. 118 B, 500 cm. from the throat. The effect of flare is to reduce the second harmonic by 9·5 db., i.e. it has approximately one-tenth the power of that in the tube.

APPENDIX II

Mathieu's Equation as a Stability Criterion

1. Consider the equation

$$\ddot{y} + \alpha y + \beta y^3 = f \cos 3\omega t, \tag{1}\dagger$$

$\alpha, \beta, f > 0$, which (as shown in § 4.190) has an exact subharmonic solution $(4f/\beta)^{\frac{1}{3}} \cos \omega t$, provided $\omega^2 = \alpha + 3(f^2\beta/4)^{\frac{1}{3}}$. We wish to ascertain whether or not this solution is stable.

Let y be increased or decreased by a very small amount $\delta y = v$, such that terms in $v^2, v^3, \dots$, may be neglected. Then with $(y+v)$ for y in (1), we get

$$\ddot{y} + \ddot{v} + \alpha(y+v) + \beta(y+v)^3 = f \cos 3\omega t, \tag{2}$$

so
$$[\ddot{y} + \alpha y + \beta y^3 - f \cos 3\omega t] + \{\beta v^2(3y+v)\} + \ddot{v} + (\alpha + 3\beta y^2)v = 0. \tag{3}$$

By (1) the part in [ ] is zero, by hypothesis that in { } is negligible, so we are left with the variational equation, linear in v, namely,

$$\ddot{v} + (\alpha + 3\beta y^2)v = 0. \tag{4}$$

Now $y = (4f/\beta)^{\frac{1}{3}} \cos \omega t$, giving $3\beta y^2 = 6(f^2\beta/4)^{\frac{1}{3}}(1 + \cos 2\omega t)$; also from above $\alpha = \omega^2 - 3(f^2\beta/4)^{\frac{1}{3}}$. Substituting these into (4), yields

$$\ddot{v} + [\{\omega^2 + 3(f^2\beta/4)^{\frac{1}{3}}\} + 6(f^2\beta/4)^{\frac{1}{3}} \cos 2\omega t]v = 0. \tag{5}$$

If the solution of (5) is stable, so also is that of (1), since the procedure is equivalent to determining whether or not the amplitude of motion of the system represented by (1) increases with increase in time, after being disturbed.

Writing $\omega t = (\frac{1}{2}\pi - z)$ in (5), and dividing throughout by ω^2, yields the standard Mathieu equation

$$v'' + (a - 2q \cos 2z)v = 0. \tag{6}$$

In (6) $a = 1 + (3/\omega^2)(f^2\beta/4)^{\frac{1}{3}}$, and $q = (3/\omega^2)(f^2\beta/4)^{\frac{1}{3}}$, so

$$a = 1 + q. \tag{7}$$

From above we have also

$$q = (3/\omega^2)(f^2\beta/4)^{\frac{1}{3}} = (1 - \alpha/\omega^2), \tag{8}$$

and since $\omega^2 > \alpha$, q lies within the range $(0, 1)$. Now the characteristic curve a_1 in Figs. 36, 38 is given by

$$a_1 = 1 + q - \frac{1}{8}q^2 - \dots, \tag{9}$$

so the segment of the line $a = 1 + q$, $0 < q < 1$, lies in a stable region. Hence the subharmonic solution is stable.

2. As a second example we shall consider the case of the vibrating thread with non-linear control discussed in § 7.20 et seq., when the parameters are such that the D.E. in § 7.230 has an exact subharmonic solution. The D.E. is

$$y'' + (\alpha - 2\gamma \cos 2z)y + \beta y^3 = 0, \tag{1}\dagger$$

$\alpha, \beta, \gamma > 0$, its solution being $y = \pm 2(\gamma/\beta)^{\frac{1}{2}} \cos z$, provided that $\alpha = (1 - 2\gamma)$.

† The change in parameters from a, b to α, β, is to permit the use of a in (6) and other Mathieu equations, since it is standard.

With the foregoing restrictions on α, γ, it is evident from Fig. 38 that when $\beta = 0$, the line $\alpha = (1-2\gamma)$ lies in the stable region between $\alpha_0\dagger$ and $\beta_1\dagger$ of the corresponding $\alpha-\gamma$ stability diagram. It corresponds to the segment of the line between $a = 1, q = 0$, and $a = 0, q = 0.5$ in Fig. 38, so γ lies in the range $0 < \gamma < 0.5$. The variational equation, linear in v, is

$$v'' + (\alpha + 3\beta y^2 - 2\gamma \cos 2z)v = 0. \tag{2}$$

Writing $3\beta y^2 = 6\gamma(1+\cos 2z)$, $\alpha = (1-2\gamma)$ in (2), leads to

$$v'' + \{(1+4\gamma) + 4\gamma \cos 2z\}v = 0, \tag{3}$$

and with $(\tfrac{1}{2}\pi - z)$ for z, this takes the standard Mathieu form

$$v'' + (a - 2q \cos 2z)v = 0, \tag{4}$$

where $a = (1+4\gamma)$, $q = 2\gamma$, giving $a = 1+2q$, $0 < q < 1$. If we imagine this line to be drawn in Fig. 38, it will lie in the stable region between a_1 and b_2. Hence the solution $y = \pm 2(\gamma/\beta)^{\frac{1}{2}} \cos z$ is stable. The reader may deal with the case $\beta < 0$, for which the solution is $y = \pm 2(\gamma/\beta)^{\frac{1}{2}} \sin z$, provided $\alpha = (1+2\gamma)$.

3. By substituting $y = C + A \cos 2z$ into the D.E.

$$y'' + \alpha y + \beta y^2 = f \cos 4z, \tag{1}$$

$\alpha, \beta, f > 0$, and equating coefficients of like terms on both sides, we find that it is satisfied if $A = \pm(2f/\beta)^{\frac{1}{2}}$, $C = \{(4-\alpha)/2\beta\} < 0$, $\alpha^2 = 16 + 4\beta f$, so $\alpha > 4$. The variational equation is

$$v'' + (\alpha + 2\beta y)v = 0. \tag{2}$$

Then

$$(\alpha + 2\beta y) = \alpha + 2\beta[\{(4-\alpha)/2\beta\} \pm (2f/\beta)^{\frac{1}{2}} \cos 2z] \tag{3}$$

$$= 4 \pm 2(2f\beta)^{\frac{1}{2}} \cos 2z. \tag{4}$$

Inserting this into (2) leads to the Mathieu equations

$$v'' + (a \pm 2q \cos 2z)v = 0, \tag{5}$$

where $a = 4$, and $q = (2f\beta)^{\frac{1}{2}}$. Now in its complete form Fig. 36, § 7.10, is symmetrical about the a-axis, and it is seen that the line $a = 4$ passes through wide unstable, but narrow stable regions, for $\pm q = \pm(2f\beta)^{\frac{1}{2}}$. Accordingly the subharmonic solutions have these attributes in the corresponding ranges of q.

4. By (6), § 4.10, the D.E. for a thermionic valve oscillator in the range $0 < \epsilon \ll 1$ is

$$d^2y/dz^2 + \epsilon(y^2 - 1) \, dy/dz + y = 0. \tag{1}$$

The circuit damping is positive or negative according as $|y| > 1$ or < 1. The variational equation, linear in v, is

$$v'' + \epsilon(y^2 - 1)v' + (1 + 2\epsilon yy')v = 0. \tag{2}$$

In accordance with § 4.10 we take the approximate solution $y = A \sin z$, and we shall determine A for stability. Substituting for y into (2) gives

$$v'' + \epsilon[\{(A^2/2) - 1\} - (A^2/2)\cos 2z]v' + (1 + \epsilon A^2 \sin 2z)v = 0. \tag{3}$$

Let $v = e^{\varphi}u(z)$, where $\varphi = -\tfrac{1}{2}\epsilon[\{(A^2/2) - 1\}z - (A^2/4)\sin 2z]$ to remove the term in v'. Neglecting terms in ϵ^2 and writing $z = (x - \tfrac{1}{4}\pi)$, we obtain the Mathieu equation

$$u'' + [1 - (\epsilon A^2/2)\cos 2x]u = 0. \tag{4}$$

† These correspond to the curves a_0, b_1 in Fig. 38.

By [185, p. 78, (3)], (4) has an unstable solution of the form

$$u(x) = e^{\mu x} \times \text{bounded periodic function, period } 2\pi \quad (\mu > 0). \tag{5}$$

Thus
$$u(z) = e^{\mu\pi/4}e^{\mu z} \times \text{b.p.f.} \tag{6}$$

so
$$v = Ce^{(\mu z+\varphi)} \times \text{b.p.f.}, \tag{7}$$

where $C = e^{\mu\pi/4}$, a constant, and

$$\mu z + \varphi = \mu z - \tfrac{1}{2}\epsilon[\{(A^2/2)-1\}z-(A^2/4)\sin 2z]. \tag{8}$$

For stability we are concerned with the non-periodic part of (8), namely,

$$\psi = \{\mu+\tfrac{1}{2}\epsilon(1-A^2/2)\}z. \tag{9}$$

In (4), $q = \epsilon A^2/4$, and by [185, (3) § 4.92], since ϵ is small,

$$\mu = (\epsilon A^2/8)-O(\epsilon^3). \tag{10}$$

Substituting from (10) into (9), yields

$$\psi = (\epsilon z/8)\{4-A^2-O(\epsilon^2)\}. \tag{11}$$

Then the solution at (7) will be either stable or unstable, according as $\psi < 0$ or > 0. Thus for

(i) stability $\qquad 4-A^2-O(\epsilon^2) < 0$, so $A^2 > 4-O(\epsilon^2)$; $\qquad$ (12)

(ii) instability $\qquad 4-A^2-O(\epsilon^2) > 0$, so $A^2 < 4-O(\epsilon^2)$; $\qquad$ (13)

(iii) neutrality $\qquad\qquad A^2 = 4-O(\epsilon^2)$. $\qquad\qquad$ (14)

Hence the amplitude decreases or increases according as (i) or (ii) is satisfied, but it is stabilized for (iii). The form at (14) agrees with that of the coefficient of $\sin\psi$ in (23), § 4.110, where $(b/\omega_0)^2 \simeq \epsilon^2$.

In (4) if ϵ^2 terms were included, the variational equation would be a Hill type [(3), § 7.413 and ref. 185, p. 127]. The index μ could be found by aid of [(1), (4), § 6.12 in 185]. For stability the real non-periodic part of $(\mu z+\varphi) < 0$. This is left as an exercise for the reader, as also is consideration of the D.E. (1), § 5.12 which pertains to an electrically maintained tuning fork.

PROBLEMS

1. A large mass m starting from rest falls under the influence of gravity and encounters a resistance proportional to the square of its velocity. Obtain the appropriate differential equation, solve it and show that when t is large enough, the velocity is substantially constant. $[y = (m/k)\log\{\cosh(kg/m)^{\frac{1}{2}}t\}$, $v = (mg/k)^{\frac{1}{2}}\tanh(kg/m)^{\frac{1}{2}}t \sim (mg/k)^{\frac{1}{2}}$, where g is gravity, and k the resistance proportionality factor.]

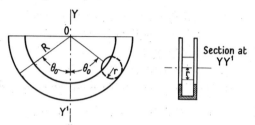

Fɪɢ. 119.

2. A spherical cavity in an unlimited volume of liquid of density ρ, has a radius r_0. Owing to an internal explosion, the gas pressure in the cavity increases suddenly to p_0 at $t = 0$. If the gas expands adiabatically when $t > 0$, the non-linear differential equation for r, the radius of the cavity, is

$$r\frac{d^2r}{dt^2}+\frac{3}{2}\left(\frac{dr}{dt}\right)^2-k^2\left(\frac{r_0}{r}\right)^{3\gamma} = 0,$$

where $k^2 = p_0/\rho$ and $\gamma = \frac{4}{3}$. Taking $\varphi = \{(r/r_0)-1\}$, solve this equation and obtain t as a function of φ. When $p_0 = 1,000$ atmospheres, $r_0 = 50$ cm. and $k \simeq 3\cdot16\times10^4$ cm. sec.$^{-1}$ Calculate the time taken for the radius to be doubled, and also the initial acceleration of the radius. $\left[t = \frac{(2\varphi)^{\frac{1}{2}}r_0}{k}\left(1+\frac{2\varphi}{3}+\frac{\varphi^2}{5}\right)\right.$; time for radius to be doubled $= 4\cdot17\times10^{-3}$ sec.; at $r = r_0$, $\frac{d^2r}{dt^2} = \frac{k^2}{r_0} = 2\times10^7$ cm. sec.$^{-2}$ Multiply the equation throughout by $2r^2\,dr/dt$, and then express it in the form of a first-order equation with t as independent variable.$\Big]$

3. A balanced circular wheel of mass m, polar moment of inertia about its axis I, outer radius r, can roll in a circular track inner radius R, mounted in a vertical plane as illustrated in Fig. 119. If the wheel starts from the position θ_0 at $t = 0$, obtain an *exact* formula for the periodic time of the motion, frictional loss being neglected. $\left[\tau_0 = 4\frac{l}{g}\Big\{\Big(1+\frac{I}{mr^2}\Big)\Big\}^{\frac{1}{2}} F(\sin\frac{1}{2}\theta_0,\frac{1}{2}\pi). \quad l(1+I/mr^2)\right.$ is the length of the equivalent simple pendulum. Compare with (12), § 3.160.$\Big]$

4. During oscillation, the tension T in the string of a simple pendulum varies periodically. If the length of the pendulum is l, mass of bob m, find an *exact* expression for T_{av}, the *time* average of T over one quarter period. Assume absence of loss, inextensibility of the string, and neglect its mass.

[$mg\{6(E/F)+(4k^2-5)\}$, where E and F are elliptic integrals of the first and second kinds, with modulus $k = \sin\frac{1}{2}\psi$, ψ being the amplitude.]

5. Referring to Fig. 120 show that the length of the arc NP of the ellipse is $aE(k,\varphi)$, E being an elliptic integral of the first kind with modulus $k = \{1-(b/a)^2\}^{\frac{1}{2}}$. $OA = ON = b$, $OB = OM = a$; at Q, $x = b\cos\psi$, $y = a\sin\psi$; at P, $x = b\cos\varphi$ and $y = a\sin\varphi$.

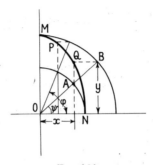

FIG. 120.

6. The weight of a balanced flywheel combination is $w = 22{,}400$ lb., and the polar moment of inertia about its axis is $\mathbf{I} = 1{\cdot}8 \times 10^4$ slug feet^2. It is mounted on a horizontal axle having a flanged wheel 3 ft. diameter at each end, the wheels running on parallel horizontal rails. Calculate the *exact* periodic time of rolling, if a weight $w_1 = 100$ lb. is fixed to the wheel at $l = 6$ ft. from the centre line of the axle, and released when the c.g. of w_1 is level with the tops of the rails. Assume absence of loss and slipping. [$\tau_0 = 4(2a/p)^{\frac{1}{2}}\{F(k,\frac{1}{2}\pi)-cE(k,\frac{1}{2}\pi)\} = 40{\cdot}1$ sec. nearly, where $a = \{\mathbf{I}+m_1 l^2+(m+m_1)r^2\}/2w_1 l$, $w_1 = m_1 g$, $w = mg$, $r = 1{\cdot}5'$, $p = (1-c) \simeq 0{\cdot}9972$, $c = b/a \simeq 2{\cdot}84 \times 10^{-3}$, $b = m_1 rl/w_1 l = r/g$, $k = \sin\frac{1}{2}\theta_0$, $\theta_0 = \frac{1}{2}\pi-\sin^{-1}(1{\cdot}5/6)$. If θ_0 is small, F, $E \simeq \frac{1}{2}\pi$ and $\tau_0 \simeq 35{\cdot}9$ sec.]

7. Determine the y, v coordinates and types of the singular points of the differential equation $\ddot{y}+ay-by^3 = 0$, a, $b > 0$. Using the method of isoclines in Chapter VIII, draw a representative set of v–y curves on squared paper, and check points on them from the v–y equation. Obtain the equation for the separatrix, and the slopes of the v–y curves on entering the cols. $\Big[y = v = 0$ is a centre, $y = \pm(a/b)^{\frac{1}{2}}$, $v = 0$ are cols. Equation of separatrix is found from $v^2 = A-ay^2+\frac{1}{2}by^4$ by taking $y = \pm(a/b)^{\frac{1}{2}}$, $v = 0$, which gives $A = a^2/2b$. Then $v^2 = \dfrac{a^2}{2b}\Big(1-\dfrac{by^2}{a}\Big)^2$, and at the cols, $dv/dy = \pm(2a)^{\frac{1}{2}}.\Big]$

8. Solve the differential equation in problem 7 for *stable* periodic motion, using the Fourier series method as far as the third harmonic. Explain the absence of a second harmonic. Calculate the periodic time τ_0 if $a = 10$, $b = 2$, $y(0) = y_0 = 1$, $v(0) = 0$, and compare it with that when $b = 0$.

[$y = 1{\cdot}0072 \cos\omega t - 0{\cdot}0072 \cos 3\omega t$; $\tau_0 \simeq 2{\cdot}16$ for $b = 2$ and $1{\cdot}99$ for $b = 0$. The condition for stability may be deduced either from the control curve $f(y) = ay-by^3$, or from the v–y curves. The exact solution and the condition for stability are given in 1°, § 3.20.]

9. A hollow cylinder, with its axis horizontal, containing air at N.T.P. is closed at one end, and at a distance l therefrom is a leakfree frictionless piston of mass m. The piston, area A, is displaced outwards a distance $y_0 \ll l$ and released at $t = 0$. Obtain the first three terms in the Fourier series for the subsequent displacement of the piston.

$$\left[y = \frac{b y_0^2}{2\omega^2} + y_0\left(1 - \frac{b y_0}{3\omega^2}\right) \cos \omega t - \frac{b y_0^2}{6\omega^2} \cos 2\omega t, \text{ with } \omega^2 \simeq \frac{A p_0 \gamma}{ml} = a, \text{ and} \right.$$

$$b = \frac{A p_0 \gamma(\gamma+1)}{2ml^2}. \text{ See § 4.199 for } \gamma \text{ and } p_0.$$

The next approximation is

$$y = \frac{b y_0^2}{2\omega^2}\left(1 - \frac{2b y_0}{\omega^2}\right) + y_0\left\{1 - \frac{b y_0}{3\omega^2} + \frac{29}{144}\frac{b^2 y_0^2}{\omega^4}\right\}\cos \omega t -$$

$$- \frac{b y_0^2}{6\omega^2}\left(1 - \frac{2b y_0}{3\omega^2}\right)\cos 2\omega t + \frac{b^2 y_0^3}{48\omega^4}\cos 3\omega t,$$

$$\text{with } \omega^2 \simeq a - 5b^2 y_0^2/6\omega^2. \Big]$$

10. Determine the singular point (coordinates and type) of the differential equation $\ddot{y} + 10y + 500y^3 = 0$, and plot the v–y curve for the initial conditions $y(0) = 1$, $\dot{y}(0) = 0$. Solve the equation by (i) the Fourier series method, (ii) perturbation method, (iii) elliptic integral. Use the Fourier series for $\operatorname{cn} u$ in § 3.19 to check the amplitude ratio of the third harmonic to the fundamental. Also, calculate from this series the amplitude ratio of the fifth and seventh harmonics to the fundamental. [The origin is a centre;

$$v^2 = 10(1 - y^2) + 250(1 - y^4);$$

(i) $y \simeq 0.953 \cos \omega t + 0.047 \cos 3\omega t$, $\qquad \omega^2 \simeq 368$;

(ii) $y \simeq 0.956 \cos \omega t + 0.0422 \cos 3\omega t + 0.0018 \cos 5\omega t$, $\qquad \omega^2 \simeq 369$;

(iii) $y = \operatorname{cn}(t\{a + bA^2\}^{\frac{1}{2}})$ with $A = 1$, so $y = \operatorname{cn} 22.6t$; the ratios are 0.0433, 0.0018, 0.000075, respectively.]

11. Using the method of iteration, extend the solution of (1), § 4.130 to the third approximation, and compare the values of y and ω with those given at (16), (17), § 4.131.

$$\left[y = -\left(\frac{b y_0^2}{2\omega^2} + \frac{b^2 y_0^3}{3\omega^4} - \frac{7}{72}\frac{b^3 y_0^4}{\omega^6}\right) + \right.$$

$$+ \left(y_0 + \frac{b y_0^2}{3\omega^2} + \frac{29b^2 y_0^3}{144\omega^4} - \frac{247}{2160}\frac{b^3 y_0^4}{\omega^6}\right)\cos \omega t + \left(\frac{b y_0^2}{6\omega^2} + \frac{b^2 y_0^3}{9\omega^4} + \frac{b^3 y_0^4}{108\omega^6}\right)\cos 2\omega t +$$

$$+ \left(\frac{b^2 y_0^3}{48\omega^4} + \frac{b^3 y_0^4}{144\omega^6}\right)\cos 3\omega t + \frac{b^3 y_0^4}{1080\omega^6}\cos 4\omega t; \ \omega^2 \text{ as in (17), § 4.131.}\Big]$$

12. Obtain the singular point (coordinates and type) of the differential equation $\ddot{y} + 2\kappa|\dot{y}|\dot{y} + \omega^2 y = 0$, κ small > 0. Solve the equation by the method of slowly varying amplitude and phase in Chapter V, taking $A = A_0$ at $t = 0$.

$$\left[\text{The origin is a stable spiral point. } y \simeq \frac{A_0 \sin(t + \varphi_0)}{(1 + 8A_0 \kappa \omega t/3\pi)}. \right]$$

13. Find the singular point (coordinates and type) of the differential equation $\ddot{y}+2\kappa|y|\dot{y}+\omega^2 y = 0$, κ small > 0. Using §§ 6.10, 6.20, obtain the equivalent linear differential equation and solve it. $\Big[$The origin is a stable spiral point. $\ddot{y}+\dfrac{8\kappa A}{3\pi}\dot{y}+\omega^2 y = 0$, $A = A_0/(1+4\kappa A_0 t/3\pi)$, $A_0 = A(0)$. Taking $C = 3\pi/4\kappa A_0$ the equation becomes $\ddot{y}+\dfrac{2\dot{y}}{(t+c)}+\omega^2 y = 0$ which may be solved by writing $x = (t+c)$, $y = u(x)/x$. Then $y = \dfrac{C\sin(\omega t+\varphi_0)}{(t+c)}.\Big]$

14. Determine the coordinates and types of the singular points of $\ddot{y}+ay+by^2 = d$ $(a, b, d > 0)$. Plot representative f–y, V–y, and v–y curves in the stable and unstable regions. What is the slope of the separatrix on entering and on leaving the col? $\Big[y = \pm\dfrac{1}{2b}\{(a^2+4bd)^{\frac{1}{2}}\mp a\}$, $v = 0$ are centre and col, respectively. The slopes at the col are $v' = \pm(a^2+4bd)^{\frac{1}{4}}.\Big]$

15. One end of a strip of metal of negligible mass is fixed to a shaped metal block, the other end being free. When a downward vertical force f is applied to that end, the free bending length is reduced in virtue of the block, such that the relationship between f and the vertical displacement y is $f = s_1 y+s_2 y^2$, s_1 and s_2 being positive non-zero constants. A weight w is attached to the free end, and prior to $t = 0$, it is supported, the strip being horizontal and unstrained. If w is released at $t = 0$, derive the differential equation for its motion. Find (i) the singular point of this equation in the range $y > 0$, (ii) the v–y relationship, and sketch the v–y curve. Also show that the solution of the equation is periodic, and express y as a function of t the time. [(i) a centre at the position of statical equilibrium $y = \theta$, $v = 0$, where $\theta = (a/2b)\{(1+4bg/a^2)^{\frac{1}{2}}-1\}$, and $a = s_1/m$, $b = s_2/m$, $w = mg$; (ii) $v^2 = y(2g-ay-\frac{2}{3}by^2)$; v–y curve is closed and symmetrical about the y-axis, which it crosses at

$$y = 0,\, y = (3a/4b)\{(1+16bg/3a^2)^{\frac{1}{2}}-1\};$$

$$v_{max} = |v_{min}| = \{(b\theta^3/3)+g\theta\}^{\frac{1}{2}}.$$

$$y = \theta(1-b\theta/2\omega^2)-\theta(1-b\theta/3\omega^2)\cos\omega t+(b\theta^2/6\omega^2)\cos 2\omega t;$$

$$\omega^2 = a+2b\theta-5b^2\theta^2/6\omega^2.$$

If $a = 10$, and $b = 100$, then $\theta = 0{\cdot}518$, $y_{max} = 0{\cdot}908$, $v_{max} = 4{\cdot}61$.]

16. Determine the singular points (coordinates and types) of the differential equation $\ddot{y}+\dot{y}+4y-y^3 = 0$. Indicate the form of the v–y curves, and plot to scale the potential energy curve (V–y). What significance pertains to maximum and minimum values of the V–y curve? [$y = v = 0$ is a stable spiral point; $y = \pm 2$, $v = 0$ are cols; see 2°, § 9.30, and Fig. 101.]

17. The differential equation for a non-linear vibrational system is

$$\frac{d^2y}{dt^2}+20y+12y^2 = 0.$$

Determine the coordinates and types of the singular points of this equation. Demonstrate that under certain conditions the solution is periodic. Use the method of perturbation to obtain a second approximation to the vibrational frequency, for initial conditions $y(0) = A$, $\dot{y}(0) = 0$. What is the largest permissible value of y if instability is to be avoided? Find the equation of the separatrix. Reference may be made to § 4.131 and Fig. 103.

[$y = v = 0$ is a centre, $y = -\frac{5}{3}$, $v = 0$ is a col; $v^2 = 20(A^2 - y^2) + 8(A^3 - y^3)$; $\omega^2 = 10\{1 + (1 - 1\cdot2A^2)^{\frac{1}{2}}\}$, $A < 0\cdot9$; for stability $|y| < 20/12 = 1\cdot667$; equation of separatrix is $v^2 = 18\cdot5 - 20y^2 - 8y^3$.]

18. Find the coordinates and types of the singular points of $\ddot{y} + ay + by^2 = 0$, $a, b > 0$. Show that under certain conditions the solution is periodic. Solve the equation in terms of Jacobian elliptic functions using initial conditions $y(0) = A$, $0 < A < a/2b$, $\dot{y}(0) = 0$, and find the periodic time. Using the Fourier series representations in § 3.19, and $a = 400$, $b = 100$, $A = 1$, compare the solution so obtained with that in (16), § 4.131. [Centre at $y = v = 0$; col at $y = -a/b$. $v = 0$ (see Figs. 11 A, 103). Solution is

$$y = \alpha_1 - (\alpha_1 - \alpha_2)\text{sn}^2 u = \alpha_2 + (\alpha_1 - \alpha_2)\text{cn}^2 u,$$

where $u = \{b(\alpha_1 - \alpha_3)/6\}^{\frac{1}{2}}t$; $\alpha_1, \alpha_2, \alpha_3$ are roots of the cubic

$$y^3 + p(y^2 - A^2) - A^3 = (y - A)\{y^2 + (p + A)y + (p + A)A\} = 0,$$

with $p = 3a/2b$. $\alpha_1 = A$, $\alpha_2 = y_{\min} < 0$,

$$\alpha_2, \alpha_3 = -\tfrac{1}{2}\{(p + A) \mp [(p + A)(p - 3A)]^{\frac{1}{2}}\}.$$

$\tau = 2\{6/b(\alpha_1 - \alpha_3)\}^{\frac{1}{2}}F(k, \tfrac{1}{2}\pi) = 0\cdot325$; by (17), § 4.131, $\tau = 0\cdot323$: $\alpha_1 = 1$, $\alpha_2 = -1\cdot208$, $\alpha_3 = -5\cdot79$, $k = \{(\alpha_1 - \alpha_2)/(\alpha_1 - \alpha_3)\}^{\frac{1}{2}} = 0\cdot57$. By (16), (17), § 4.131, $y = -0\cdot155 + 1\cdot102\cos\omega t + 0\cdot052\cos 2\omega t + 0\cdot001\cos 3\omega t$, $\omega = 19\cdot45$. To get the elliptic function solution put $v = dy/dt$, and then take

$$\sin\varphi = \{(\alpha_1 - y)/(\alpha_1 - \alpha_2)\}^{\frac{1}{2}}.$$

For stability, $0 < A < a/2b = 2$, which makes $k^2 < 1$.]

19. Determine the coordinates and types of singular points of the differential equation $\ddot{y} + ay^2 = c$, with $a, c > 0$, (i) from the control characteristic, (ii) from the potential energy curve, (iii) using Poincaré's criteria. Take $a = 3, c = 6$ and plot the curves for (i) and (ii). Draw representative v–y curves also; include the separatrix, and find its equation and the slopes as it enters and leaves the col. [Centre at $y = (c/a)^{\frac{1}{2}}$, $v = 0$; col at $y = -(c/a)^{\frac{1}{2}}$, $v = 0$; equation of separatrix is $v^2 = \tfrac{4}{3}(c^3/a)^{\frac{1}{2}} + 2cy - \tfrac{2}{3}ay^3$, and it has slopes $dv/dy = \pm(4ac)^{\frac{1}{4}}$ at the col.]

20. The differential equation for a system similar to that described in problem 15 is $m\ddot{y} + sy^2 = mg$. Plot representative control, V–y, and v–y curves, and demonstrate that the solution is periodic. Obtain the solution in elliptic integral form, and find the periodic time in terms of the gamma function. Obtain also the first three terms in the Fourier expansion type of solution. [The singular point in $y \geqslant 0$ is a centre at $y = (mg/s)^{\frac{1}{2}}$, $v = 0$; solution is

$$t = (3/Cb)^{\frac{1}{2}}\{F(1/2^{\frac{1}{2}}, \tfrac{1}{2}\pi) - F(1/2^{\frac{1}{2}}, \psi)\},$$

$C = (3mg/s)^{\frac{1}{2}}$ being the maximum downward displacement, and $\cos\psi = y/C$;

$$\tau = (3m/16\pi^2 gs)^{\frac{1}{4}}\Gamma^2(\tfrac{1}{4}) \simeq 4\cdot88(m/gs)^{\frac{1}{4}}.$$

$$y = (mg/s)^{\frac{1}{2}}(0\cdot793 - 0\cdot868\cos\omega t + 0\cdot075\cos 2\omega t)$$

is an approximate solution; $\omega = 2\pi/\tau$.]

21. The differential equation for the free oscillations of an undamped system is $\ddot{y} + ay + by^2 + cy^3 = 0$, with $a, b, c > 0$. Sketch the forms of the force-displacement curves for (i) $b^2 > 4ac$, (ii) $b^2 = 4ac$, (iii) $3ac < b^2 < 4ac$,

(iv) $b^2 < 3ac$. Determine the coordinates and types of the singular points in each case, indicate the shapes of the v–y curves and discuss the corresponding forms of solution. If the amplitude of oscillation about $y = 0$ in (i)–(iii) is such that the minimum of the control characteristic is not reached, take initial conditions $y(0) = A$, $\dot{y}(0) = 0$, and obtain an approximation to the periodic solution using the method of perturbation. $\bigg[$(i) centres at $y = 0$, and

$-(1/2c)\{b+(b^2-4ac)^{\frac{1}{2}}\}$, $v = 0$; col at $y = -(1/2c)\{b-(b^2-4ac)^{\frac{1}{2}}\}$, $v = 0$; (ii) centre at $y = v = 0$; centre-col at $y = -(b/2c)$, $v = 0$; (iii), (iv) centre at $y = v = 0$.

$$y = -\frac{bA^2}{2\omega^2}+A\left\{1+\frac{bA}{3\omega^2}-\frac{cA^2}{32\omega^2}\right\}\cos\omega t+\frac{bA^2}{6\omega^2}\cos 2\omega t+\frac{cA^3}{32\omega^2}\cos 3\omega t.$$

Assume that c is of order b and put $c = \epsilon b$, ϵ being constant.

$$\omega^2 = a+\frac{3cA^2}{4}-\frac{5b^2A^2}{6\omega^2}+\frac{bcA^3}{4\omega^2}.$$

Put $c = 0$ and compare with §§ 4.130, 4.131.$\bigg]$

22. Determine the coordinates and types of singular points of the differential equation $\ddot{y}+ay+by^3+cy^5 = 0$, with a, b, $c > 0$. Show that for any initial conditions $y(0) = A$, $\dot{y}(0) = v_0$, the solution is periodic. Sketch the forms of the control, potential energy, and v–y curves. Solve the equation approximately for initial conditions $y(0) = A > 0$, $\dot{y}(0) = 0$, using the method of perturbation. If $c = 0$, verify that the solution reduces to that in problem 21 when $b = 0$ and c is replaced by b. In the equation $\ddot{y}+ay+cy^5 = 0$ take $a = 10$, $c = 100$, and write down the solution for $A = 1$, $y(0) = 0$. Compare (i) the amplitude ratio of the third harmonic to the fundamental with that in problem 21 when $b = 0$, (ii) the two values of ω. Also obtain the results for $A = 1.5$, $\dot{y}(0) = 0$, and explain why they differ from those for $A = 1$, $\dot{y}(0) = 0$.

$\bigg[y = v = 0$ is a centre; $v^2 = a(A^2-y^2)\left\{1+\frac{b}{2a}(A^2+y^2)+\frac{c}{3a}(A^4+A^2y^2+y^4)\right\};$

$$y = A\left(1-\frac{bA^2}{32\omega^2}-\frac{cA^5}{24\omega^2}\right)\cos\omega t+\frac{A^3}{32\omega^2}\left(b+\frac{5cA^2}{4}\right)\cos 3\omega t+\frac{cA^5}{384\omega^2}\cos 5\omega t;$$

$\omega^2 = a+\frac{3bA^2}{4}+\frac{5cA^4}{8}$; (i) $y = 0.942\cos\omega t+0.054\cos 3\omega t+0.004\cos 5\omega t$; the

ratios are 0.0385 and 0.0574; (ii) $\omega^2 = 72.5$ and $85.\bigg]$

23. Determine the coordinates and types of singular points of

$$\ddot{y}+2\kappa\dot{y}+y-6y^3+9y^5 = 0,$$

for $\kappa \geqslant$ or < 0. Plot the control characteristic, the potential energy and v–y curves for $\kappa = 0$, $-.1 < y < 1$. Using the method of isoclines in Chapter VIII, draw representative sets of v–y curves for $\kappa = 0.5$ and 2 (see Fig. 101). When $\kappa = 2$, find two values for the slope as the curves enter the origin, and draw the 'exceptional' curve (see 2°, § 9.50). $[y = 0, v = 0$ is (i) a stable node if $\kappa > 1$, (ii) a stable spiral point if $0 < \kappa < 1$, (iii) a centre if $\kappa = 0$, (iv) an unstable node if $\kappa \leqslant -1$, (v) an unstable spiral point if $-1 < \kappa < 0$; if $\kappa = 0$, centre-col at $y = -1/3^{\frac{1}{2}}$, $v = 0$ and col-centre at $y = 1/3^{\frac{1}{2}}$, $v = 0$. The slopes at the origin are $-\kappa \pm (\kappa^2 - 1) = -2 \pm 3^{\frac{1}{2}}$ for $\kappa = 2$. $V = \frac{1}{2}y^2(1 - 3y^2 + 3y^4)$.]

24. Determine the coordinates and types of the singular points of the differential equation $\ddot{y} + \dot{y} + 20y - 5y^3 = 0$. Using the method of isoclines in Chapter VIII, plot a representative set of v-y curves. [Stable spiral point at $y = v = 0$; the cols at $y = \pm 2$, $v = 0$. $V = \frac{1}{4}(40y^2 - 5y^4)$ when $\kappa = 0$.]

25. Determine the coordinates and type of singular point of the differential equation $\ddot{y} + 0 \cdot 1\dot{y}^2 + y = 0$. Assume that $\dot{y}^2 = v^2 = w$, and obtain a first order equation in w and y. Solve this for w by aid of (4), (5), § 2.12. Use $A = -20$, $-10, 0, 10, 20$, and plot the corresponding v-y curves. What information may be deduced from these curves? [$v^2 = Ae^{-0 \cdot 2y} - 10y + 50$; the origin is a centre; the separatrix corresponds to $A = 0$, so $v = \pm (50 - 10y)^{\frac{1}{2}}$.]

26. The substitution $y = u'/u = (du/dx)/u$ transforms the differential equation $u''' + 2\kappa u'' + \omega^2 u' = 0$, $\omega > \kappa > 0$, to

$$y'' + (2\kappa + 3y)y' + \omega^2 y + 2\kappa y^2 + y^3 = 0.$$

Solve the original equation by putting $v = u'$, and thence solve the equation for y. [$y = \omega \cos(\alpha t + \theta + \tan^{-1}\kappa/\alpha)/\{\sin(\alpha t + \theta) + Fe^{\kappa t}\}$, where θ, F are constants of integration, and $\alpha^2 = (\omega^2 - \kappa^2)$.]

27. Obtain the periodic solution of the differential equation in § 8.12 to the first order in ϵ ($0 < \epsilon < 0 \cdot 25$) using the method of *iteration*, with initial conditions $y(0) = 0$, $\dot{y}(0) = A$. [$y = 2\sin t + \frac{1}{4}\epsilon(\cos t - \cos 3t)$, $A = 2$.]

28. Using the method of isoclines in Chapter VIII (see Fig. 60), draw a v-y curve for $\ddot{y} - 0 \cdot 5(1 - y^2)\dot{y} + y = 0$. From this curve obtain approximate values of the ultimate amplitude and the periodic time of the steady oscillation.

29. Determine the coordinates and type of singular point of $\ddot{y} + \epsilon y^2 \dot{y} + y = 0$, $\epsilon > 0$. Apply the method of slowly varying amplitude and phase in Chapter V to obtain an approximate solution if $0 < \epsilon \ll 1$. Using the method of isoclines in Chapter VIII, draw a v-y curve for $\epsilon = 0 \cdot 1$.

$$\left[y = v = 0 \text{ is a stable spiral point. } y = \frac{A_0 \sin(t + \varphi_0)}{(1 + \epsilon A_0^2 t/4)}. \right]$$

30. Obtain the periodic solution of $\ddot{y} - \epsilon(1 - y^2)\dot{y} + by^3 + y = 0$ to the first order in b and ϵ, $0 < b < 0 \cdot 25$, $0 < \epsilon < 0 \cdot 25$. Take $y(0) = 0$, $\dot{y}(0) = A$, and use the method of iteration. [$y = A \sin t - (b - \epsilon)(A^3/32)(\cos t - \cos 3t)$, with $A = 2/(1 + 3b/\epsilon)^{\frac{1}{2}}$. When $b = \epsilon$, $y = \sin t$ is an *exact* solution. This remark applies also to (1), § 5.12 if $a = 1$, and $3c = 8\kappa$. When $b = 0$, the solution is that given for problem 27.]

31. Find the transient solution of the equation in problem 30 using the method of slowly varying amplitude and phase in Chapter V, with $A = A_0$ when $t = 0$.

$$\left[y = \frac{A_0 e^{\epsilon t/2}\sin(t + \varphi_0)}{\{1 + kA_0^2(e^{\epsilon t} - 1)\}^{\frac{1}{2}}} \rightarrow \frac{\sin(t + \varphi_0)}{k^{1/2}} \text{ as } t \rightarrow +\infty, \text{ where } k = \frac{1}{4}(1 + 3b/\epsilon). \right.$$

If $b = \epsilon$, then $k = 1$, and $y \rightarrow \sin(t + \varphi_0)$ as $t \rightarrow +\infty$. For initial conditions $y(0) = 0$, $\dot{y}(0) = A_0$, we have $\varphi_0 = 0$ and $y \rightarrow \sin t$ as in problem 30, for the steady state. $\Big]$

32. Determine the conditions under which the solution of $\ddot{y} + 2\kappa y\dot{y} + ay = d$, is periodic, with $\kappa, a > 0$. Obtain the periodic solution to order two in κ, using the method of perturbation. For initial conditions take (i) $y(0) = A$, $\dot{y}(0) = 0$, (ii) $y(0) = 0$, $\dot{y}(0) = \omega A$.

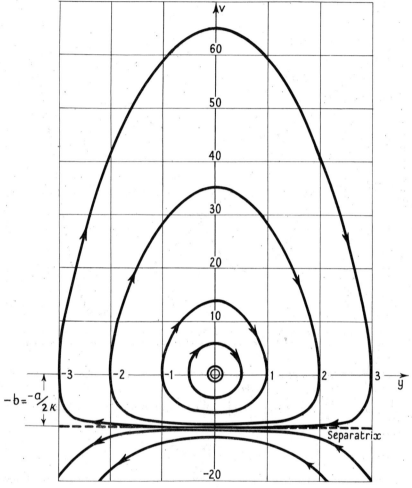

FIG. 121. v–y curves for $\ddot{y} + 10y\dot{y} + 100y = 0$, showing stable (above the separatrix) and unstable regions (below the separatrix). The origin is a centre.

$\left[\dot{y} = v > -a/2\kappa,\ d = 0.\right.$

(i) $\quad y = A\left(1 - \dfrac{23\kappa^2 A^2}{72\omega^2}\right)\cos\omega t + \dfrac{\kappa A^2}{3\omega}(2\sin\omega t - \sin 2\omega t) +$

$$+ \dfrac{\kappa^2 A^3}{72\omega^2}(32\cos 2\omega t - 9\cos 3\omega t);$$

(ii) $y = A\left(1 - \dfrac{2\kappa A}{3\omega} + \dfrac{37\kappa^2 A^2}{72\omega^2}\right)\sin\omega t + \dfrac{\kappa A^2}{3\omega}\left(1 - \dfrac{4\kappa A}{3\omega}\right)\sin 2\omega t + \dfrac{\kappa^2 A^3}{8\omega^2}\sin 3\omega t;$

$\omega^2 = (a - \kappa^2 A^2/3)$ where $\kappa^2 A^2/3 \ll a$ in both cases. See [243].$\Big]$

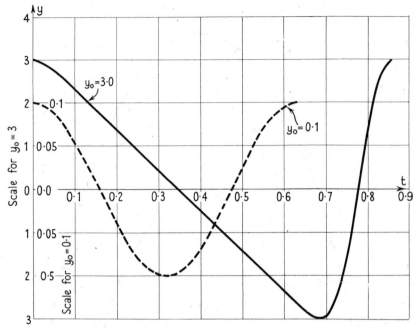

Fig. 122. y–t curves for $\ddot{y} + 10y\dot{y} + 100y = 0$ for initial conditions
(i) $y_0 = 0.1$, $v_0 = 0$ (broken curve), and (ii) $y_0 = 3$, $v_0 = 0$ (solid curve).

33. In problem 32, if $d = 0$, find the equation of the v–y curves when
(i) $v > -a/2\kappa$, (ii) $v < -a/2\kappa$.

$\left[\text{(i)}\ \ y = \pm\left\{\dfrac{1}{\kappa}\left[-v + b\log\left(\dfrac{b+v}{v}\right)\right] + y_0^2\right\}^{\frac{1}{2}}\right.$, the initial conditions being $y(0) = y_0$,
$v(0) = 0$, and $b = a/2\kappa$;

(ii) $y = \pm\left\{\dfrac{1}{\kappa}\left[(v_0 - v) - b\log\left(\dfrac{b+v_0}{b+v}\right)\right] + y_0^2\right\}^{\frac{1}{2}}$,

the initial conditions being $y(0) = y_0$, $v(0) = v_0 < -a/2\kappa$. In (i) the curves
are closed about the singular point $y = v = 0$, whereas in (ii) $y \to \pm\infty$ as
$v \to -\infty$ whatever the value of y_0, which entails instability. See Figs. 121, 122,
and [243]. The y–t curve resembles a saw tooth form if y_0 is large enough.$\Big]$

34. Determine the coordinates and type of singular point of the differential
equation $\ddot{y} + 2\kappa\dot{y} + ay + by^3 = d$, with $a, b, d, \kappa > 0$. Indicate the form of a
typical v–y curve. $\Big[$Put $y = (x + \theta)$, where θ is the only real root of

$$b\theta^3 + a\theta - d = 0.$$

The singular point is $y = \theta$, $v = 0$. If $\kappa^2 \geqslant a + 3b\theta^2$ it is a stable node; if $\kappa^2 < a + 3b\theta^2$, it is a stable spiral point. The singularities are unstable in type for $\kappa < 0$.]

35. In a capacitor having a non-linear dielectric, e.g. rochelle salt crystal, the capacitance is $C(Q) = C_0/(1 + aQ + bQ^2)$, Q being the charge, C_0 the capacitance when $Q = 0$, while a and b are positive constants < 1, such that $4b > a^2$. At $t = 0$ the capacitor has a charge Q_0, and it is then put in series with a coil of inductance L_0. Write the differential equation for Q and determine the co-ordinates and type of its singular point. Indicate the form of the I–Q curves (analogous to v–y curves for a mechanical system), where $I = dQ/dt$.

$\Big[\ddot{Q} + \omega_0^2 Q(1 + aQ + bQ^2) = 0$, where $\omega_0^2 = 1/L_0 C_0$. Centre at $Q = I = 0$.

If L_0 has resistance R_0, the origin is a stable node for $\kappa_0 \geqslant \omega_0$ and a stable spiral point for $\kappa_0 < \omega_0$, where $\kappa_0 = R_0/2L_0$.

$$I = \pm\omega\Big\{(Q_0^2 - Q^2) + \frac{2a}{3}(Q_0^3 - Q^3) + \frac{b}{2}(Q_0^4 - Q^4)\Big\}^{\frac{1}{2}}.\Big]$$

36. Using theorem 4, § 9.50, show that $\ddot{y} + 2\kappa|y|\dot{y} + ay = F(t)$, where κ, $a > 0$, and $F(t)$ is a continuous periodic function of t having period τ, has a periodic solution with period τ.

37. Using theorem 3, § 9.50, show that $\ddot{y} + 2\kappa\dot{y} + ay + by^2 = f\cos\omega t$, κ, a, $b > 0$, has a periodic solution with period $2\pi/\omega$, provided $y > -b/a$. Why is this restriction essential?

38. The differential equation for a direct radiator loudspeaker having a coil-driven conical diaphragm is $\ddot{y} + 2\kappa\dot{y} + ay + by^2 + cy^3 = f\cos\omega t$, where $a, b, c, f, \kappa > 0$. To avoid a maximum or a minimum in the control characteristic, take $b^2 < 3ac$, so that the only real zero of $cy^3 + by^2 + ay = 0$, is $y = 0$. Then an inflexion occurs at $y = -b/3c$ and the control curve

$$f(y) = ay + by^2 + cy^3$$

is an asymmetrical type, e.g. if $a = 1$, $b = 2$, $c = 3$. Using theorem 3, § 9.50, show that the equation has a periodic solution for $\kappa \geqslant 0$. Take $\kappa = 0$, f constant, and solve by the method of perturbation with initial conditions $y(0) = A$, $\dot{y}(0) = 0$. Assume absence of subharmonics.

$\Big[$Put $z = \omega t$, $c = bk$, $f = bF$, k and F being constants.

$$y = -\frac{bA^2}{2a} + A\Big\{1 + \frac{A}{a}\Big(b - \frac{cA}{32}\Big)\Big\}\cos\omega t + \frac{bA^2}{6a}\cos 2\omega t + \frac{cA^3}{32a}\cos 3\omega t;$$

$$\omega^2 = a + A^2\Big\{\frac{3c}{4} - \frac{5b^2}{6a}\Big\} + \frac{3cA^4}{4a}\Big(b - \frac{cA}{16}\Big) - \frac{f}{A},$$

from which A may be calculated. $-bA^2/2a$ represents a unidirectional displacement in virtue of asymmetry of the control characteristic. The 'centre of oscillation' moves away from the origin in the direction of minimum slope (at the inflexion). The combined effect of asymmetry and variation in the radial magnetic field along the axis of the magnet causes an appreciable unidirectional displacement of the coil either into or out of the magnet in the low audio frequency range provided f is large enough. In practice κ is likely to be relatively large (due to mechanical loss mainly), and the curves corresponding to those in

Fig. 16 A may not have vertical tangents. Thus the jump phenomenon (see § 4.170) will not occur. If, however, κ is small enough, this phenomenon will occur. These statements have been confirmed experimentally.$\big]$

39. An electrical circuit comprises a fixed inductance L_0 and periodically varying capacitance $C = C_0(1+2q\cos 2\omega t)$, $0 < q < 0.05$. Determine a condition under which the current will increase indefinitely with increase in time. What type of impedance must be connected in circuit to cause the current to attain a steady value? Explain why this happens.

$$[(1-q) < (\omega/\omega_0)^2 < (1+q), \qquad \omega_0^2 = 1/L_0 C_0.]$$

40. An electrical circuit comprises a fixed capacitance C_0 and periodically varying inductance $L = L_0(1+2q\cos 2\omega t)$, $0 < q < 0.05$. Determine a condition under which the current will increase indefinitely with increase in time (in a theoretical sense). What type of impedance must be connected in circuit so that the current will attain a steady value? Explain why this happens. [See the answer to problem 39 for the condition to be satisfied.]

41. The differential equation for a stretched string driven *along* its length, thereby causing variation in tension, may be written in the form

$$\frac{d^2y}{dz^2}+(a-2q\cos 2z)y+by^3 = 0,$$

where y is the transverse displacement of any point in the string, and $z = \omega t$. Take $a = 1, b = 0.1, 0 < q < 0.25$ and find the periodic solution to the second order in b, q, using the method of perturbation, with initial conditions $y(0) = A$, $\dot{y}(0) = 0$.

$\bigg[$Put $q = b\epsilon$.

$$y = A\bigg\{1+\frac{q}{8}\bigg(1-\frac{A^2}{4\epsilon}\bigg)+\frac{5q^2}{192}\bigg(1+\frac{3A^2}{20\epsilon}\bigg)\bigg\}\cos z -$$

$$-\frac{Aq}{8}\bigg(1-\frac{A^2}{4\epsilon}\bigg)\bigg\{\bigg(1+\frac{1}{4}q\bigg)\cos 3z-\frac{q}{24}\bigg(1-\frac{3A^2}{4\epsilon}\bigg)\cos 5z\bigg\};$$

$$a = \bigg(1-\frac{3A^2b}{4}+\frac{3A^4b^2}{128}\bigg)+\bigg(1-\frac{A^2b}{16}\bigg)q-\frac{1}{8}q^2; \qquad A = \bigg(\frac{4q}{3b}\bigg)^{\frac{1}{2}}.$$

With this value of A, $y \simeq A\{(1+\frac{1}{12}q+\frac{1}{32}q^2)\cos z-\frac{1}{12}(q+\frac{1}{4}q^2)\cos 3z\}$. When $q = 0.2$ the amplitude ratio of the third harmonic to the fundamental is approximately 0.017, i.e. 1.7 per cent. See [239] for additional information.$\big]$

42. The differential equation for y, the lateral displacement of an electrically-driven tuning fork is $\ddot{y}+(c\dot{y}^2-2\kappa)\dot{y}+ay = 0$, with $a > 0$, c, κ small > 0. Show that $y = \dot{y} = 0$ is the only singular point of the equation. Discuss the v-y curves, as in 3°, § 9.23, and show that the equation has a periodic solution. If we put $y = (2\kappa/c)^{\frac{1}{2}}x$, $2\kappa = \epsilon$, the equation becomes $\ddot{x}+\epsilon(\dot{x}^2-1)\dot{x}+ax = 0$.

Obtain the periodic solution to the second order in ϵ, using the method of perturbation, with initial conditions $x(0) = A$, $\dot{x}(0) = 0$. The transient solution is given in § 5.12.

$$\left[x = \frac{2}{3^{\frac{1}{2}}\omega}\left\{\left(1 - \frac{5\epsilon^2}{192\omega^2}\right)\cos\omega t - \frac{\epsilon}{24\omega}(3\sin\omega t - \sin 3\omega t) + \right.\right.$$

$$\left.\left. + \frac{\epsilon^2}{192\omega^2}(6\cos 3\omega t - \cos 5\omega t)\right\} \quad \omega^2 = (a - \tfrac{3}{8}\epsilon^2).\right.$$

See [240] for additional information.$\Big]$

43. Using the procedure in § 4, Appendix II, investigate the stability of motion of the tuning fork in problem 42. As a first approximation take $x = A\cos\omega t$. $\Big[$Stable if $A^2 > \dfrac{4}{3\omega^2} - O(\epsilon^2)$; unstable if $A < \dfrac{4}{3\omega^2} - O(\epsilon^2)$; neutral and periodic if $A^2 = \dfrac{4}{3\omega^2} - O(\epsilon^2)$. The v–x or v–y curves entail a limit cycle as in § 8.12. See [240] for additional information.$\Big]$

44. Solve $\ddot{\theta} + 0{\cdot}1\dot{\theta} + 2\sin\theta = H(t)$ approximately, for the range $0 \leqslant t \leqslant 1$, using Maclaurin's theorem and the procedure in § 8.35.

$$[\theta \simeq 0{\cdot}5t^2(1 - 0{\cdot}0333t - 0{\cdot}1658t^2 + 0{\cdot}00665t^3 + 0{\cdot}10944t^4).]$$

45. Continue the solution of (6), § 8.33 as given in Table 4, p. 169, as far as $t = 6$. Take a common interval $0{\cdot}1$. Plot θ and t in $0 \leqslant t \leqslant 6$.

46. By aid of Maclaurin's theorem, obtain an approximate solution of $d^2\theta/dx^2 + x\sin\theta = 0$ for boundary conditions $\theta(0) = \theta_0$, $\theta'(0) = 0$. Calculate the first three non-zero coefficients in the formula for θ, with $\theta_0 = 30°$.

$$\left[\theta \simeq \frac{\pi}{6} - \frac{x^3}{2{.}3!} + \frac{3^{\frac{1}{2}}}{6!}x^6.\right]$$

47. The differential equation for an undamped pendulum is

$$d^2\theta/dt^2 + a\sin\theta = 0,$$

where $a = gh/k^2$, g = acceleration due to gravity, h = distance of c.g. from support, k = radius of gyration about support. Find the positions and types of the singular points of the equation in the range $-4\pi \leqslant \theta \leqslant 4\pi$ by three different methods. Sketch the v–θ curves, and determine the slopes when they enter and leave the cols. [Centres at $\theta = 0$, $\pm 2\pi$, $\pm 4\pi$, $v = 0$; cols at $\theta = \pm\pi$, $\pm 3\pi$, $v = 0$; slopes at cols are $\pm a^{\frac{1}{2}}$.]

48. The differential equation for longitudinal wave motion of *finite* amplitude in a uniform rubber rod is

$$\frac{\partial^2\xi}{\partial x^2} = \left(\frac{3}{c^2}\right)\frac{\partial^2\xi}{\partial t^2}\{(1 + \xi')^3/[2 + (1 + \xi')^3]\},$$

where $\xi(x, t)$ is the displacement at a point distant x from the end $x = 0$ at time t, $\xi' = \partial\xi/\partial x$, and c is the velocity of propagation of waves of infinitesimal amplitude. If the rod is driven at $x = 0$ by an axial force such that $\xi(0, t) = \xi_0\cos\omega t$, and the far end is terminated to avoid reflection, determine the periodic part of the displacement $\xi(x, t)$, to the second order in ξ_0.

$\Big[\xi = \xi_0 \cos\theta - (\xi_0^2 k^2 x/4)\cos 2\theta.$ $k = \omega/c,$ $\theta = (\omega t - kx),$ $\xi_0 k^2 x \leqslant 1.$ To the third order in $\xi_0,$

$$\xi = \xi_0\Big(1 - \frac{\xi_0^2 k^4 x^2}{8}\Big)\cos\theta - \tfrac{1}{8}\xi_0^3 k^3 x \sin\theta - \tfrac{1}{4}\xi_0^2 k^2 x \cos 2\theta +$$
$$+ \tfrac{1}{8}\xi_0^3 k^4 x^2 \cos 3\theta - \tfrac{1}{24}\xi_0^3 k^3 x \sin 3\theta.$$

The method of solution is that in Appendix I, also that in [241].$\Big]$

49. The differential equation for plane sound waves of *finite* amplitude in air is $\dfrac{\partial^2\xi}{\partial x^2} = \dfrac{1}{c^2}\dfrac{\partial^2\xi}{\partial t^2}(1+\xi')^{\gamma+1},$ the symbols having the same meaning as in problem 48; $\gamma = 1\cdot 4$ for air. If $\xi = \xi_0\cos\omega t$ at $x = 0,$ obtain the periodic part of $\xi(x,t)$ to the second order in $\xi_0.$

$\Big[\xi = \xi_0\cos\theta - \dfrac{(\gamma+1)}{8}\xi_0^2 k^2 x \cos 2\theta;$ $\Big(\dfrac{\gamma+1}{2}\Big)\xi_0 k^2 x \leqslant 1$ to restrict $x.$ See [241] for third order in $\xi_0.\Big]$

50. In problem 49, if the particle displacement at $x = 0$ is

$$\xi = \xi_1\cos\omega_1 t + \xi_2\cos\omega_2 t, \qquad \omega_1 \neq \omega_2 \neq 0,$$

obtain the periodic part of the solution to the second order in $\xi_1, \xi_2.$

$\Big[\xi = \xi_1\cos\theta_1 + \xi_2\cos\theta_2 - \dfrac{(\gamma+1)x}{8}\{\xi_1^2 k_1^2\cos 2\theta_1 + \xi_2^2 k_2^2\cos 2\theta_2 +$

$$+ 2\xi_1\xi_2 k_1 k_2\cos(\theta_1+\theta_2) - 2\xi_1\xi_2 k_1 k_2\cos(\theta_1-\theta_2)\};$$

$k_m = \omega_m/c,$ $\theta_m = (\omega_m t - k_m x);$ restriction on x as in problem 49. Non-linearity of the medium introduces the respective sum and difference frequencies $(\omega_1+\omega_2)$ and $(\omega_1-\omega_2).$ See §§ 4.20–4.22.$\Big]$

51. Water waves of *finite* amplitude in a very long uniform canal of rectangular cross-section. If u is the *horizontal* velocity of the water particles at abscissa $x,$ η the elevation of the water surface at x from its quiescent level h above the bottom of the canal, the non-linear differential equations of motion are

$$\frac{\partial u}{\partial t} + u\frac{\partial u}{\partial x} = -g\frac{\partial\eta}{\partial x} \quad\text{and}\quad \frac{\partial\eta}{\partial t} + u\frac{\partial\eta}{\partial x} = -(h+\eta)\frac{\partial u}{\partial x},$$

g being the acceleration due to gravity. The non-linear terms are $u\,\partial u/\partial x,$ $u\,\partial\eta/\partial x,$ and $-\eta\,\partial u/\partial x.$ The canal is open to the sea at $x = 0,$ where owing to tidal motion, the water elevation is $\eta = \eta_0\cos\omega t,$ and the effect of reflection from the far end of the canal at an intermediate point is negligible. Determine the values of η and u at any $x > 0$ to the second order in $\eta_0.$ $\Big[$In the first approximation neglect the non-linear terms and solve the equations, so reduced, to satisfy the boundary condition at $x = 0.$

$$\eta = \eta_0\cos\theta - \frac{3\eta_0^2 g\omega}{4c^3}x\sin 2\theta, \qquad u = \frac{\eta_0 g}{c}\cos\theta - \frac{\eta_0^2 g^2}{8c^3}\cos 2\theta - \frac{3\eta_0^2 g^2\omega x}{c^4}\sin 2\theta,$$

where $\theta = (\omega t - kx)$, $k = \omega/c$, $c = (gh)^{\frac{1}{2}}$ the velocity of wave propagation in an unlimited expanse of water.]

52. Using the Maclaurin series method of solution, obtain an Abac for calculating the coefficients, as far as the term in η^{14}, in the solution of $w''' + ww'' = 0$, with boundary conditions $w(0) = w'(0) = 0$, $\lim_{\eta \to \infty} w'(\eta) = \frac{1}{2}$. Take $w_0^{(2)} = \alpha$, and evaluate the first five non-zero coefficients in terms thereof. Given that $w(2) = 0.325$, and that α lies between 0.164 and 0.169, calculate its value using the first four terms of the series for $w(\eta)$ and linear interpolation. Find also a solution of the equation valid at $\eta = \infty$.

$$\left[w(\eta) = \alpha \eta^2 \left(\frac{1}{2!} - \frac{\alpha \eta^3}{5!} + \frac{11\alpha^2 \eta^6}{8!} - \frac{375\alpha^3 \eta^9}{11!} + \frac{27897\alpha^4 \eta^{12}}{14!} - \dots \right); \right.$$

$$\left. \alpha \simeq 0.166; \qquad w = \frac{1}{2}\eta - b, \, b > 0, \text{ at } \eta = \infty. \right]$$

REFERENCES

Abbreviations used in Section A

1. *A.M.*   *Annals of Mathematics* (America).
2. *A.P.*   *Annalen der Physik.*
3. *A.P.T.T.*   *Annales des Postes Télégraphes et Téléphones.*
4. *B.S.M.*   *Bulletin des Sciences Mathématiques.*
5. *C.R.*   *Comptes Rendus des séances de l'Académie des Sciences.*
6. *D.M.J.*   *Duke Mathematical Journal* (America).
7. *J.A.M.*   *Journal Applied Mechanics* (America).
8. *J.A.P.*   *Journal Applied Physics* (America).
9. *J.F.I.*   *Journal Franklin Institute.*
10. *J.I.E.E.*   *Journal Institution Electrical Engineers* (London).
11. *J.M.P.*   *Journal Mathematics and Physics* (Mass. Inst. Tech. America).
12. *J.T.F.*   *Journal Tekhnitcheskoi Fisiki* (Moscow).
13. *M.A.*   *Mathematische Annalen.*
14. *P.I.A.C.S.*   *Proceedings Indian Association for Cultivation of Science.*
15. *P.I.R.E.*   *Proceedings Institute Radio Engineers* (America).
16. *P.M.*   *Philosophical Magazine.*
17. *P.N.A.S.W.*   *Proceedings National Academy of Sciences, Washington.*
18. *P.R.S.E.*   *Proceedings Royal Society, Edinburgh.*
19. *Q.A.M.*   *Quarterly Applied Mathematics* (America).
20. *T.A.I.E.E.*   *Transactions American Institute Electrical Engineers.*
21. *T.P.U.S.S.R.* *Technical Physics of the U.S.S.R.* (Leningrad).
22. *Z.A.M.M.*   *Zeitschrift für angewandte Mathematik und Mechanik.*

The items in sections A, B marked with an asterisk may be consulted for information relating to analytical proofs and justification of the methods used in the text.

A. SCIENTIFIC PAPERS

1. ABELÉ, J. Définition cinématique des oscillations de relaxation. *Jour. de Physique*, **6**, 96, 1945.

2. ABRAHAM, M., and BLOCH, A. Mesure en valeur absolue des périodes des oscillations de haute fréquence. *Annales de Physique*, **12**, 237, 1919.

3. ANDRONOW, A. Les cycles limités de Poincaré et la theorie des oscillations autoentretenues. *C.R.* **189**, 559, 1929.

4. —— and WITT, A. Zur Theorie des Mitnehmens. *Archiv für Elektr.* **24**, 99, 1930.

5. —— —— Sur la théorie mathématique des auto-oscillations. *C.R.* **190**, 256, 1930.

6. —— —— Sur la théorie mathématique des systèmes auto-oscillatoires a deux degrés de liberté. *T.P.U.S.S.R.* **1**, 249, 1934.

7. APPLETON, E. V., and POL, B. VAN DER. Form of free triode oscillations. *P.M.* **42**, 201, 1921.

8. —— —— oscillation hysteresis in triode. *P.M.* **43**, 177, 1922.

9. —— Automatic synchronization of triode oscillators. *Proc. Camb. Phil. Soc.* **21**, 231, 1922.

10. APPLETON, E. V., and GREAVES, W. M. H. Solution of representative differential equation of triode oscillator. *P.M.* **45**, 401, 1923.

11. —— Anomalous behaviour of a galvanometer. *P.M.* **47**, 609, 1924.

12. ARTEMJEW, N. Periodische Lösungen nichtlinearer partieller Differentialgleichungen. *J.T.F.* **1**, No. 2, 1934.

13. BANERJI, D. Theory and application of sub-synchronous pendulums. *P.I.A.C.S.* **7**, 145, 1923.

*14. BENDIXON, I. Sur les courbes définies par des équations différentielles. *Acta Mathematica*, **24**, 1, 1901.

15. BICKLEY, W. G. Simple method for numerical solution of differential equation. *P.M.* **13**, 1006, 1932; **15**, 1174, 1933.

16. —— The heavy elastica. *P.M.* **17**, 603, 1934.

17. —— The plane jet. *P.M.* **23**, 727, 1937.

18. —— Secondary flow due to sphere rotating in viscous fluid. *P.M.* **25**, 746, 1938.

*19. BIRKHOFF, G. D. Quelques théorèmes générales sur le mouvement des systèmes dynamiques. *B.S.M.* **40**, 1912.

*20. —— *Acta Math.* **43**, 80, 1922.

21. BOWSHEWEROW, V. Experimentelle Untersuchung des Phasenraumes Autoschwingender Systeme. *T.P.U.S.S.R.* **2**, 43, 1935.

22. BULGAKOV, B. V. Problems of control theory with non-linear characteristics. *Appl. Math. Mech.* [*Akad. Nauk U.S.S.R. Prikl. Mat. Mech.*], **10**, 313, 1946.

23. CARRIER, G. F. Non-linear vibration problem of elastic string. *Q.A.M.* **3**, 157, 1945.

24. —— On the buckling of elastic rings. *J.M.P.* **26**, 94, 1947.

25. CARTAN, E. and H. Note sur la génération des oscillations entretenues. *A.P.T.T.* **14**, 1196, 1925.

*26. CARTWRIGHT, M. L., and LITTLEWOOD, J. E. Non-linear differential equation of the second order. *Jour. Lond. Math. Soc.* **20**, 180, 1945.

*27. —— —— Non-linear differential equations of the second order. *A.M.* **48**, 472, 1947.

*28. —— Forced oscillations in nearly sinusoidal systems. *J.I.E.E.* **95**, part III, 88, 1948.

*29. —— Topological aspect of forced oscillations. *Research*, **1**, 601, 1948.

30. COLE, R. S. *Surge chamber in hydro-electric installations.* Selected paper No. 55, Institution Civil Engineers (London), 1927.

31. DUFFIN, R. J. Non-linear networks. *Bull. Amer. Math. Soc.* **52**, 833, 1946; **53**, 963, 1947; **54**, 119, 1948.

32. EARNSHAW, S. On the mathematical theory of sound. *Phil. Trans. Roy. Soc. Lond.* **150**, 133, 1860.

33. EDGERTON, H. E., and ZAK, F. J. Pulling into step of synchronous motors. *J.I.E.E.* **68**, 1205, 1930.

34. —— —— and FOURMARIER, P. Pulling into step of salient pole synchronous motor. *T.A.I.E.E.* **50**, 769, 1931.

35. FRAZER, R. A. Representation of non-linear motion by series of damped time exponentials. *P.M.* **23**, 866, 1937.

36. FOWLER, R. H. *Monthly Notices Roy. Astron. Soc.* **91**, 63, 1930.

37. —— *Quart. Jour. Math.* **45**, 289, 1914; **2**, 259, 1931 (Oxford).

38. FRIEDRICHS, K. O., and STOKER, J. J. Forced vibrations of systems with non-linear restoring force. *Q.A.M.* **1**, 97, 1943.

39. —— and WASOW, W. R. Singular perturbations of non-linear oscillations. *D.M.J.* **13**, 367, 1946.

40. GAPONOW, V. I. Theory of entrainment. *J.T.F.* **5**, 821, 1935.

41. GOLDSTEIN, S., and McLACHLAN, N. W. Sound waves of finite amplitude in an exponential loudspeaker horn. *Wireless Engineer*, **11**, 427, 1934; *Jour. Acous. Soc. Amer.* **6**, 275, 1935.

42. GOLZ, J. Jahrbuch der drahtlosen Telegraphie und Telephonie. **19**, 281, 1922.

*43. HADAMARD, J. Sur l'itération et les solutions asymptotiques des équations différentielles. *B.S.M.* **26**, 1901.

44. HAMBURGER, L. Een nieuwe weg voor conjunctuur onderzoek en een nieuwe richtlijn voor conjunctuur politiek. *De Economist*, January 1930.

45. HAMEL, G. Über erzwungene Schwingungen bei endlichen Amplituden. *M.A.* **86**, 1922.

46. HAMMERSTEIN, A. Eine nichtlineare Randwertaufgabe. *Jahrb. d. D. Math. Ver.* **39**, 59, 1930.

47. HARTOG, J. P. DEN. Amplitudes of non-harmonic vibrations. *J.F.I.* **216**, 459, 1933.

48. —— and MIKINA, S. J. Forced vibrations with non-linear spring constants. *Trans. Amer. Soc. Mech. Eng.* **54**, 157, 1932.

49. —— and HEILES, R. M. Forced vibrations in non-linear systems. *J.A.M.* **3**, A-127, 1936.

50. HARTREE, D. R. Boundary layer equations. *Proc. Camb. Phil. Soc.* **33**, 223, 1937.

51. ——, PORTER, A., and CALLENDER, A. Time lag in control system. *Phil. Trans. Roy. Soc.* (A), **235**, 415, 1936.

52. —— —— —— and STEVENSON, A. B. Time lag in a control system. *Proc. Roy. Soc.* (A), **161**, 460, 1937.

53. HERR, D. L. Oscillations in certain non-linear driven systems. *P.I.R.E.* **27**, 396, 1939.

*54. IGLISCH, R. Zur theorie der Schwingungen. *Monatsh. für Math. u. Phys.* **37**, 525, 1930; **39**, 173, 1932; **42**, 7, 1935.

*55. —— Über die Lösungen des Duffingschen Schwingungproblems bei grossen Parameterwerten. *M.A.* **111**, 568, 1935.

*56. —— Die erste Resonanzkurve beim Duffingschen Schwingungproblem. *M.A.* **112**, 221, 1936.

*57. —— Über den Resonanzbegriff bei nichtlinearen Schwingungen. *Z.A.M.M.* **17**, 249, 1937.

58. JACOBSEN, L. S., and JESPERSEN, H. J. Steady forced vibrations of single mass systems with non-linear restoring elements. *J.F.I.* **220**, 615, 1940.

59. JAMES, H. M., and GUTH, E. Wave equation for finite elastic strains. *J.A.P.* **16**, 643, 1945.

60. JANET, P. Note sur une ancienne expérience d'électricité appliquée. *A.P.T.T.* December 1925.

61. KADEN, H. Frequenzmesser nach dem Kompensationverfahren. *Elektr. Nach. Tech.* **16**, 1939.

REFERENCES   261

62. KÁRMÁN, TH. VON. The Engineer grapples with non-linear problems.
    Bull. Amer. Math. Soc. **46**, 615, 1940. (Contains 178 classified
    references.)
63. KAUFMANN, W. Elektrodynamische Eigentümlichkeiten leitender
    Gase. *A.P.* **2**, 158, 1900.
64. KELLER, E. G. Resonance theory of series non-linear control circuits.
    J.F.I. **225**, 561, 1938.
65. —— Beat theory of non-linear circuits. *J.F.I.* **228**, 319, 1939.
66. —— Non-linear problems in electrical and aeronautical industries.
    Q.A.M. **2**, 72, 1944.
67. KELVIN, LORD. Graphical solution of dynamical problems. *P.M.* **34**,
    1892.
68. —— (THOMSON, W.). Homer Lane's problem of a spherical gaseous
    nebula. *P.R.S.E.* **27**, 375, 1907.
69. KLEINHOONTE, A. *De door het licht geregelde autonome bewegingen der
    Canavalia bladeren.* Thesis, Delft, 1928.
70. KLOTTER, K. *Ingenieur-Archiv.* **7**, 87, 1936.
71. —— and KOTOWSKI, G. Über die Stabilität der Bewegungen des Pen-
    dels mit oszillierendem Aufhängepunkt. *Z.A.M.M.* **19**, 289, 1939.
72. KOBSAREV, J. B. Asynchronous action in self excited oscillatory systems.
    J.T.F. **3**, 138, 1933.
73. KRYLOFF, N., and BOGOLIUBOFF, N. Quelques exemples d'oscillations
    non-linéares. *C.R.* **194**, 957, 1932.
74. —— —— Sur le phénomène de l'entraînement en radiotechnique. *C.R.*
    194, 1064, 1932.
75. —— —— Les phénomènes de démultiplication de fréquence en radio-
    technique. *C.R.* **194**, 1119, 1932.
76. —— —— Über einige Methoden der nichtlinearen Mechanik in
    ihren Anwendungen auf der Theorie der nichtlinearen Resonanz.
    Schweizer Bauzeitung, **103**, 225, 267, 1934.
77. —— —— Méthodes approchées de la mécanique non-linéaire dans leur
    application à l'étude de la perturbation des mouvements pério-
    diques, et de divers phénomènes de résonance s'y rapportant.
    Acad. Sci. d'Ukraine, No. 14, 112, 1935.
78. LANE, J. HOMER. *Amer. Jour. Sci.* **50**, 57, 1870.
79. LECORBEILLER, PH. Oscillations of triodes and regulators. *Proc.
    Third Cong. App. Mech. Stockholm*, **3**, 205, 1931.
80. —— Non-linear theory of maintenance of oscillations. *J.I.E.E.* **79**,
    361, 1936.
*81. LEFSCHETZ, S. Existence of periodic solutions of certain differential
    equations. *P.N.A.S.W.* **29**, 90, 1943.
*81a. LEVENSON, M. L. *Harmonic and subharmonic response for the Duffing
    Equation.* Dissertation, New York University, 1948, abridgement
    in *J.A.P.* **20**, 1045, 1949.
*82. LEVINSON, N., and SMITH, O. K. General equation for relaxation
    oscillations. *D.M.J.* **9**, 382, 1942.
*83. —— Existence of periodic solutions of second order differential equa-
    tions with a forcing term. *J.M.P.* **22**, 41, 1943.
*84. —— A non-linear differential equation of the second order. *J.M.P.* **22**,
    181, 1943.

*85. LEVINSON, N. Transformation theory of non-linear differential equations of the second order. *A.M.* **45**, 723, 1944.

*86. —— Perturbations of discontinuous solutions of non-linear systems of differential equations. *P.N.A.S.W.* **33**, 214, 1947.

*87. LIAPOUNOFF, M. A. Problème général de la stabilité du mouvement. *Annales de la Faculté des Sci. de Toulouse*, **9**, 1907: translation from the Russian by E. Davaux, 1947.

*88. LIÉNARD, A. Étude des oscillations entretenues. *Rev. Gén. d'Électricité.* **23**, 901, 1928.

*89. —— Oscillations auto-entretenues. *Proc. Third Cong. App. Mech. Stockholm*, **3**, 173, 1931.

*90. LINDSTEDT, A. Differentialgleichungen der Störungstheorie. *Mém. de l'Acad. Imp. des Sci. de St. Pétersbourg*, **31**, No. 4, 1883.

91. LUDEKE, C. A. Resonance. *J.A.P.* **13**, 418, 1942.

92. —— Experimental investigation of forced oscillations in system having non-linear restoring force. *J.A.P.* **17**, 603, 1946.

92a. —— Mechanical model for demonstrating sub-harmonics. *Amer. Jour. Phys.* **16**, 430, 1948.

92b. —— Electromechanical device for solving non-linear differential equations. *J.A.P.* **20**, 600, 1949.

93. LYON, W. V., and EDGERTON, H. E. Transient torque-angle characteristics of synchronous motors. *T.A.I.E.E.* **49**, 686, 1930.

94. MANDELSTAM, L., and PAPALEXI, N. Über Resonanzschwingungen bei Frequenzteilung. *Zeitschr. für Phys.* **73**, 223, 1932.

95. —— ——, ANDRONOW, A., CHAIKIN, S., and WITT, A. Exposé des recherches récentes sur les oscillations non-linéares *T.P.U.S.S.R.* **2**, 81, 1935. (Has an extensive reference list.)

96. MARIN, J. Creep deflexions in columns. *J.A.P.* **18**, 103, 1947.

97. MARTIENSSEN, O. Über neue Resonanzerscheinungen in Wechselstromkreisen. *Phys. Zeitschr.* **11**, 448, 1910.

98. MARTIN, H. Über Tonhöhe und Dämpfung der Schwingungen von Saiten in verschiedenen Flüssigkeiten. *A.P.* **77**, 627, 1925.

99. McCRUMM, J. D. Experimental investigation of sub-harmonic currents. *T.A.I.E.E.* **60**, 533, 1941.

100. McLACHLAN, N. W., and MEYERS, A. L. Spherical sound waves of finite amplitude. *Proc. Phys. Soc. Lond.* **47**, 644, 1935.

101. —— —— Über die Bildung von Kombinationstönen in sich ausbreitenden Schallwellen endlicher Amplitude. *Elektr. Nach. Tech.* **12**, 259, 1935.

102. —— Subharmonics. *Wireless World*, **37**, 666, 1935.

103. MEISSNER, E. *Schweizerische Bauzeitung* **104**, 1934.

103a. —— *Z.A.M.M.* **15**, 62, 1935.

104. MELDE, F. *Pogg. Annalen*, **109**, 193, 1860.

105. MILLER, J. C. P. *Emden Functions, tables for n = 3/2, 2, 3.* British Association Mathematical Tables Committee, 1932.

106. MINORSKY, N. Self-excited oscillations in dynamical systems possessing retarded actions. *J.A.M.* **9**, A65–A71, 1942.

107. —— Mechanical self-excited oscillations. *P.N.A.S.W.* **30**, 308, 1944.

108. —— Non-linear phenomena in self-rolling of ships. *P.N.A.S.W.* **31**, 346, 1945.

109. MINORSKY, N. Parametric excitation. *J.F.I.* **240**, 25, 1945.

110. —— Experiments with activated tanks. *Trans. Amer. Soc. Mech. Eng.* October 1947.

111. —— Self-excited mechanical oscillations. *J.A.P.* **19**, 332, 1948.

112. MÖLLER, H. G. Über störungsfreien Gleichstromempfang mit dem Schwingaudion. *Zeitschr. für draht. Teleg. u. Teleph.* 17 April 1921.

113. PARODI, H. and M. Les équations de relaxation, cas particulier des équations de la marche d'un train. *La Revue Scientifique.* **81**, 110, 1943.

114. PEDERSEN, P. O. Sub-harmonics in forced oscillations in dissipative systems. *Jour. Acous. Soc. Amer.* **6**, 227, 1935; **7**, 64, 1935.

115. PIPES, L. A. Operational analysis of non-linear dynamical systems. *J.A.P.*, **13**, 117, 1942.

116. POINCARÉ, J. H. Sur les courbes définies par une équation différentielle. *Jour. de Math.* **8**, 251, 1882.

117. POL, B. VAN DER. Oscillation hysteresis in a triode generator. *P.M.* **43**, 700, 1922.

118. —— Relaxation oscillations. *P.M.* **2**, 928, 1926.

119. —— Forced oscillations in circuit with non-linear resistance. *P.M.* **3**, 65, 1927.

120. —— and MARK, J. VAN DER. *Nature*, **120**, 363, 1927.

121. —— —— Le battement du cœur considéré comme oscillation de relaxation. *Onde Électrique*, **7**, 365, 1928.

122. —— Oscillations sinusoïdales et de relaxation. *Onde Électrique*, **9**, 293, 1930.

123. —— Non-linear theory of electric oscillations. *P.I.R.E.* **22**, 1051, 1934. (Has an extensive list of references.)

124. PRAGER, W. Strain hardening under combined stresses. *J.A.P.* **16**, 837, 1945.

125. —— Introduction to the mathematical theory of plasticity. *J.A.P.* **18**, 375, 1947. (See additional references therein.)

126. —— Theory of plastic flow versus theory of plastic deformation. *J.A.P.* **19**, 540, 1948 (see additional references therein.)

127. RAMAN, C. V. Experimental investigations on maintenance of vibrations. *P.I.A.C.S. Bull.* **6**, 1, 1912.

128. —— Dynamical theory of motion of bowed strings. *P.I.A.C.S. Bull.* **11**, 43, 1914.

129. RAUSCHER, M. Steady oscillations of systems with non-linear and unsymmetrical elasticity. *J.A.M.* **5**, A-169, 1938.

130. —— Steady forced oscillations of permanent non-linear systems. *Proc. Fifth Int. Cong. App. Mech.* **5**, 681, 1939.

131. RAYLEIGH, LORD. On maintained vibrations. *P.M.* **15**, 229, 1883.

131a. REUTER, G. E. H. Subharmonics in non-linear system with unsymmetrical restoring force. *Quart. Jour. Mech. and App. Math.* **2**, 198, 1949.

132. RJASIN, P. Einstellungs- und Schwebungsprozesse bei der Mitnahme. *T.P.U.S.S.R.* **2**, 195, 1935.

133. ROBB, A. Graphical solutions of differential equations of the type $\ddot{y} + f(y)\dot{y} + ay = \phi(t)$. *P.M.* **43**, 206, 1922.

134. RÜDENBERG, R. Einige unharmonische Schwingungsformen mit grosser Amplitude. *Z.A.M.M.* **3**, 454, 1923.

135. SALINGER, H. Propagation of telegraph signals in Krarup cables. *Archiv. für Elektrotechnik*, **12**, 268, 1923.

136. SHOHAT, J. A. Non-linear differential equations. *J.A.P.* **15**, 568, 1944.

137. SILVERMAN, I. K. Forced pseudo-harmonic vibrations. *J.F.I.* **217**, 743, 1934.

138. STRAUB, H. Über selbsterregte nicht lineare Röhrenschwingungen. *Helv. Phys. Acta*, **6**, 337, 1933.

139. STRELKOFF, S. Froude's pendulum. *J.T.F.* **3**, 563, 1933.

140. SUITS, C. G. Studies in non-linear circuits. *T.A.I.E.E.* **50**, 724, 1931.

141. TAEGER, W. Die Entdämpfung von Schwingungskreisen durch Eisendrossen. *Arch. für Elektr.* **35**, 193, 1941.

142. THEODORCHIK, K., and CHAIKIN, S. Acoustical entrainment. *J.T.F.* **2**, 111, 1932.

143. TREFFTZ, E. Zur Berechnung der Stabilität periodischer Bewegungsvorgänge. *Z.A.M.M.* **5**, 473, 1925.

144. —— Zu den Grundlagen der Schwingungstheorie. *M.A.* **95**, 307, 1926.

145. VINCENT, J. H. Experiments in which two neighbouring maintained circuits affect a resonating circuit. *Proc. Phys. Soc. Lond.* **32**, 84, 1919.

146. VLASOV, N. Oscillations of a synchronous motor. *J.T.F.* **9**, 1939.

147. VOLTERRA, V. Variations and fluctuations of number of individuals in animal species living together. *Jour. de Conseil International pour l'Exploration de la mer*, **3**, 1, 1928.

148. WANATABE, Y. On non-harmonic oscillations. *Proc. Fifth Int. Cong. App. Mech.* **5**, 686, 1939.

149. WEDDERBURN, J. H. M. Isoclinal lines of a differential equation of the first order. *P.R.S.E.* **24**, 400, 1902.

150. WEGEL, R. L. Theory of vibration of the larynx. *Bell. Syst. Tech. Jour.* **9**, 209, 1930.

B. BOOKS AND REPORTS

151. AIGNER, F. *Unterwasserschalltechnik*, p. 158 (1922).

152. AKIMOFF, M. J. *Sur les fonctions de Bessel à plusieurs variables et leur applications en mécanique* (1929).

153. ANDRONOW, A., and CHAIKIN, S. *Theory of Oscillations* (Moscow, 1937).

154. APPELL, P. *Traité de la mécanique rationelle*, vol. i (Paris).

155. BARKHAUSEN, G. H. *Lehrbuch der Elektronenröhren* (1937).

156. BIEBERBACH, L. *Differentialgleichungen*, part 1, chap. 4, (Berlin, 1930).

157. BIRKHOFF, G. D. *Dynamical Systems* (New York, 1927).

158. BROWN, E. E. W. *Elements of Theory of Resonance.* Rice Institute Pamphlet, **19**, No. 1, 1932.

158a. CARTWRIGHT, M. L. Non-linear vibrations. Report for the Brit. Assn. published in *The Advancement of Science*, **6**, No. 21, April 1949. Additional references are given therein.

159. CHANDRASEKHAR, S. *Introduction to Study of Stellar Structure* (Chicago, 1939).

160. COURANT, R., and FRIEDRICHS, K. O. *Supersonic Flow and Shock Waves* (1948).

161. DREFUS, L. *Elektrotechnik und Maschinenbau* (1911).
162. DUFFING, G. *Erzwungene Schwingungen bei veränderlicher Eigenfrequenz* (Braunschweig, 1918).
*163. ECKWEILER, H. J., FLANDERS, D. A., FRIEDRICHS, K. O., JOHN, F., and STOKER, J. J. *Studies in Non-linear Vibration Theory* (New York University, 1946).
164. EDDINGTON, A. S. *Internal Constitution of the Stars.*
165. EMDEN, V. R. *Gaskugeln* (1908).
166. FORCHHEIMER, P. *Hydraulik* (1930).
167. FORSYTH, A. R. *Treatise on Differential Equations* (1933).
*168. GOURSAT, E. Differential equations II, being part of *A Course of Mathematical Analysis*, translated from the French by E. R. Hendrick and O. Dunkel (Boston, 1917).
169. HELMHOLTZ, H. VON. *Sensations of Tone* (London, 1893).
170. HORT, W. *Technische Schwingungslehre* (Berlin, 1922).
171. —— *Die Differentialgleichungen des Ingenieurs* (Berlin, 1925).
*172. INCE, E. L. *Ordinary Differential Equations* (London, 1927).
173. JAHNKE, E., and EMDE, F. *Tables of Functions with Formulae and Curves* (New York, 1943).
173a. KAMKE, E. *Differentialgleichungen, Lösungsmethoden und Lösungen* (1944).
174. KRYLOFF, A. N. *Approximate Numerical Integration of Ordinary Differential Equations* (Berlin, 1923.)
*175. KRYLOFF, N., and BOGOLIUBOFF, N. *Introduction to Non-linear Mechanics.* Translated from the Russian by S. Lefschetz (Princeton, 1943). Contains a list of papers by these authors.
176. LAMB, H. *Dynamical Theory of Sound*, 2nd edition (1925).
177. —— *Hydrodynamics*, 4th edition (1932).
178. LECORBEILLER, PH. *Les Systèmes auto-entretenues et les oscillations de relaxation* (Paris, 1931).
179. LEHR, E. *Schwingungstechnik*, vol. ii (1934).
180. LIEBENSON, L. S. *Elements of Mathematical Theory of Plasticity* (1943). Translation by Graduate Division of Applied Mathematics, Brown University (1947).
181. LIN, C. C. *Introduction to Dynamics of Compressible Fluids.* Report of Grad. Div. of App. Math. Brown University (1947).
182. LOTKA, J. *Elements of Physical Biology*, p. 66 (Baltimore, 1925).
183. MCLACHLAN, N. W. *Loudspeakers* (Oxford, 1934).
184. —— *Bessel Functions for Engineers* (Oxford, 1946).
185. —— *Theory and Application of Mathieu Functions* (Oxford, 1947).
186. MEISSNER, E. *Graphische Analysis vermittelst des Linienbildes einer Funktion* (Zürich, 1932).
187. MINORSKY, N. *Introduction to Non-linear Mechanics* (Ann Arbor, U.S.A., 1947).
188. MISES, R. VON. *Dynamical Problems in Theory of Machines.* Enzykl. der Math. Wiss. vol. iv, 2, p. 254, 1911.
189. NADAI, A., and WAHL, A. M. *Plasticity; Mechanics of the Plastic State of Matter* (New York, 1931).
190. National Research Council U.S.A., Report No. 92 on Numerical Solution of Differential Equations (1933).

191. NEWMAN, M. H. A. *Elements of the Topology of Plane Sets of Points* (Cambridge, 1939).
*192. POINCARÉ, J. H. *Œuvres*, vol. i (Paris, 1893).
*193. —— *Les méthodes nouvelles de la mécanique céleste*, vol. i (1892); vol. ii (Paris, 1893).
194. PRAGER, W. *Mécanique des solides isotropes au delà du domaine élastique.* Mem. des Sc. Math., Fascicule No. 87 (Paris).
195. *Proceedings first International Congress Applied Mechanics* (Delft, 1924).
196. —— *second International Congress Applied Mechanics* (Zurich, 1926).
197. —— *third International Congress Applied Mechanics* (Stockholm, 1931).
198. —— *fourth International Congress Applied Mechanics* (Cambridge, England, 1934).
199. —— *fifth International Congress Applied Mechanics* (Cambridge, U.S.A., 1939).
200. —— *sixth International Congress Applied Mechanics* (Paris, 1946).
201. —— *seventh International Congress Applied Mechanics* (London, England, 1948).
202. RAYLEIGH, LORD. *Theory of Sound*, vol. i, § 68a (1894).
203. —— *Scientific Papers*, vol. ii, p. 188 (1883).
204. RIEMANN, G. *Göttinger Abhandlungen*, viii (1860).
205. SANDEN, H. VON. *Practical Mathematical Analysis* (New York, 1926).
206. SOUTHWELL, R. V. *Introduction to Theory of Elasticity* (Oxford, 1941).
207. STOKER, J. J., and PETERS, A. *Seminar Notes* (New York University, 1943).
208. TRJITZINSKY, W. J. *Analytic Theory of Non-linear Singular Differential Equations.*
209. VOLTERRA, V. *Leçons sur la théorie mathématique de la lutte pour la vie* (Paris, 1931).
210. WEIERSTRASS, K. *Monatsberichte der Berliner Akademie* (1866).
211. WHITTAKER, E. T., and ROBINSON, G. *Calculus of Observations* (1942).

C. ADDITIONAL REFERENCES

212. BINNIE, A. M. Approximate methods in surge tank calculations. *Proc. Camb. Phil. Soc.* **42**, 156, 1946. See references therein.
213. BOTHWELL, F. E. Transients in multiply periodic non-linear systems. *Q.A.M.* **8**, 247, 1950.
214. BOYAJIAN, A. Mathematical analysis of non-linear circuits. *Gen. Elec. Rev.* **34**, 531 and 745, 1931.
215. CARTWRIGHT, M. L. On non-linear differential equations of the second order. *Proc. Camb. Phil. Soc.* **45**, 495, 1949.
216. COHEN, H. The stability equation with periodic coefficients. *Q.A.M.* **10**, 266, 1952.
217. DRESSLER, R.F. Hydraulic resistance effect upon the Dam-break functions. *Jour. Res. Nat. Bureau Standards*, **49**, 217, 1952. See references therein.
218. —— and POHLE, F. V. Resistance effects of hydraulic instability. *Communications on Pure and Applied Mathematics*, N.Y. University, **6**, 93, 1953. See references therein.

219. EDMAN, J. L. Graphical solution of simultaneous second order non-linear differential equations. *Amer. Soc. Mech. Eng. Mid-western Conference on Solid Mechanics*, 1953.

220. FRIEDLANDER, F. G. On the forced vibrations of quasi-linear systems. *Quart. Jour. Mech. and Appl. Math.* 3, 364, 1950.

221. —— On the asymptotic behaviour of the solutions of a class of non-linear differential equations. *Proc. Camb. Phil. Soc.* 46, 406, 1950.

222. GOMORY, R., and RICHMOND, D. E. Boundaries for limit cycle of $\ddot{x} + \mu(x^2 - 1)\dot{x} + x = 0$. *Q.A.M.* 9, 205, 1951.

223. HAAG, J. *Ann. Sci. École Norm. Sup.* 64, 3, 1947, and 65, 285, 1948.

224. —— *C.R.* 233, 117, 1951.

225. HAYASHI, C. *Forced Oscillations in Non-linear Systems* (1953).

226. KLOTTER, K. *Non-linear Vibration Problems treated by the Averaging Method of W. Ritz.* Techn. Rep. 17, parts 1, 2, done at Stanford Univ., for Off. Air Res. and Off. Nav. Res. 1951. See references therein.

226a. KOITER, W. T. Niet-lineaire vraagstukken in de toegepaste mechanica. *Ned. T. Natuurkunde*, 17, 258, 1951.

226b. —— Linearisation of the equations for torsional vibration of crank-shafts. *Proc. Koninkl. Nederl. Akademie van Wetenschappen, Amsterdam*, Series B, 54, 464, 1951.

227. KU, Y. H. Non-linear analysis of electromechanical problems. *J.F.I.* 255, 9, 1953. See references therein.

228. —— A method of solving third and higher order non-linear differential equations. *J.F.I.* 256, 229, 1953.

228a. —— Analysis of multiloop non-linear systems. *P.I.R.E.* vol. CT–I, 6, 1954.

228b. —— Analysis of non-linear systems with more than one degree of freedom by means of space trajectories. *J.F.I.*, 259, 115, 1955.

229. LANDSBERG, P. T. On the present state of the theory of contact rectifiers. *Zeitschr. Phys. Chem.* 198, 75, 1951.

230. LaSALLE, J. Relaxation oscillations. *Q.A.M.* 7, 1, 1949. See references therein.

231. LEFSCHETZ, S. (Editor). *Contributions to the Theory of Non-linear Oscillations. Ann. Math. Stud.* vol. 1, 1950; vol. 2, 1952.

232. —— On Liénard's differential equation. See ref. 243, p. 149.

233. LEVY, H., and BAGGOTT, E. A. *Numerical Studies in Differential Equations.* (1934).

234. LUDEKE, C. A. Predominantly subharmonic oscillations. *J.A.P.* 22, 1321, 1951.

235. —— and PONG, W. Extinction of predominantly subharmonic oscillations in non-linear systems. *J.A.P.* 24, 96, 1953.

236. —— and EVANS, R. T. Coupling analog for non-linear systems with more than one degree of freedom. *J.A.P.* 24, 119, 1953.

237. —— and MORRISON, C. L. Analog computer elements for solving non-linear differential equations. *J.A.P.* 24, 243, 1953.

238. MacCOLL, L. A. Pseudo closed trajectories defined by a system of differential equations. *Q.A.M.* 8, 255, 1950.

239. McLACHLAN, N. W. Non-linear differential equation having a periodic coefficient. *Math. Gaz.* 35, 32, 1951.

240. —— Application of Mathieu's equation to stability of non-linear oscillator. *Math. Gaz.* 35, 105, 1951.

241. McLachlan, N. W. *Theory of Vibrations* (1951).

242. —— An oscillation problem involving elliptic integrals of the first and second kinds. *Math. Gaz.* **38**, 141, 1953.

243. —— On a non-linear equation in hydraulics. *Proc. 5th Sympos. App. Math. of Amer. Math. Soc.*, p. 49, 1954.

244. Mettler, E. Zum Problem der Stabilität erzwungerer Schwingungen elastischer Körper. *Z.A.M.M.* **31**, 263, 1951.

245. Milne-Thomson, L. M. *Theoretical Hydrodynamics*, 2nd ed. (1949).

246. Minorsky, N. Sur l'excitation paramétrique. *C.R.* **231**, 1417, 1950.

247. —— Parametric excitation. *J.A.P.* **22**, 49, 1951.

248. —— Sur une équation différentielle de la physique. *C.R.* **232**, 1060, 1951.

249. —— Sur l'oscillateur non-linéaire de Mathieu. *C.R.* **232**, 2179, 1951.

249a. —— Stationary solutions of certain non-linear differential equations. *J.F.I.*, **254**, 21, 1952.

250. Obi, C. Subharmonic solutions of non-linear differential equations of the second order. *Jour. Lond. Math. Soc.* **25**, 217, 1950.

251. Pipes, L. A. *Operational Methods in Non-linear Mechanics.* Rep. 51–10, Dept. of Eng., Univ. of Calif., Los Angeles (1951).

252. —— Reversion method for solving non-linear differential equations. *J.A.P.* **23**, 202, 1952.

253. —— Mathematical analysis of a dielectric amplifier. *J.A.P.* **23**, 818, 1952.

254. Reuter, G. E. H. A boundedness theorem for non-linear differential equations of the second order. *Proc. Camb. Phil. Soc.* **47**, 49, 1951.

254a. —— On certain non-linear differential equations with almost periodic solutions. *Jour. Lond. Math. Soc.* **26**, 215, 1951.

254b. —— Boundedness theorems for non-linear differential equations of the second order. *Journ. Lond. Math. Soc.* **27**, 48, 1952.

255. Rosenberg, R. M., and Wang, A. J. *Periodic Solutions of a Non-linear Differential Equation.* Bull. No. 118, p. 77, Univ. of Wash. Eng. Exper. Stn. (1951).

256. Ryder, J. D. Ferroinductance as a variable electric circuit element. *T.A.I.E.E.* **64**, 962, 1945. See references therein.

257. Schlichting, H. Boundary layer theory. Part 1 on laminar flow. *Nat. Adv. Comm. for Aero., Tech. Memo. No. 1217* (1949).

258. Serbin, H. Periodic motions of a non-linear dynamic system. *Q.A.M.* **8**, 296, 1950.

258a. Stoker, J. J. *Non-linear Vibrations* (1950).

259. Torda, T. P. Compressible flow through reed valves for pulse jet engines. *Reissner Anniversary Volume*, p. 469, 1949.

260. —— and Hoff, N. J. Aerodynamic heating and thermal stresses in aircraft structures. *Proc. Anglo-Amer. Aero. Conf. Brighton, England*, 1951.

261. —— Approximate theory of compressible air inflow through reed valves for pulse jet engines. *Proc. 1st Mid-western Conf. on Fluid Mechanics, Michigan*, p. 362, 1951.

262. —— Boundary layer control by continuous surface suction or injection. *J.M.P.* **31**, 206, 1952.

263. —— Ackermann, W. O., and Burnett, H. R. Symmetric turbulent mixing of two parallel streams. *J.A.M.* **20**, 63, 1953.

264. —— Wake of a flat plate in laminar flow. *Proc. 3rd Mid-western Conf. on Fluid Mechanics*, p. 613, 1953.

265. TORDA, T. P., HILTON, H. H., and HALL, F. C. Analysis of viscous laminar compressible flow through axial-flow turbo-machines with infinitesimal blade spacing. *J.A.M.* **20**, 401, 1953.

266. —— Boundary layer control by distributed suction or injection. Biparametric general solution. *J.M.P.* **32**, 312, 1954.

267. TRAVIS, I., and WEYGANDT, C. N. Subharmonics in circuits containing iron-cored reactors. *T.A.I.E.E.* **57**, 423, 1938; **58**, 735, 1939.

268. WEIDENHAMMER, F. Nicht-lineare Biegeschwingungen des axial-pulsierend belasteten Stabes. *Ingenieur-Archiv*, **20**, 315, 1952.

269. —— Biegeschwingungen des Stabes mit nichtlinearem Elastizitäts-gesetz. *Z.A.M.M.* **32**, 265, 1952.

270. YOUNG, D. Forced vibration of system with non-linear restoring force. *Amer. Soc. Mech. Eng., Mid-western Conference on Solid Mechanics*, p. 164, 1953.

By aid of the lists of references in [62, 95, 123, 158a, 175, 187, 212, 217, 218, 226, 227, 230, 256], the number of items may be increased to more than 350.

Additional references will be found from time to time in *Mathematical Reviews* and *Zentralblatt für Mathematik*.

INDEX

PRINTED IN
GREAT BRITAIN
AT THE
UNIVERSITY PRESS
OXFORD
BY
CHARLES BATEY
PRINTER
TO THE
UNIVERSITY